TIME TO BE YOUNG

Youth is alive, and once we too were young,
Dreamed we could make the world all over new,
Tossed eager projects lightly from the tongue,
And hoped the hurrying years would prove them true.

Wellesley at Fifty—1881–1931

TIME TO BE YOUNG

GREAT STORIES OF THE GROWING YEARS

EDITED BY WHIT BURNETT

PHILADELPHIA AND NEW YORK

J. B. LIPPINCOTT COMPANY

Printed in the United States of America by H. Wolff, New York
Designed by Stefan Salter

A STORY PRESS BOOK

Story Press Books are published by J. B. Lippincott Company
in association with Story Magazine, Inc.

This book has been produced in full compliance with all government regulations for the conservation of paper, metal and other essential materials

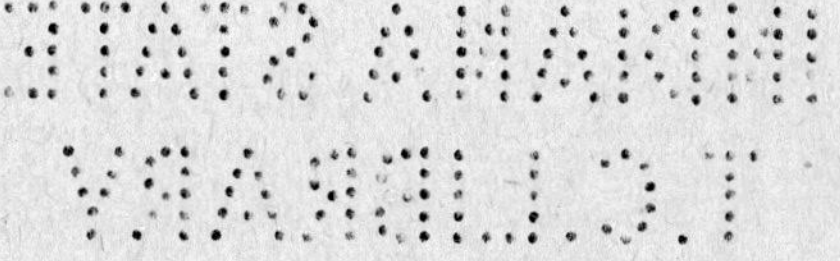

FOR DAVID, JOHN AND BILL

WHOSE YOUNG, DISCERNING

EYES HAVE OFTEN SEEN

THEIR ELDERS

(IF NOT THEIR BETTERS)

OFF GUARD

CONTENTS

III. *Early Spring*

FOREWORD

Some go in for stamps. Others pewter. I know a full-grown man of high executive calibre who collects old milk glass. There are others who favor election buttons, G.A.R. Encampment ribbons, or Staffordshire deer. Wealthy males of one part of Europe, I am told, used to collect beautiful women the way the French collect paintings. Only a fortunate lack of means once prevented my amassing a magnificent collection of the world's most priceless fiddles. At another time with me it was Oriental rugs. And although today I can still distinguish a Gasparo da Salo from a Markneukirchen Amati and a Kazak rug from an antique Sarouk, collecting of this type—the assembling of material show-pieces—has never deeply, for any length of time, held my interest.

I have, however, collected stories. In 1931, I began the professional collecturing of short stories in Vienna, and for the fourteen years or so since, as editor of *Story,* stories of one kind or another have been so constantly passing through my hands that I have begun to feel I can detect a good one when I read it. It is true, a short story is art in a small frame, but size in such matters, as size in a Royal Bokhara, is not the main thing; a viola may carry as much melody as a bull fiddle. I felt so, anyway. And I liked short stories. I still do. I have even sometimes written one. So, from merely conning over stories, or rugs, or fiddles, to assembling and exhibiting one's collection for the edification of others seems only the natural order of progress.

And yet who wants to be known as an Anthologist? For such, it must be conceded, is the technical term for one who collects stories for others to read, at least if the collection appears in book form and not in a magazine which, God willing, he may there edit to suit no one but himself. The fact is, anthologists are merely editors trying to make their editorial selections more permanent than periodicals permit. And of anthologists there are many kinds and varieties. Your early anthologists (*anthos,* flower, plus *legein,* to gather) were your true collectors of literary floral pieces, the epigrams and pretty passages of literatures, usually dead. Those were the days of the pressed-flower books, the aversion to which is everywhere known as *anthologophobia,* from which we all today in some way suffer. Later there have been the comprehensive anthologists, who encompass everything from Sanskrit to Thomas Wolfe, composing monumental volumes it would take a library's research to duplicate. There are anthologists, too, like W. Somerset Maugham who not only select the best or the greatest works in prose and poetry in their time but the greatest and best in prose and poetry in their estimation of all time. And there are the Personal Readers and the What I Likers, after Woollcott. One young woman I know is currently collecting the world's great love stories and my family doctor confesses that he has for years been assembling his own loose-leaf anthology of poetry.

In editing an anthology one may pursue various courses. He may, as I did in *This Is My Best,* simply ask the authors to choose their own favorite works; he may, as in *Two Bottles of Relish,* publish in his own magazine for several years oddly appealing stories he personally likes and these he may sometime later issue in a book; he may cull from one periodical—as in *The Pocketbook of Story*; or he may, having in mind a special kind of unity for a book, assemble through his own taste and that of the authors and other specialists in the field, a book like *The Seas of God,* stories of the human spirit. The authors, the editor and dozens of others brought that book into shape.

There is still another kind of anthology where the mood and subject are such that the book almost seems to grow into shape itself. Gaiety, tenderness, simplicity, charm, youthfulness, candor, the good old days . . . when we were very young . . . With such qualities infusing a wealth of literature, what was more natural than that someone should assemble such stories, particularly someone who has, for many years, been seeing these stories pass under his editorial eye, and bring out an anthology of childhood and early youth under the simple, clear, and comprehensive title, *Time to be Young?* The project seemed downright inescapable. Here, surely, the subject literally radiated its storied manifestations. This would be a collection as loose and free, as open-eyed and honest, as complex, paradoxical, comic and tragic, as youth itself; young and foolish, young and wise, young and fanciful; moody, full of a "nameless sorrow," and lost in the tragi-comedy of being neither six nor sixty. In short, a young book. A book, so to say, for your real *anthologophiles.*

In the fiction of adult against adult in the adult world, we have the story of human relations, in which the highest point of revelation is who marries whom. In collecting stories for *The Seas of God,* it was a deep pleasure to consider stories where merely human relations were not the end-all and be-all of mortal preoccupation. Joseph Wood Krutch has quoted Eugene O'Neill: "Most modern plays are concerned with the relation between man and man, but that does not interest me at all. I am interested only in the relation between man and God." * In the stories in *Time to be Young,* a kindred sense of other than merely human relations is constantly being encountered. The world is the Golden Apple, said Meredith, and thirst for it is common during youth. A child is more than a child when seen through the eyes of a writing artist who once was a child himself; a child is an individual up against the world, and the world is more than the visible, tangible world we see. It is the world of fantastic adults, of gods and aspirations, of depths of despair and strange predicaments. The world is to be accepted or rejected, wholly, open-eyed, and it is something serious, something at times hilariously funny, something at times most utterly stupid and ridiculous, and unworthy.

There is a time to be young,
(said my Great Aunt Eliza in Idaho)
Not always the same time, either, for all of us . . .

My great Aunt Eliza would have liked *Time to Be Young,* for Aunt Eliza was young at all times. Hardy, earthy, she had lived her days of earliest wedlock in New Zealand, where her husband, at Christchurch, had, among other things, built the first jail. It was his lot, too, since he was an exuberant fellow, to be the jail's first guest, for his celebration exceeded sobriety. Eliza herself was a kind of lusty philosopher; she believed in life, its aspirations and its appetites, and was a friend to the young in her day. She passed occasionally through a story of my own remote childhood, not full-bodied, but ineffectively, like a cry of Coooeee in the wilderness; I never did her justice. At 93 she succumbed. She never wore glasses. She was chipper and hale to the night of her death, and doubtless would still be with us but for the accident when, in the middle of the night, she slipped on the stairs, getting up out of bed, as was her custom at times, to raid the icebox.

The scope of this anthology is somewhat limited. These are writers of our times. There is practically nothing here from the Bhagavad-Gita. And by our times I mean as far back as Mark Twain. Some in its pages are no longer young in years; they are young immemorably. And there are many newcomers whose names have not yet grown to fame.

The shape of the book is simple; the first section is called "Sunrise," the middle is "The Great Mountains," and the book concludes with "Early Spring." The stories are an affectionate selecting of many charming fragments from the days of innocence. Some are gay, some are tender, some nostalgic. The book is the book of the fresh young world of a child, the groping of a growing spirit, the love and social awakening of early youth.

* Preface to *Nine Plays by Eugene O'Neill,* Modern Library.

It was not a difficult task to find authors. Indeed, it is surprising how so many authors who pride themselves on being tough-minded and hairy-chested, have written so tenderly of children. It could even be a parlor game: surveying contemporary authors to see which ones present other than the adult world of human relations, and which ones seem never to have been children and have nothing left in their style or nature that is childlike.

Some of these stories are veritable autobiography. Some are steeped in memory. There is Thomas Wolfe discoursing on a world of youthful reading. Havelock Ellis aroused to poetry, at ten, at the touch of a young girl's hand. Yet some of these autobiographies have their flair, one feels, for fiction. Or shall we take as a later revelation of the whole truth Winston S. Churchill's frank statement that he had another lad do his Latin for him at Harrow, and swallow with Mencken the family boast that the Sage of Baltimore at three had a fine Spencerian hand?

It doesn't matter. These stories, these autobiographies, are of the essence true. No man is a liar who varies from the facts with art. The childhood of great men often dances in the past behind a play of colored veils. But in Mark Twain's sights and smells of his uncle's farm in Missouri (a wonderful set of pages from the old humorist's *Autobiography*) there is everyone's lost boyhood who has ever climbed a tree for nuts or sat down to dinner on a farm.

"I can see," wrote the reminiscent Clemens, "the woods in their autumn dress, the oaks purple, the hickories washed with gold, the maples and the sumachs luminous with crimson fires, and I can hear the rustle made by the fallen leaves as we plowed through them. I can see the blue clusters of wild grapes hanging among the foliage of the saplings, and I remember the taste of them and the smell. I know how the wild blackberries looked, and how they tasted, and the same with the pawpaws, the hazelnuts and the persimmons; and I can feel the thumping rain, upon my head, of hickory nuts and walnuts when we were out in the frosty dawn to scramble for them with the pigs, and the gusts of wind loosed them and sent them down. . . . I know the stain of walnut hulls, and how little it minds soap and water, also what grudged experience it had of either of them. I know the taste of maple sap, and when to gather it, and how to arrange the troughs and the delivery tubes, and how to boil down the juice, and how to hook the sugar after it is made, also how much better hooked sugar tastes than any that is honestly come by, let bigots say what they will . . ."

And too there is everyone's lost childhood—everyone's who has ever been kissed good night—in a part of perhaps the most nostalgic book in the world, *A la Recherche du Temps Perdu.* "Many years have passed," wrote Proust, "since that night." (It was the night when M. Swann called and the child-autobiographer was sent to bed without the good night kiss from his mother.) "The wall of the staircase, up which I had watched the light of my father's candle gradually climb, was long ago demolished. And in myself, too, many things have perished which, I imagined, would last for ever, and new structures have arisen, giving birth to new sorrows and new joys which in those days I could not have foreseen, just as now the old are difficult of comprehension. It is a long time, too, since my father has been able to tell Mamma to 'Go with the child.' Never again will such hours be possible for me. But of late I have been increasingly able to catch, if I listen attentively, the sound of the sobs which I had the strength to control in my father's presence, and which broke out only when I found myself alone with Mamma. Actually, their echo has never ceased: it is only because life is now growing more and more quiet round about me that I hear them afresh, like those convent bells which are so effectively drowned during the day by the noises of the streets that one would suppose them to have been stopped for ever, until they sound out again through the silent evening air."

But an anthology of living matter is not composed alone of memories, however the structures of the past appeal. *Time to Be Young* was not designed as a book of philosophizing. The editor is not an anthologo-philosopher.

Actually, some very funny fellows once were young: Robert Benchley, plagued by the problem of the Visiting Schoolmate and what on earth to do with him; Mencken, once a chubby infant, so chubby in fact that the remark was sometimes passed to his frailish mother: "Good God, girl, is that baby *yours*?" James Thurber had his troubles in the University. Cornelia Otis Skinner sometimes has to furnish complete outfits for the Young. And there is, as well, George Jean Nathan, the bachelor, giving advice, perhaps the soundest of the century, to both children and adults, on how to get along each with the other.

Time to be Young, it is hoped, is a refuge-book for the imagination, for the freshness of the vision of the young. It is a child's first glimpse of a sunrise; it is Clarence Day lugging his first ponderous watch, an heirloom, which was no watch at all for a boy, no matter what rôle it played in making him prompt for Father. It is the "Intimations of Philosophy in Early Childhood" of Irwin Edman, who says: Many moral philosophers, I suspect now, began through being accidentally disquieted (at thirteen, when he was so disquieted) and the search for the Good began usually because some boy somewhere discovered early that there was something wrong with the *good* people he knew and found people outside his own family who had other standards of good than he had ever dreamed of. It is William Saroyan's first bicycle which, finally, slowly, when he and his brother Krikor were riding it double, collapsed, and it is that day some time later when everyone thought it all so funny and the meaning of it came when he and all his relatives were bursting with laughter . . . "And because I had been laughing, and because tears had come from my eyes, I sat on my bed and began to cry."

. . . Youth is such a wonderful thing, a wise man said, that it is a pity it has to be wasted on the young. Evanescent it is, but a reader who is a collector of stories can here find surely that it has not always been wasted. It has been experienced and recreated. It was Edward J. O'Brien's belief that Americans wrote their best stories (in our days) about childhood because the writers he was encountering being mainly young people were writing, he said, about what was their only "usable past." As an editor and collector of stories, I know I have received a full share of excellent stories of childhood. Many I have printed in *Story*. Some of the stories, in fact, were by very young people, some no older than sixteen.

Kenneth Grahame, a British contributor to this volume, wrote three books, ostensibly for children, but one critic said: "They are not really for children to read, but for adults to remember." Mr. Grahame had his own reservation. He wrote for children, he said, because they were "the only really living people." Most of the other contributors have children of their own. Of the thirty-five men authors, twenty-seven are sober married men, and twenty-one of these fellows have a total of forty-four children with all the problems pertaining thereto. . . . Of the women writers, all but three are married and seven of them have a total of nineteen children. Eight male authors in the book are unmarried. Proust hated noise and had to work in a cork-lined room—he obviously was allergic to anything as unpredictable as an infant; two of the young men writers are currently busy in the Army, and the three outstanding bachelors who have foresworn family life as the others know it are notably two philosophers, Santayana and Edman, and one critic of the make-believe world of the theatre, Mr. George Jean Nathan.

The stories in this anthology have come from many sources. From books, magazines, and authors' out-of-print files. Some have not before appeared in type. They are all, I think, exceedingly good. They are honest. They are true. They are lyric, passionate with youth, or candid with the retrospect of after years. There is Helen Keller's first spoken word which opened to her the world of speech and made her blindness bearable. There is a little girl's all-consuming wish for a pair of bright red shoes, a boy going fishing with his father. There is Ludwig Bemelmans' little daughter bravely bearing with the tortures of a camp for little girls, and there is Fessier's classic of the high school boy who was a practically unlimited standing high-jumper; there is James Street's boy and a bird dog and Jesse Stuart's boy and a gun, and Sally Benson's junior miss in her dressup coat and the doll beneath the Christmas tree. And finally there are the odd, disquieting stories of Early Spring.

Sherwood Anderson, who sometimes has been accused of being a simple, animalistic writer (incorrectly), concludes the stories in this book with a story seldom gathered with the flowers of literature. The story is "Sophistication," and deals with young George Willard, who at eighteen has decided to leave Winesburg, Ohio, and he makes a timid call on a girl in the village he wants to see before he leaves. Awkwardly they talk, walk, and finally, unaccountably, break into a childish race. . . . "It was so they went down the hill. In the darkness they played like two splendid young things in a young world. Once, running swiftly forward, Helen tripped George and he fell. He squirmed and shouted. Shaking with laughter, he rolled down the hill. Helen ran after him. For just a moment she stopped in the darkness. There is no way of knowing what woman's thoughts went through her mind but, when the bottom of the hill was reached and she came up to the boy, she took his arm and walked beside him in dignified silence. For some reason they could not have explained they had both got from their silent evening together the thing needed. Man or boy, woman or girl, they had for a moment taken hold of the thing that makes the mature life of men and women in the modern world possible."

We were all young once. In a way, I think this book is a testament to the fact. My great Aunt Eliza would have liked it. It reminds me of her best advice when I saw her as a very young man in Idaho:

> *Just remember* (this was what she said to me),
> *When you are old, you may be very, very old,*
> *So when you are young, you should be youthful.*

—THE EDITOR.

ACKNOWLEDGMENTS

Anderson, Sherwood: from WINESBURG, OHIO, copyright 1919 by B. W. Huebsch. By permission of The Viking Press, Inc., New York.

Bemelmans, Ludwig: from I LOVE YOU, I LOVE YOU, I LOVE YOU, copyright 1939, 1940, 1941, 1942 by Ludwig Bemelmans. By permission of The Viking Press, Inc., New York.

Benchley, Robert: from THE TREASURER'S REPORT, copyright 1930 by Robert Benchley. By permission of Harper & Brothers, New York.

Benét, Stephen Vincent: from SELECTED WORKS OF STEPHEN VINCENT BENÉT, published by Farrar & Rinehart, Inc. Copyright 1933 by The Butterick Company. By permission of Brandt & Brandt for the Estate of Stephen Vincent Benét.

Benson, Sally: from JUNIOR MISS, copyright 1939, 1940, 1941 by Sally Benson. By permission of Random House, Inc.

Boyle, Kay: first appeared in *The New Yorker*. Copyright by Kay Boyle. By permission of Kay Boyle and Ann Watkins, Inc.

Brookhouser, Frank: copyright 1940 by Story Magazine, Inc.

Callaghan, Morley: first published in *Story*. Copyright 1943 by Story Magazine, Inc., copyright by Morley Callaghan. By permission of Harold Matson.

Canfield, Dorothy: copyright 1940 by Story Magazine, Inc. By permission of Dorothy Canfield Fisher.

Churchill, Winston S.: from A ROVING COMMISSION, copyright 1930 by Charles Scribner's Sons. By permission of Charles Scribner's Sons. In Canada MY EARLY LIFE by Winston S. Churchill, published by The Macmillan Company of Canada, Ltd.

Damon, Bertha: from GRANDMA CALLED IT CARNAL, copyright 1938 by Bertha Damon. By permission of Simon and Schuster, Inc.

Day, Clarence: from LIFE WITH FATHER, copyright 1920, 1922, 1923, 1924, 1933, 1934, 1935 by Clarence Day. By permission of Alfred A. Knopf, Inc.

Edman, Irwin: from PHILOSOPHER'S HOLIDAY, copyright 1938 by Irwin Edman. By permission of The Viking Press, Inc., New York.

Eisenberg, Frances: from THERE'S ONE IN EVERY FAMILY, published by J. B. Lippincott Company (A Story Press Book), copyright 1941 by Frances Eisenberg. By permission of J. B. Lippincott Company.

Ellis, Havelock: from MY LIFE, copyright 1940 by William Heinemann Ltd. By permission of Houghton Mifflin Company.

Farnham, Alice: copyright 1944 by Story Magazine, Inc. By permission of Alice Farnham Russell and Harry Altshuler.

Faulkner, William: first published in *The Saturday Evening Post,* copyright 1942 by Curtis Publishing Company. By permission of William Faulkner.

Fessier, Michael: first published in *Story*. Copyright 1935 by Story Magazine, Inc., copyright by Michael Fessier. By permission of Harold Matson.

Fifield, William: copyright 1941 by Story Magazine, Inc.

Fishbaugh, W. E.: copyright 1939 by Story Magazine, Inc.

Gibbs, Wolcott: copyright 1929 by *The New Yorker*. By permission of Wolcott Gibbs.

Gill, Brendan: first published in *The New Yorker*. Copyright 1940 by The F-R Publishing Corporation. Reprinted by permission of Brendan Gill and *The New Yorker*.

Grahame, Kenneth: from THE GOLDEN AGE. By permission of Dodd, Mead & Company, Inc.

Grove, Walt: copyright 1945 by Story Magazine, Inc. By permission of Walt Grove.

Hemingway, Ernest: from THE FIFTH COLUMN AND THE FIRST FORTY-NINE STORIES, copyright 1938 by Ernest Hemingway. By permission of Charles Scribner's Sons.

Huxley, Aldous: from MORTAL COILS, copyright 1922 by Aldous Huxley. By permission of Harper & Brothers. In Canada by permission of Oxford University Press for Chatto and Windus.

Kantor, MacKinlay: from AUTHOR'S CHOICE, copyright 1944 by MacKinlay Kantor. By permission of Coward-McCann, Inc.

Keller, Helen: from THE STORY OF MY LIFE, copyright 1902, 1903 by Helen Keller. By permission of Doubleday, Doran & Company, Inc.

Lincoln, Victoria: from GRANDMOTHER AND THE COMET, published by Farrar & Rinehart, Inc., copyright 1944 by Victoria Lincoln. By permission of Victoria Lincoln.

Mansfield, Katherine: from THE SHORT STORIES OF KATHERINE MANSFIELD, copyright 1922, 1923, 1924, 1926, 1937 by Alfred A. Knopf, Inc. By permission of Alfred A. Knopf and Constable & Company, Ltd., London, and Society of Authors, by Denys Kilham Roberts.

Marks, Marjorie: copyright 1939 by Story Magazine, Inc. By permission of Marjorie M. Mayer.

Mencken, H. L.: from HAPPY DAYS, copyright 1939, 1940 by Alfred A. Knopf, Inc. By permission of Alfred A. Knopf, Inc.

Nathan, George Jean: from BEWARE OF PARENTS, copyright 1943 by George Jean Nathan. By permission of Farrar & Rinehart, Inc., Publishers.

Porter, Katherine Anne: from THE LEANING TOWER, copyright 1944 by Katherine Anne Porter. Reprinted by permission of Harcourt, Brace and Company, Inc.

Proust, Marcel: from SWANN'S WAY, copyright 1943 by Modern Library, Inc. By permission of Random House, Inc.

Rawlings, Marjorie Kinnan: from WHEN THE WHIPPOORWILL, copyright 1931, 1932, 1933, 1934, 1936, 1939, 1940 by Marjorie Kinnan Rawlings. By permission of Charles Scribner's Sons.

Santayana, George: from PERSONS AND PLACES, copyright 1944 by Charles Scribner's Sons. By permission of Charles Scribner's Sons.

Saroyan, William: copyright by William Saroyan. By permission of Harold Matson.

Singer, Jeanne: copyright 1943 by Story Magazine, Inc.

Skinner, Cornelia Otis: from SOAP BEHIND THE EARS, copyright 1941 by Cornelia Otis Skinner. By permission of Dodd, Mead & Company, Inc.

Steinbeck, John: from THE LONG VALLEY, copyright 1938 by John Steinbeck. By permission of The Viking Press, Inc.

Street, James: Copyright by James Street. By permission of Harold Matson.

Stuart, Jesse: first published in *Household Magazine.* Copyright 1943 by Capper Publications, Inc., Publishers of *Household.* By permission of Jesse Stuart.

Tarkington, Booth: from PENROD, published by Doubleday, Doran & Company, Inc., copyright 1914, 1942 by Booth Tarkington. By permission of Brandt & Brandt.

Thurber, James: from MY LIFE AND HARD TIMES, copyright 1933 by James Thurber. By permission of James Thurber.

Traver, Robert: from TROUBLE SHOOTER, copyright 1943. By permission of The Viking Press, Inc.

Twain, Mark: from Mark Twain's AUTOBIOGRAPHY, published by Harper & Brothers, copyright 1924 by Clara Gabrilowitsch. By permission of Harper & Brothers.

Ware, Edmund: copyright 1934 by Story Magazine, Inc. By permission of Brandt & Brandt for Edmund Ware Smith.

Welty, Eudora: from A CURTAIN OF GREEN, copyright 1936, 1937, 1938, 1939, 1941 by Eudora Welty. By permission of Doubleday, Doran & Company, Inc.

Wolfe, Thomas: from LOOK HOMEWARD, ANGEL, copyright 1927, 1928 by *The New Republic,* copyright, 1929 by Charles Scribner's Sons. By permission of Charles Scribner's Sons.

1. *SUNRISE*

Roof Sitter

FRANCES EISENBERG

FROM THE very beginning there were two things wrong with my brother Joe. He was shy and he was stubborn. This is the way he did. If somebody tried to make him not shy, then he got stubborn. Like the time when he was only four years old and he was supposed to be a butterfly in the Sunday school entertainment, and Miss Willson tried and tried to push Joe out on the stage and make him flutter his wings, but Joe lay down on the floor of the stage and wouldn't get up no matter how much the other butterflies stepped on him.

And when he started to kindergarten and his teacher kept asking him to come up in front and tell the other children about his pets, Joe ran out of the room and hid downstairs in the boys' toilet until they had to call the janitor to get him out.

My mother had tried her best to make Joe not like he was, but when he was six years old she had to give up. She said she hoped he would outgrow it. And she asked Joe's teacher please not to try to draw Joe out any more because of the way it made him act. So after that everybody let him alone.

One morning in June just after school was out we got a telegram from Nashville saying that my father's Aunt Sadie was in a dying condition, and for them to come quick. At first my mother didn't know what to do, because she knew they wouldn't want any children there, and there wasn't anybody to leave us with. And she thought a while, and then all of a sudden she said, "Sarah Blevins."

"Who is that?" I asked. I was standing there watching my mother.

"She is a College Student," said my mother. "She is Mrs. White down the street's niece, and she is staying with her and earning her way through college by taking care of children and things like that this summer."

So my mother hurried down to Mrs. White's house, and I went too, and Mrs. White was out in the yard, and she said that Sarah Blevins would be glad to take care of us while my mother and father were gone. "She is very good with children," Mrs. White said. "She has had some courses in child training at the College, and she knows all about them. She will try out some new ideas on your children."

Then Mrs. White called Sarah Blevins out and she was a tall skinny girl with glasses on and a serious look. She told my mother that she would be glad to stay with us, and would give us the best of care. "How old are these children?" Sarah Blevins asked, looking at me, and stretching her mouth a little, like a smile.

"This is Helen," my mother said. "She is nine. And Joe, her little brother, is six."

"Oh, that's very fortunate," Sarah Blevins said, "because I have just finished a course in the child from six to twelve years, and that includes both of your children."

"Yes," said my mother. "But please be careful with little Joe. He is a very shy child, and doesn't like to be noticed. As long as he's left alone though, he's very nice. Just so you don't try to draw him into the limelight."

Sarah Blevins looked interested. "I'm very good on behavior problems," she said. "I will try to adjust your little boy. I have done a lot of field work on problem children."

My mother looked worried. "Oh, there's nothing wrong with Joe," she said. "He's just a little young for his age. If you let him alone he'll be all right."

"I'm sure we'll get along splendidly together," said Sarah Blevins, stretching her mouth at me again. She went into her aunt's house and came out with her clothes in a little bag, and we all hurried back to our house because my mother had to meet my father in town and catch the one o'clock train.

When we got to our yard Joe was playing under the sweet-gum tree. He had some rocks and little sticks, and when he saw Sarah Blevins he stared at her for a minute and went on playing.

"This is Joe," said my mother in a hurry. "Joey this is Sarah Blevins. She is going to take care of you while mother is gone, and you must be a good little boy and do what she says." Then my mother went into the house to get ready.

Joe stared at Sarah Blevins again, and then he began to hammer a stick into the ground with a rock. Sarah Blevins went over to Joe and held out her hand. "How do you do, Joe," she said.

Joe began to look nervous. He twisted his head around so he couldn't see her, but she kept on holding her hand out for him to shake. When she saw he wasn't going to shake hands with her finally she put her hand down. She looked at the sticks and the rocks he was playing with.

"Oh, a house," she said. "Joe is building a nice house. Who will live in your house when it is built? Is it a fairy house? Will a tiny fairy live in it?"

Joe put his arm up and hid his face. Then he went over and stood behind a bush where Sarah Blevins couldn't see him. All you could see was a piece of his head.

"He doesn't like for people to talk to him," I told Sarah Blevins. "Just the family. He's shy of people."

Sarah Blevins looked a little mad. "Yes, but that's very wrong to encourage him in it," she said. "That way he'll get conditioned and then it will be hopeless. He should be drawn out."

"He doesn't like to be drawn out," I told her. "That just makes him worse."

"Not if it's done right," she said. She began to pretend that she didn't know where Joe was. "There was a little boy here a minute ago," she said. "Where did he go? Maybe he had on a pair of magic shoes, or maybe he changed into a flower or a butterfly?"

Joe heard what she was saying and he squatted down quickly behind the bush. He tried to crawl into it, but it was full of stickers.

Just then my mother came out of the house with her hat on. She kissed me good-bye. "Joe is behind the bush," I told her.

My mother went over and kissed him good-bye. "Be a good boy," she told him. "Good-bye," she said to Sarah Blevins. "I know you're going to be fine with the children. Just take charge of things, and order what you need from the grocery. We'll be back by Wednesday at least."

Then she got into the taxi and rode away.

It seemed very lonely without her. Sarah Blevins stood still a minute, then she said, "I will just leave your little brother alone for the time being." And she took her bag and we went into the house and I showed her where to put her things.

After a while, when she had looked in the icebox to see what food there was, she got a piece of paper and began to write on it. She told me she was writing out what for me to do every hour of the day and beginning tomorrow I must do exactly what it said. She stuck the paper on the kitchen door with some thumbtacks.

"Now you must take care of everything for a few minutes," she said. "I am going to run down to the grocery store and get some celery. Your little brother seems to be lacking in iron."

While she was gone I went out and hunted for Joe. He was digging holes in the back yard.

"Is she gone yet?" he asked. I knew he meant Sarah Blevins.

"She is gone, but she is coming back in a minute," I told him. "She has gone to get something for you to eat to give you iron."

"I don't want iron," Joe said.

"But listen, Joe," I told him. "She is supposed to take care of us, and we are supposed to mind her while mother and father are away. So don't be stubborn. Do what she says, and maybe they will bring us something nice."

"I don't like her," Joe said.

I didn't know what else to say to Joe. I could see that he was going to be stubborn, but I didn't know how to make him not be.

Pretty soon I could hear Sarah Blevins in the kitchen fixing the supper, and after a while she called us in to eat it.

It was mostly lamb chops and celery and carrots with nothing for dessert. All through supper Sarah Blevins talked to Joe. She asked him things like did he like furry kittens, and did he ever see a brownie, and things like that. But Joe was so hungry that he didn't hide anywhere. He would take a bite of whatever it was, and then he would put his head under the table to chew it so he wouldn't have to look at Sarah Blevins. And just as soon as he got through eating he went into the living room and turned on the radio to the Krunchy Krispy Kiddies hour and I went in there too, and we listened to it.

It had got to the place where the twins had sailed to the moon in their rocket ship and found the palace of King Zoozag, the moon king. While the twins were looking around for the moon pearl, King Zoozag's magician had caught them and locked them up in a dungeon with a ceiling that kept coming down closer and closer to crush the twins to pieces. It was very exciting. The roof was just above their heads and you could hear it giving awful creaks, and you could hear the king laughing an awful laugh, hahahaha, when all of a sudden Sarah Blevins came rushing in there looking like she was going to faint. She ran over and turned off the radio.

"My goodness," she said. She sat down in a chair and got her breath. "No wonder," she said. "No wonder your little brother has got a complex if your mother lets him listen to such things as that. Especially at night."

Joe had been sitting up close to the radio listening with his mouth open, but when Sarah Blevins turned it off, he turned around and stared at her with his mouth still open.

"Now," Sarah Blevins said, after a minute, in a cheerful voice. "Let's tell stories. Shall we? First I'll tell a story, then Helen will tell one and then Joe will. Or maybe Joe would tell his first."

Joe kept looking at her for just a minute, and then he shook his head. But Sarah Blevins paid no attention to that. "Joe's going to tell us a story, Helen," she said. "Won't that be nice? I wish Joe would tell us a story about a little white rabbit. Don't you?"

"Yes, but he won't," I told her. "He doesn't like to talk before people."

"Oh, yes, Joe will. I know he will," Sarah Blevins said. She gave me a kind of a mad look. "Joe will tell us a story."

Joe put his head down in a corner of the chair, and pulled a cushion over it.

"You see," I said. "He won't."

"Shhhh," hissed Sarah Blevins, frowning at me. "Yes he will," she said out loud. "Just as soon as he thinks awhile he will. Let's be quiet and let him think. Oh, what a nice story Joe is going to tell us."

For a little while we were quiet and Joe didn't take his head out.

"Now," Sarah Blevins said finally. "Now I think Joe is ready to begin. But where is Joe?" she asked in a surprised voice. "Why he was here just a minute ago. Where can he be? Is he behind the radio?" She went over there and looked. "No, he's not there. Is he behind the door? No." Then she went over to the chair where Joe was and lifted up the cushion. "Why *here* he is."

But before she could say anything else Joe slid out of the chair and ran upstairs.

"I guess he's going to hide in the bathroom," I told Sarah Blevins. "Sometimes he does that when ladies bother him because they can't go in there after him."

Sarah went to the foot of the stairs. "Joe's sleepy," she said in a loud voice. "I guess he wants to go to bed. He will tell us a story tomorrow. Good night Joe."

Then she came back and sat down in the living room. She looked sort of mad. "Helen," she said, "you must keep quiet when I'm talking to Joe. What's wrong with him now is that he's heard people say he's shy so much that he thinks he is shy. So he acts shy. He isn't really shy, he only thinks he is. When he withdraws like this you must pretend it's just a game he's playing, or you must explain it to him like I did just now and make it reasonable. Have I made it clear to you? Do you understand?"

"I don't know if I do or not," I said.

"Well it doesn't matter. Just so you keep quiet and let me manage your little brother my own way. By the time your mother comes back I'll have him adjusted. But you must co-operate."

"All right," I told her. Because it would be nice and my mother would be glad if she got home and Joe was talking to people and not running from them any more, and not being stubborn and singing little songs when they asked him to, and making speeches and things like that. So I would do like Sarah Blevins said, and be quiet and pretend I didn't know why he was hiding.

The next morning we had breakfast and I looked on the paper to see what I was supposed to do. I was supposed to do Household Tasks for a half an hour. Sarah Blevins told me to go upstairs and make up my bed, and then come down and play outdoors until lunch. So I went up and began to clean up the bedroom, and I looked out of the window and saw Joe playing in the front yard. He had some marbles and he was putting them in a row on the grass.

Pretty soon I saw Sarah Blevins coming out there and she had some papers in her hands. "Hello, Joe," she said. She sat down on the grass beside him.

"May I play with you?" she asked, stretching her mouth into a smile at him.

Joe looked down at the ground and began to pick up the marbles one at a time. He would not look at Sarah Blevins.

"Would you like to play a game that I have here?" Sarah Blevins said. She put one of the papers down on the grass. "It's a game with pictures. Look. It's fun. Do you want to play it with me?"

Joe began to shake his head. He began to slide away from her a little toward the bush.

"See the little girl in the picture," Sarah Blevins told him, holding it up. "She is rolling a hoop. But something is missing. Can you take the red pencil and put in what is missing?"

Joe kept shaking his head and Sarah kept holding out the pencil to him. Finally Joe got up and ran to the bush and hid behind it. But Sarah went over there too and sat down. "It's nicer over here, isn't it Joe?" she said. "Let's don't play that game then, let's play another one. Listen."

She took another piece of paper and began to read off of it.

"The sun was shining on the sea, shining with all its might. Can you say that, Joe? Listen. The sun was shining on the sea, shining with all its might. Now you say it."

But Joe began to look more nervous than ever, and he went around to the other side of the bush, and Sarah followed him around there. She kept on talking. "This is fun, isn't it, Joe?" she said. "It's like a game I know called follow the leader. Did you ever play that game?"

Joe began to look kind of wild. He looked for another place to hide. There wasn't any. He ran toward the front porch, but I guess he thought that wouldn't be any good, and all of a sudden he started climbing up the rose trellis. There weren't many roses on it, and it was just like a ladder. He went halfway up and then he turned his head around to see if Sarah was coming.

This time she did not follow him. But anyway he climbed on higher until he got to the porch roof, and then he crawled up on it and sat there and looked down at Sarah.

I spread up the bed in a hurry and went on downstairs and out into the yard to where they were. I wanted to see what Sarah was going to do next to adjust Joe.

Sarah was standing there on the ground looking up at the roof. Her face was red and she looked sort of mad, but she laughed and said to me, "Did you see Joe go up the trellis? He's playing that he's a little squirrel, I guess. Did you see him climb?"

"Yes," I said. I was not going to say anything else, because I was supposed to co-operate with her and keep quiet.

"I wonder how a little squirrel comes down off a roof," Sarah Blevins said. "Can you show us, Joe?"

We waited about ten minutes, but Joe did not come down. He went over and sat down behind the chimney. We could just see his legs and a piece of his blouse.

Then I forgot. "We could get the stepladder and get him down that way," I told Sarah Blevins. She gave me an awful mad look.

"Be quiet," she said under her breath. Then she said in a loud voice, "Why, we don't want to get a little squirrel down with a ladder. He will come down himself in a little while to get some nuts."

"Or maybe he thinks he's a bird," I said.

But Sarah Blevins didn't pay any attention to me. "I'm going to fix your lunch now, and when I get back I wouldn't be surprised if Joe is on the ground playing with you, Helen," she said. "Being a squirrel is fun, but after all it's nicer to be a little boy, isn't it?" And she took the papers and things and went into the house.

I sat down on the ground and looked up at Joe.

After a while I said, "Sarah Blevins has gone inside now, Joe. Why don't you come down off of the roof and surprise her?"

Joe got from behind the chimney. "No," said Joe. After a minute he asked, "When is she going home?"

"Maybe not till next Wednesday," I said. "So come on down and do what she says. We're supposed to."

"I'll come down next Wednesday," Joe said.

I could see that he was going to be stubborn and not come down off of the roof, and then Sarah Blevins couldn't adjust him before mother came back. I didn't know what to do, so I just sat there and tried to think of something.

After a while some children from the next block came skating along the sidewalk. "What are you doing, Helen?" they asked.

"Nothing," I told them. "Only sitting here waiting for my little brother Joe to come down off of the roof."

They came up in the yard and looked up at Joe's face, which was sticking over.

"What is he doing up there?" they asked.

"Just waiting. He's going to sit there until next Wednesday."

They all stood there staring at Joe with their mouths open.

Just then an automobile with two men in it came driving slowly along the street. The men looked out at us and stopped the car. A fat one stuck his head out the window. "Hey, kids," he said. "Having a big time with school out and everything?"

"Yes sir," we said.

"Well sir, how would you like to have your pictures on the Kiddies Vacation page of the *Morning Journal* so all the other kids all over the city can see what fun you are having. Would you like that?"

"Yes sir," we told him.

So they got out of the car and the thin one had a camera. The fat one told us to stand in a line with our hands on each others shoulders and pretend that we were skating. One of the other children said, "Hey, mister, can Joe be in the picture?"

"Sure, sure," the fat man said. "Who is Joe, your dog?"

"No," I told him. "He's my little brother. He's up there." I pointed up at the roof.

"Sure Joe can be in it," the fat man said. "Hold everything Bill," he said to the man with the camera. "Come on down, Joe," he said.

"He can't be in the picture if he has to come down to be in it," I told the man. "He's going to stay up there all the rest of this week and some more too."

"Ha, ha," laughed the fat man. "That's a new one, ain't it. All over town they're sitting in trees, but he's the first roof sitter. Well, I'll tell you what. We wouldn't want Joe to spoil his record, so we'll take a picture of him from the ground. The rest of you can stand around and be looking up at Joe. We'll give him some free publicity."

So we all stood around and pointed up at the roof, and the cameraman clicked the picture so quick that Joe couldn't hide his face or do anything about it. Then the man asked us our names and how old we were, what grades at school we were in, and then they got in their car and drove away. And the children from the next block hurried home to tell their mothers about having their pictures taken. And just then Sarah Blevins came to the door and said lunch was ready. "We have peanut butter sandwiches, Helen," she said. "Maybe Joe will come down and get some."

But he didn't. I went in and sat down at the table.

"A man took our pictures," I told Sarah Blevins.

But she didn't pay any attention. I guess she was thinking what to do next to adjust Joe. When we finished lunch she said we would just let Joe alone until he got hungry, and she put the dishes to soak and sat down and began to look at a magazine.

I went outside and stayed in the front yard. So the afternoon went by and it was beginning to get dark, and after a while it was really dark, and still Joe was on the roof.

I went in the house to see if supper was ready and to ask Sarah Blevins what she was going to do.

"It's dark," I said, "and Joe is still up on the roof. He still won't come down."

"Go out and tell him that supper is ready," said Sarah Blevins. "But do not tell him to come down. He must decide that for himself. He must make up his own mind what he is going to do. If I make him come down now, everything will be ruined."

So I went out and told Joe supper was ready. "Don't you want any?" I asked him.

His voice sounded very weak and far away. "No," he said.

"Are you going to sleep up there?" I asked him.

"Yes," he said, and he sounded scared and stubborn at the same time.

I went back and told Sarah Blevins. "Very well," she said.

So we ate supper and it was bedtime, and I went upstairs. I went to the window of my mother and father's bedroom. The moon was shining and I could look down on the porch roof and see Joe, sitting up close to the chimney.

"Are you awake, Joe?" I asked him.

"Yes," his voice came up.

"Good night, then," I said. I went to bed and I felt awful. I thought well anyway he can't roll off, because the roof is wide and flat, but it would be hard and maybe he would be hungry. So after a while I got two pillows and a blanket, and I went to the window and dropped them down to Joe. I didn't care if I had promised Sarah to co-operate. I knew my mother wouldn't want Joe to sleep out-of-doors without a blanket. "Do you want something to eat, Joe?" I asked him low so she wouldn't hear.

"Yes," he said. "I want a peanut butter sandwich and some crackers."

So I went into the kitchen and when I went past the living room I told Sarah Blevins I was going for a drink of water, and I got some peanut butter sandwiches and a whole box of crackers, and I went back up to the window and let them down to Joe by a string.

"But you oughtn't to be so stubborn, Joe," I told him while he was eating them. "You ought to do more what people say and mind them better, or something awful might happen to you."

"I don't care," Joe said. He was fixing the blanket and the pillow. He lay down on them and went to sleep.

The next morning Joe was still on the roof. We talked to him from the upstairs window, but he turned his back because Sarah was there and he wouldn't say anything to her. "Your little brother is a very strange case," Sarah Blevins said to me. She told me to get a bottle of milk and let it down to him, because we couldn't have him starving. And she would think what to do next.

About ten o'clock people began to drive past the house and they would drive slow and point up to our roof. A few of them stopped their cars and came up on the sidewalk and looked. "Little girl," they said to me, "is this where the little boy lives that's sitting on the roof, that his picture was in the *Journal* this morning?"

I went and got the paper and there we all were on the vacation page, and under it it said "Out to establish new record," and "Little Joe Marsden, 7, has joined the ranks of marathon sitters and declares that he will stay on his roof until next Wednesday afternoon."

You couldn't see much of Joe in the picture, only his head. But the rest of us were plain. I ran and showed the paper to Sarah Blevins. "Look!" I said. "Joe got his picture in the paper and look out in the street at the people."

Sarah looked and she turned sort of pale. She asked me some questions, but she didn't listen to what I said. She straightened out her mouth and looked mad. "I'm going out there and try one more time," she said to herself. "And this is the last straw."

"You mean you're not going to try to adjust him any more?" I asked her, following her out into the yard, but she didn't answer me.

She looked up at him from the sidewalk. She changed her voice from mad to sweet. "Helen, do you believe in magic?" she said to me. "I do. I'm going to close my eyes and count to ten, and when I open them I believe Joe will be down off of the roof, standing right here on the grass." Then she shut her eyes and began to count.

By now there were two cars parked in front of the house and a fat man and a woman was in one of them and his face was red and he acted funny. He made funny motions at Joe and he yelled, "Don't you do it, sonny. You stay there. She's just trying to get you down." But he didn't talk plain, and he smelled funny. "Shhhh," the woman in the car said, "shhhh." But she was giggling herself and she acted nearly as funny as her husband.

"Six, seven, eight," Sarah was saying very slow.

But just then something funny seemed to happen to Joe. He looked down and saw the people looking up at him and he heard the fat man yelling, "Don't you do it, sonny." Then all of a sudden instead of hiding from them he began to jump up and down on the roof and yell at Sarah, "This is my house. Let me alone." And then he called her a bad name. "Go home, old jackass," he said.

Sarah opened her mouth and looked surprised. I guess she was surprised that Joe could talk. He had not said anything before her until now.

The fat man began to laugh as loud as he could. "That's telling her!" he said and he drove the car away, and he was sort of whooping as he went and so was his wife. "That's telling her," they said.

The people in the other car stayed though. Twice Sarah started to climb the trellis so she could talk to Joe better, but both times he said, "Let me alone," and looked like he was going to jump. So Sarah had to get down, and she went over and talked to a woman. She told her that in all the time she had worked with children she had never in her life seen one as stubborn as Joe. But she said if everyone had just let him alone she could have had him adjusted, but now everything was spoiled.

But nobody paid much attention to her, because now Joe had turned out to be famous, because he was the only roof sitter in town, and nobody cared what Sarah thought.

The more people stopped and looked up at Joe, the more I got proud of him, and I would tell everybody I was his sister and that he had stayed up there all day and all night and was going to stay on until Wednesday, and everybody asked me questions about him and laughed, and about three o'clock some newsreel cameramen that were in town for something else took some pictures of Joe for the movies.

It was just after this that my father and mother came home. When they got out of the taxi my mother saw the people standing there and began to look scared. "What is it?" she said. "What's happened?"

"Look, Mother. Look, Daddy," I yelled, pointing up to the roof. "Joe's up there. He's been up there nearly two days. He had his picture in the paper, and the people have been coming to see him all day. He's famous now."

Then Sarah Blevins ran over and began talking fast, and she was really crying. She kept saying things about how she had tried to adjust Joe, and then these people began to come and notice him and encourage him, and everything was spoiled.

"And he called her a jackass," I said. "And this is the stubbornest he ever was in his life. But now he's not shy any more. He didn't hide from the people. Aren't you glad Joe's going to be in the movies, and everybody will get to see him?"

But my father and mother didn't seem to be glad. And my father climbed up the trellis to get Joe, and Joe started to jump off, but when he saw that Sarah was leaving he said he would come down now. And Sarah went away with her little black bag, and she said she was so nervous she didn't know what she was doing. All the people went away, and that was the end of Joe being a roof sitter. He had to eat his supper and go to bed, even if it wasn't dark, and he couldn't have any of the box of candy they had brought from Nashville where they had left and come home because my father's Aunt Sadie had turned out not to be so sick after all.

But Joe was famous for several days and all over town children began sitting on roofs, trying to break the record. One of them, a little girl named Gladys Potts, sat on her garage roof for ninety-three hours, but a storm came up, and she had to come down.

And another thing, it seemed that all the attention he had got had adjusted Joe, because he was hardly at all shy after that, and not so stubborn. He stopped hiding from people, and he would be in plays and things if he could have some bananas afterward. And at school the next year he let them dress him up in a long-tailed coat and long trousers and be an usher in a Tom Thumb wedding. So I guess it was a good thing after all.

The Sunrise

W. E. FISHBAUGH

THEY WERE at breakfast and his father, looming big at the head of the table, was buttering a slice of bread with enthusiasm. The house was still chilly. The fire had not "come up" yet, they both had said, and he was thickly wrapped in his woolens with even blankets swathed around his feet for warmth. His mother was reaching around in front of him busily tucking in a napkin and drawing up his dish of oatmeal and beneath the table, seeming at a great distance, he rubbed one foot against the other contentedly.

She sugared his oatmeal and gave him a spoon to eat it with.

"A wonderful sunrise this morning!" his father remarked loudly and warmly from the table end.

With a chuckle of remembrance he reached for the coffeepot, swooped it toward him and tipped it up above his cup.

"Was it?" his mother murmured. "I didn't notice."

The coffee poured glittering dark amber. He watched it.

She took the pitcher of milk and refilled his oatmeal dish. He looked down in front of him and saw it swim over the warm, gray porridge.

"Rose and gold!" his father said, with a tremor of worship. "Rose and gold!"

He clumped the pot heavily back on its pad and then began spooning coffee into his mouth noisily.

"I didn't notice," his mother murmured.

She lifted small spoonfuls to her mouth, humbly.

He only played at eating his oatmeal. Usually he much enjoyed it. Also his warm feet. But he was waylaid now by the strange talk.

What was a sunrise? he wondered, stirring with his spoon.

"Wouldn't have missed it for the world," his father commented between gulps.

He ate his bread butter side to the tongue, always with great gestures, and he leaned his shoulders over and dominated his place at the table as though he would take the whole thing in, tablecloth and all.

"Great sight! Something to miss, I can tell you!"

He sat then, with a stilled spoon watching his father's heavy, swooping gestures fascinatedly, and a little mistrustfully. He was almost too much for him. His great activity was bewildering, disturbing. His voice boomed and he handled everything with great hearty movements of his arms and shoulders.

When his father had finally gone away from the table to work he finished his oatmeal very quickly. He pushed the empty dish away from him, not thinking about it.

"What's a sunrise?" he asked his mother.

She took his napkin off and wiped his mouth with it.

"Why, you know what the sun is, don't you, Paul?"

"Yes, but what's a sunrise?"

"Why—it's just the sun. When it comes up, you know. It rises every morning. Sun . . . rising . . . that's the sunrise."

"Well—but what's it like?"

"Oh, it's—always different. . . . It's before you *see* the sun, really . . . and the sky gets colored."

She looked off trying to think how to explain it to him.

"Why! Like a sun*set*!" she exclaimed, suddenly realizing. "Like a sun*set,* only it's *behind* our house instead of in front of it! And it's in the morning, of course."

"Like a *sunset*?" he asked doubtfully.

He had seen *them*. *They* weren't strange, like his father seemed to make out sunrises were. The birds got silent then, and other things began to make a noise (crickets they told him). That was what happened at sunset. There wasn't any of that strangeness any more. But he couldn't make his mother understand what he meant. He didn't have the words.

"Yes. That's what it's like. Just like a sunset," she told him, starting to clear the table. "Only it's turned around, you see."

But he knew it couldn't be. His father had never acted like that about sunsets. Nothing at all like that.

"Rose and gold!" his father had said. And the tone of the voice and its trembling had struck deep down in his mind.

What were they really like? he wanted to know. What could a sunrise be that it did that to his father? He would like to feel that way.

One night at supper his father, before the rest of the family had sat down to the table, looked at him in a queer way and said, "Your mother tells me you want to know what a sunrise is."

And then his feeling of strangeness about his father was gone, suddenly.

He swallowed and looked up at him and said eagerly, "Yes. What is it?"

His father paused a moment, and then said, still looking queerly, "Well, it can't be told very well. You'll have to see one yourself, first."

And of course he realized he couldn't do that and he began to feel bad.

But they kept on looking at each other. "Sometime," his father said, "when I see one at the proper time, maybe I'll wake you up and show it to you. Shall I?"

"Yes," he said, squirming forward. "I want to!"

"All right," his father said, picking up the carving knife, "sometime soon."

"What's this? What's this?" the others who had now come to the table were asking.

"Tend to your plates," his father told them. "It's between Paul and me. Tend to your plates, now!"

Then his mother came and set the platter of meat on the table.

"It's rather fat beef," she said. "You'd better not give them too much at first . . ."

Each night after that he lay in his bed in the dimming light listening to the sparrows chirping monotonously in the eaves outside his window, and hearing the clatter of the dishes being washed downstairs and he would wonder if the next morning would be the one. Moving sleepily beneath the warm covers he would wonder drowsily how it would be.

At the proper time, his father had said, and rose and gold. And you hear the milkman then, one of his brothers had told him. He would like looking out the window at the fading light, seeing the branches of the maples becoming less and less distinct against the sky, and sometimes hearing people walking by on the sidewalk below, and sometimes horses' hoofs and with them the grind of wheels, or far off he would hear shouts, or laughter. And sometimes he would hear the older neighbor kids playing Stillwaters. Then after a while everything would become too warm and comfortable for listening and it would all get hazy and soft and he would forget it all and lie there and sink down far away, with the room darkening.

When it did happen the bed was shaking and everything was dark. Everything was shaking and someone big and dark was there, leaning over him and the shaking bed and saying over and over, "Are you awake? . . . Are you awake?"

And then he suddenly knew he was awake. But he was too frightened to think of answering and then the bed stopped shaking.

"Come on now," his father said then, "there's a fine one this morning."

And then the air was cold as the covers suddenly went back off of him and he was lying there in the center of the bed with no covers, shivering in the cold, and he couldn't think at first, or do anything. But his father helped him. He lifted him up then, and wrapped a blanket around him and held him up against his shoulder and carried him off through his dark unfamiliar room and down the dim, cold hall and he saw that the wallpaper was a color he had never seen it before and the light all looked different and as he passed them he saw all the doors to the others' bedrooms were closed yet, and there was the side gas jet glinting with the new light on one wall and there wasn't any sound at all except what they made themselves.

His father's footsteps were just thumps along the hall because he didn't have shoes on and he was carried along like a baby, swaying with the lilt of his stride out into the East storeroom where it was cold and all the trunks were.

He saw they had the same strange light on them and then he was swung around and his eyes hurt from the many windows the light was coming in, and his stomach turned over from the swinging, but then suddenly there it was, all over the sky. And his father said, gently, "There it is. Right up there in the East. Do you see it? It's always there in the East!"

And it was. It was there. He saw it.

There were things that from the shape of them ought to be clouds, but he had never seen clouds a color like they were, and there were bars, or something, going up from behind the furthest houses, but he couldn't look at them long; they hurt his eyes when he tried to. He saw it all, though. He saw everything. And the *East* his father called it. The *East*. So the *East* was the *sunrise* to him, then.

He stared silently at it a long time, and his father looked down at him and chuckled inside. Then he shifted him in his arms. His eyes were strange and flashing.

"Well, now you've seen one," he said. "You've seen your first one."

He pulled the blanket up closer around him, but he couldn't speak yet. He could just keep looking.

"What do you think of it?" his father asked him, chuckling. "There's your sunrise—what do you think of it? Hm-m-m?"

And he looked up quickly into his father's eyes and then back at the sky.

"Has it come up to your expectations?" his father asked. "Hm-m-m? Has it?"

But he couldn't really say anything. He just kept pulling at the blanket and looking out at the sky, and somehow he couldn't release himself from it. He didn't have any words to say anything with and he hardly had any thoughts. The sunrise had him. Something about it had him. While he looked he didn't matter any more. He was gone from himself. And he looked at it for such a long time without speaking that his father began to get tired. He would have looked at it a lot longer, but his father finally said, "Come on, I've got to start the fire and you'd better get back to bed."

So they went back thumping along the hall and he got into his cold bed again and his father went on downstairs.

Then he lay there in the cold bed, thinking, and listening to the noises his father made down in the kitchen. He had seen a sunrise! He didn't know whether it was rose and gold for he didn't know colors. He only knew it had been there, and he had seen it. He had seen a sunrise. It was in the *East* that it came. In the *East. Sunrise.* He thought about it a long time and even though the bed got warm again he did not fall asleep.

Then, later, downstairs at breakfast, he sat again in his special chair at the table and watched his father and mother.

He had a different feeling inside him now.

His mother tucked in his napkin and drew up his oatmeal dish. Then she reached down and felt of his feet. They were cold, and so she got his usual blanket and wrapped them in it. She gave him a spoon to eat with and then she turned away and prepared her own dish.

His father was gulping his coffee and reaching for things the way he always did at breakfast, and soon his mother was lifting her small spoonfuls, humbly.

He ate erratically this morning, in spurts. He would take four spoonfuls of oatmeal in quick succession, and then he would sit still, watching his father, wonderingly. Now and then he glanced at his mother. He wondered why his father didn't speak about it.

After a while he saw his father looking at him.

And then he realized that his father meant there was something new between them.

So they both stopped eating and looked at each other a while.

His mother noticed the stillness and looked up.

She looked over at his father but he was looking down at him. So then she turned and then they both were looking down at him. His mother's look was questioning. His father chuckled and reached for another slice of bread.

"He was up pretty early this morning," he said.

His mother smiled at him, still questioningly.

"Was he?" she asked.

"He saw a sunrise this morning," his father told her.

"Did you, Paul?" his mother asked him.

She smiled and wiped his mouth clean with his napkin.

"He didn't have much to say about it though," his father said. "Lost his tongue there for a minute."

His knife flashed in the buttering.

"*Did* you lose your tongue, Paul?" she asked him, smiling.

She poured more milk on his oatmeal.

He began eating it again.

"So now you *know* what a sunrise is!" she said a little later. "And we don't have to tell you. What *is* a sunrise, Paul? Maybe you can tell *us,* now. . . ."

And he let his spoon rest in the dish and sat back, thinking. Could he?

He remembered it all right. The hallway, the cold storeroom, the new light, the tremendous sky, the cold, the *East.*

"Yes . . ." he began unsurely. "Yes . . . it's like—it's like. . . ." And then he felt very moved.

"But it's *not* like you said," he told her, shaking his head anxiously. "It's not! It's not like a sunset. . . . It's like . . . it's . . . it's a . . . why, it's a *sunrise*!"

And he laughed then.

"It's a *sunrise*!" he went on jubilantly. And suddenly he looked wildly, wide-eyed with the new understanding, at his father.

"It *is*!" he said.

And his father nodded, laughing.

"Yes, it *is*!" he said.

Then he sat back thoughtfully in his chair.

Somehow, it didn't sound quite right, said that way. Something seemed missing. And yet, it was really very clear to him, now he had seen one. . . . The Sunrise. . . .

Very Special Shoes

MORLEY CALLAGHAN

All that winter and into the spring while the rest of the Johnson family waited anxiously for the doctor to decide what was really the matter with Mrs. Johnson, eleven-year-old Mary, who had only been told that her mother was troubled with pains in the legs from varicose veins, stayed home from school to help with the housework and dreamed of a pair of red leather shoes. The shoes had been in a shoestore window over on the avenue. Mary had seen them one day in the winter when she had been walking along slowly with her mother, doing the shopping.

All winter she had dreamed of the shoes. Now she could hardly believe that the day she had been waiting for had come at last. Every Saturday she got twenty-five cents for doing the housework all by herself and today it finally added up to the six dollars which was the price of the shoes. Moving around quietly so she would not wake her mother, Mary finished up the last of the dusting in the living room. She hurried to the window and looked out: on such a day she had been afraid it might rain but the street was bright in the afternoon sunlight. Then she went quickly into the bedroom where her mother slept, with one light cover thrown half over her. "Mother, wake up," she whispered excitedly.

Mrs. Johnson, a handsome woman of fifty with a plump figure and a high color in her cheeks, was lying on her left side with her right arm hanging loosely over the side of the bed: her mouth was open a little, but she was breathing so softly Mary could hardly hear her. Every day now she seemed to need more sleep, a fact which worried Mary's older sisters, Barbara and Helen, and was the subject of their long whispering conversations in their bedroom at night. It seemed to trouble Mr. Johnson too, for he had started taking long walks by himself and he came home with his breath smelling of whiskey. But to Mary her mother looked as lovely and as healthy as ever. "Mother," she called again. She reached over and gave her shoulder a little shake, and then watched her mother's face eagerly when she opened her eyes to see if she had remembered about the shoes.

When her mother, still half asleep, only murmured, "Bring me my purse, Mary, and we'll have our little treat," Mary was not disappointed. She gleefully kept her secret. She took the dime her mother gave her and went up to the store to get the two ice-cream cones, just as she did on other days, only it seemed that she could already see herself coming down the street in the red leather shoes: she seemed to pass herself on the street, wearing the outfit she had planned to wear with the shoes, a red hat and a blue dress. By the time she got back to the house she had eaten most of her own cone. It was always like that. But then she sat down at the end of the kitchen table to enjoy herself watching her mother eat her share of the ice cream. It was like watching a big eager girl. Mrs. Johnson sat down, spread her legs, and sighed with pleasure and licked the ice cream softly and smiled with satisfaction and her mouth looked beautiful. And then when she was finished and was wiping her fingers with her apron Mary blurted out, "Are we going to get my shoes now, Mother?"

"Shoes. What shoes?" Mrs. Johnson asked.

"The red leather shoes I've been saving for," Mary said, looking puzzled. "The ones we saw in the window that we talked about."

"Oh. Oh, I see," Mrs. Johnson said slowly as if she hadn't thought of those particular shoes since that day months ago. "Why, Mary, have you been thinking of those shoes all this time?" And then as Mary only kept looking up at her she went on fretfully, "Why, I told you at the time, child, that your father was in debt and we couldn't afford such shoes."

"I've got the six dollars saved, haven't I? Today."

"Well, your father . . ."

"It's my six dollars, isn't it?"

"Mary, darling, listen. Those shoes are far too old for a little girl like you."

"I'm twelve next month. You know I am."

"Shoes like that are no good for running around, Mary. A pair of good serviceable shoes is what you need, Mary."

"I can wear them on Sunday, can't I?"

"Look, Mary," her mother tried to reason with her, "I know I said I'd get you a pair of shoes. But a good pair of shoes. Proper shoes. Your father is going to have a lot more expense soon. Why, he'd drop dead if he found I'd paid six dollars for a pair of red leather shoes for you."

"You promised I could save the money," Mary whispered. And then when she saw that worried, unyielding expression on her mother's face she knew she was not going to get the shoes; she turned away and ran into the bedroom and threw herself on the bed and pulled the pillow over her face and started to cry. Never in her life had she wanted anything as much as she wanted the red shoes. When she heard the sound of her mother moving pots and pans in the kitchen she felt that she had been cheated deliberately.

It began to get dark and she was still crying, and then she heard her mother's slow step coming toward the bedroom. "Mary, listen to me," she said, her voice almost rough as she reached down and shook Mary. "Get up and wipe your face, do you hear?" She had her own hat and coat on. "We're going to get those shoes right now," she said.

"You said I couldn't get them," Mary said.

"Don't argue with me," her mother said. She sounded blunt and grim and somehow faraway from Mary. "I want you to get them. I say you're going to. Come on."

Mary got up and wiped her face, and on the way up to the store her mother's grim, silent determination made her feel lonely and guilty. They bought a pair of red leather shoes. As Mary walked up and down in them on the store carpet her mother watched her, unsmiling and resolute. Coming back home Mary longed for her mother to speak to her, but Mrs. Johnson, holding Mary's hand tight, walked along, looking straight ahead.

"Now if only your father doesn't make a fuss," Mrs. Johnson said when they were standing together in the hall, listening. From the living room came the sound of a rustled newspaper. Mr. Johnson, who worked in a publishing house, was home. In the last few months Mary had grown afraid of her father: she did not understand why he had become so moody and short-tempered. As her mother, standing there, hesitated nervously, Mary began to get scared. "Go on into the bedroom," Mrs. Johnson whispered to her. She followed Mary and had her sit down on the bed and she knelt down and put the red shoes on Mary's feet. It was a strangely solemn, secret little ceremony. Mrs. Johnson's breathing was heavy and labored as she straightened up. "Now don't you come in until I call you," she warned Mary.

But Mary tiptoed into the kitchen and her heart was pounding as she tried to listen. For a while she heard only the sound of her mother's quiet voice, and then suddenly her father cried angrily, "Are you serious? Money for luxuries at a time like this!" His voice became explosive. "Are we going crazy? You'll take them back, do you hear?" But her mother's voice flowed on, the one quiet voice, slow and even. Then there was a long and strange silence. "Mary, come here," her father suddenly called.

"Come on and show your father your shoes, Mary," her mother urged her.

The new shoes squeaked as Mary went into the living room and they felt like heavy weights that might prevent her from fleeing from her father's wrath. Her father was sitting at the little table by the light and Mary watched his face desperately to see if the big vein at the side of his head had started to swell. As he turned slowly to her and fumbled with his glasses a wild hope shone in Mary's scared brown eyes.

Her father did not seem to be looking at the shoes. With a kind of pain in his eyes he was looking steadily at her as if he had never really been aware of her before. "They're fine shoes, aren't they?" he asked.

"Can I keep them? Can I really?" Mary asked breathlessly.

"Why, sure you can," he said quietly.

Shouting with joy Mary skipped out of the room and along the hall, for she had heard her sisters come in. "Look, Barbara, look, Helen," she cried. Her two older sisters, who were stenographers, and a bit prim, were slightly scandalized. "Why, they're far too old for you," Barbara said. "Get out, get out," Mary laughed. "Mother knows better than you do." Then she went out to the kitchen to help her mother with the dinner and watch her face steadily with a kind of rapt wonder, as if she was trying to understand the strange power her mother possessed that could make an angry man like her father suddenly gentle and quiet.

Mary intended to wear the shoes to church that Sunday, but it rained, so she put them back in the box and decided to wait a week. But in the middle of the week her father told her that her mother was going to the hospital for an operation.

"Is it for the pains in her legs?" Mary asked.

"Well, you see, Mary, if everything comes off all right," her father answered, "she may not have any pains at all."

It was to be an operation for cancer, and the doctor said the operation was successful. But Mrs. Johnson died under the anaesthetic. The two older sisters and Mr. Johnson kept repeating dumbly to the doctor, "But she looked all right. She looked fine." Then they all went home. They seemed to huddle first in one room then in another. They took turns trying to comfort Mary, but no one could console her.

In the preparations for the funeral they were all busy for a while because the older sisters were arranging for everyone to have the proper clothes for mourning. The new blue dress that Helen, the fair-haired one, had bought only a few weeks ago, was sent to the cleaners to be dyed black, and of course Mary had to have a black dress and black stockings too. On the night when they were arranging these things Mary suddenly blurted out, "I'm going to wear my red shoes."

"Have some sense, Mary. That would be terrible," Helen said.

"You can't wear red shoes," Barbara said crossly.

"Yes, I can," Mary said stubbornly. "Mother wanted me to wear them. I know she did. I know why she bought them." She was confronting them all with her fists clenched desperately.

"For heaven's sake, tell her she can't do a thing like that," Helen said irritably to Mr. Johnson. Yet he only shook his head, looking at Mary with that same gentle, puzzled expression he had had on his face the night his wife had talked to him about the shoes. "I kind of think Mary's right," he began, rubbing his hand slowly over his face.

"Red shoes. Good Lord, it would be terrible," said Helen, now outraged.

"You'd think we'd all want to be proper," Barbara agreed.

"Proper. It would be simply terrible, I tell you. It would look as if we had no respect."

"Well, I guess that's right. All the relatives will be here," Mr. Johnson agreed reluctantly. Then he turned hopefully to Mary, "Look, Mary," he began. "If you get the shoes dyed you can wear them to the funeral and then you'll be able to wear them to school every day too. How about it?"

But it had frightened Mary to think that anyone might say she hadn't shown the proper respect for her mother. She got the red shoes and handed them to her father that he might take them up to the shoemaker. As her father took the box from her, he fumbled with a few apologetic words. "It's just what people might say. Do you see, Mary?" he said.

When the shoes, now dyed black, were returned to Mary the next day she put them on slowly, and then she put her feet together and looked at the shoes a long time. They were no longer the beautiful red shoes, and yet as she stared at them, solemn-faced, she suddenly felt a strange kind of secret joy, a feeling of certainty that her mother had got her the shoes so that she might understand at this time that she still had her special blessing and protection.

At the funeral the shoes hurt Mary's feet for they were new and hadn't been worn. Yet she was fiercely glad that she had them on. After that she wore them every day. Of course now that they were black they were not noticed by other children. But she was very careful with them. Every night she polished them up and looked at them and was touched again by that secret joy. She wanted them to last a long time.

Introduction to the Universe

H. L. MENCKEN

AT THE instant I first became aware of the cosmos we all infest I was sitting in my mother's lap and blinking at a great burst of lights, some of them red and others green, but most of them only the bright yellow of flaring gas. The time: the evening of Thursday, September 13, 1883, which was the day after my third birthday. The place: a ledge outside the second-story front windows of my father's cigar factory at 368 Baltimore Street, Baltimore, Maryland, U. S. A., fenced off from space and disaster by a sign bearing the majestic legend: AUG. MENCKEN & BRO. The occasion: the third and last annual Summer Nights' Carnival of the Order of Orioles, a society that adjourned *sine die,* with a thumping deficit, the very next morning, and has since been forgotten by the whole human race.

At that larval stage of my life, of course, I knew nothing whatever about the Order of Orioles, just as I knew nothing whatever about the United States, though I had been born to their liberties, and was entitled to the protection of their army and navy. All I was aware of, emerging from the unfathomable abyss of nonentity, was the fact that the world I had just burst into seemed to be very brilliant, and that peeping at it over my father's sign was somewhat hard on my still gelatinous bones. So I made signals of distress to my mother and was duly hauled into her lap, where I first dozed and then snored away until the lights went out, and the family buggy wafted me home, still asleep.

The latter details, you will understand, I learned subsequently from historians, but I remember the lights with great clarity, and entirely on my own. They constitute not only the earliest of all my earthly recollections, but also one of my most vivid, and I take no stock in the theories of psychologists who teach that events experienced so early in life are never really recalled, but only reconstructed from family gossip. To be sure, there is a dead line beyond which even the most grasping memory does not reach, but I am sure that in my own case it must have run with my third birthday. Ask me if I recall the occasion, probably before my second, when I was initiated into the game of I-spy by a neighbor boy, and went to hide behind a wire screen, and was astonished when he detected me—ask me about that, and I'll admit freely that I recall nothing of it whatever, but only the ensuing anecdote, which my poor mother was so fond of telling that in the end I hid in the cellar every time she started it. Nor do I remember anything on my own about my baptism (at which ceremonial my father, so I have heard, made efforts to get the rector tight, and was hoist by his own petard), for I was then but a few months old. But not all the psychologists on earth, working in shifts like coal-miners, will ever convince me that I don't remember those lights, and wholly under my own steam.

They made their flash and then went out, and the fog again closed down. I don't recall moving to the new house in Hollins Street that was to be my home for so many years, though we took possession of it only a few weeks later. I don't recall going into pants at about a quarter to four years, though it must have been a colossal experience, full of pride and glory. But gradually, as my consciousness jelled, my days began to be speckled with other events that, for one reason or another, stuck. I recall, though only somewhat vaguely, the deck of an excursion-boat, *circa* 1885, its deafening siren, and the wide, gray waters of Chesapeake Bay. I recall very clearly being taken by my father to a clothing-store bright with arc-lights, then a novelty in the world, and seeing great piles of elegant Sunday suits, and coming home with one that was tight across the stern. I recall a straw hat with flowing ribbons, a cat named Pinkie, and my brother Charlie, then still a brat in long clothes, howling like a catamount one hot Summer night, while my mother dosed him with the whole pharmacopoeia of the house, and frisked him for outlaw pins. I recall, again, my introduction to the wonderland of science, with an earthworm (*Lumbricus terrestris*) as my first subject, and the experiment directed toward finding out how long it would take him, laid out in the sun on the backyard walk, to fry to death. And I recall my mother reading to me, on a dark Winter afternoon, out of a book describing the adventures of the Simple Simon who went to a fair, the while she sipped a cup of tea that smelled very cheerful, and I glued my nose to the frosty windowpane, watching a lamplighter light the lamps in Union Square across the street and wondering what a fair might be. It was a charming, colorful, Kate Greenaway world that her reading took me into, and to this day I can shut my eyes and still see its little timbered houses, its boys and girls gamboling on village greens, and its unclouded skies of pale blue.

I was on the fattish side as an infant, with a scow-like beam and noticeable jowls. Dr. C. L. Buddenbohn, who fetched me into sentience at 9 p.m., precisely, of Sunday, September 12, 1880, apparently made a good (though, as I hear, somewhat rough) job of it, despite the fact that his surviving bill, dated October 2, shows that all he charged "to one confinement" was ten dollars. The science of infant feeding, in those days, was as rudimentary as bacteriology or social justice, but there can be no doubt that I got plenty of calories and vitamins, and probably even an overdose. There is a photograph of me at eighteen months which looks like the pictures the milk companies print in the rotogravure sections of the Sunday papers, whooping up the zeal of their cows. If cannibalism had not been abolished in Maryland some years before my birth I'd have butchered beautifully.

My mother used to tell me years afterward that my bulk often attracted public notice, especially when it was set off dramatically against her own lack of it, for she was of slight frame and less than average height, and looked, in her blue-eyed blondness, to be even younger than she actually was. Once, hauling me somewhere by horse-car, she was confronted by an old man who gaped at her and me for a while with senile impertinence, and then burst out: "Good God, girl, is that baby *yours?*" This adiposity passed off as I began to run about, and from the age of six onward I was rather skinny, but toward the end of my twenties my cross-section again became a circle, and at thirty I was taking one of the first of the anti-fat cures, and beating it by sly resorts to malt liquor.

My gradually accumulating and clarifying memories of infancy have to do chiefly with the backyard in Hollins Street, which had the unusual length, for a yard in a city block, of a hundred feet. Along with my brother Charlie, who followed me into this vale when I was but twenty months old, I spent most of my pre-school leisure in it, and found it a strange, wild land of endless discoveries and enchantments. Even in the dead of Winter we were pastured in it almost daily, bundled up in the thick, scratchy coats, overcoats, mittens, leggings, caps, shirts, over-shirts and under-drawers that the young then wore. We wallowed in the snow whenever there was any to wallow in, and piled it up into crude houses, forts and snow-men, and inscribed it with wavering scrolls and devices by the method followed by infant males since the Würm Glaciation. In Spring we dug worms and watched for robins, in Summer we chased butterflies and stoned sparrows, and in Autumn we made bonfires of the falling leaves. At all times from March to October we made a Dust Bowl of my mother's garden.

The Hollins Street neighborhood, in the eighties, was still almost rural, for there were plenty of vacant lots near by, and the open country began only a few blocks away. Across the street from our house was the wide green of Union Square, with a fishpond, a cast-iron Greek temple housing a drinking-fountain, and a little brick office and tool-house for the square-keeper, looking almost small enough to have been designed by Chick Sale. A block to the westward, and well within range of our upstairs windows, was the vast, mysterious compound of the House of the Good Shepherd, with nuns in flapping habits flitting along its paths and alleys, and a high stone wall shutting it in from the world. In our backyard itself there were a peach tree, a cherry tree, a plum tree, and a pear tree. The pear tree survives to this day, and is still as lush and vigorous as it was in 1883, beside being thirty feet higher and so large around the waist that its branches bulge into the neighboring yards. My brother and I used to begin on the cherries when they were still only pellets of hard green, and had got through three or four powerful bellyaches before the earliest of them was ripe. The peaches, pears and plums came later in the year, but while we were waiting for them we chewed the gum that oozed from the peach-tree trunk, and practised spitting the imbedded flies and June bugs at Pinkie the cat.

There was also a grape-arbor arching the brick walk, with six vines that flourished amazingly, and produced in the Autumn a huge crop of sweet Concord grapes. My brother and I applied ourselves to them diligently from the moment the first blush of color showed on them, and all the sparrows of West Baltimore helped, but there was always enough in the end to fill a couple of large dishpans, and my mother and the hired girl spent a hot afternoon boiling them down, and storing them away in glass tumblers with tin tops. My brother and I, for some reason or other, had no fancy for the grape jelly thus produced with so much travail, but we had to eat it all Winter, for it was supposed, like camomile tea, to be good for us. I don't recall any like embalming of the peaches, plums and pears; in all probability we got them all down before there were any ripe enough to preserve. The grapes escaped simply because some of them hung high, as in the fable of the fox. In later years we collared these high ones by steeple-jacking, and so paid for escape from the jelly with a few additional belly-aches.

But the show-piece of the yard was not the grape-arbor, nor even the fruit-trees; it was the Summer-house, a rococo structure ten feet by ten in area, with a high, pointed roof covered with tin, a wooden floor, an ornate railing, and jig-saw spirals wherever two of its members came together. This Summer-house had been designed and executed by my mother's father, our Grandfather Abhau, who was a very skillful cabinet-maker, and had also made some of the furniture of the house. Everything of his construction was built to last, and when, far on in the Twentieth Century, I hired a gang of house-wreckers to demolish the Summer-house, they sweated half a day with their crowbars and pickaxes. In the eighties it was the throne-room and justice-seat of the household, at least in Summer. There, on fair Sunday mornings, my father and his brother Henry, who lived next door, met to drink beer, try out new combinations of tobacco for their cigar factory, and discuss the credit of customers and the infamies of labor agitators. And there, on his periodical visitations as head of the family, my Grandfather Mencken sat to determine all the delicate questions within his jurisdiction.

My mother was an active gardener, and during her forty-two years in Hollins Street must have pulled at least a million weeds. For this business, as I first recall her, she had a uniform consisting of a long gingham apron and an old-time slat-bonnet—a head-dress that went out with the Nineteenth Century. Apron and slat-bonnet hung on nails behind the kitchen door, and on a shelf adjoining were her trowels, shears and other such tools, including always a huge ball of twine. My brother Charlie and I, as we got on toward school age, were drafted to help with the weeding, but neither of us could ever make out any difference between weeds and non-weeds, so we were presently transferred to the front of the house, where every plant that came up between the cobblestones of Hollins Street was indubitably verminous. The crop there was always large, and keeping it within bounds was not an easy job. We usually tackled it with broken kitchen knives, and often cut our hands. We disliked it so much that it finally became convict labor. That is to say, it was saved up for use as punishment. I recall only that the maximum penalty was one hour, and that this was reserved for such grave offenses as stealing ginger-snaps, climbing in the pear-tree, hanging up the cat by its hind leg, or telling lies in a gross and obvious manner.

Charlie was somewhat sturdier than I, and a good deal fiercer. During most of our childhood he could lick me in anything approximating a fair fight, or, at all events, stall me. Civil war was forbidden in Hollins Street, but my Grandfather Mencken, who lived in Fayette Street, only three blocks away, had no apparent objection to it, save of course when he was taking his afternoon nap. I remember a glorious day when eight or ten head of his grandchildren called on him at once, and began raising hell at once. The affair started as a more or less decorous pillow-fight, but proceeded quickly to much more formidable weapons, including even bed-slats. It ranged all over the house, and must have done a considerable damage to the bric-a-brac, which was all in the Middle Bismarck mode. My grandmother and Aunt Pauline, fixed by my grandfather's pale blue eye, pretended to be amused by it for a while, but when a large china thunder-mug came bouncing down the third-story stairs and a black hair-cloth sofa in the parlor lost a leg they horned in with loud shrieks and lengths of stove-wood, and my grandfather called time.

Charlie and I were very fond of Aunt Pauline, who was immensely hospitable, and the best doughnut cook in all the Baltimores. When the creative urge seized her, which was pretty often, she would make enough doughnuts to fill a large tin wash-boiler, and then send word down to Hollins Street that there was a surprise waiting in Fayette Street. It was uphill all the way, but Charlie and I always took it on the run, holding hands and pretending that we were miraculously dashing car-horses. We returned home an hour or so later much more slowly, and never had any appetite for supper. The immemorial tendency of mankind to concoct rituals showed itself in these feasts. After Charlie had got down his first half dozen doughnuts, and was taking time out to catch his breath and scrape the grease and sugar off his face, Aunt Pauline would always ask "How do they taste?" and he would always answer "They taste like more." Whether this catechism was original with the high contracting parties or had been borrowed from some patent-medicine almanac or other reference-work I don't know, but it never varied and it was never forgotten.

There were no kindergartens, playgrounds or other such Devil's Islands for infants in those innocent days, and my brother and I roved and rampaged at will until we were ready for school. Hollins Street was quite safe for children, for there was little traffic on it, and that little was slow-moving, and a cart approaching over the cobblestones could be heard a block away. The backyard was enough for us during our earliest years, with the cellar in reserve for rainy days, but we gradually worked our way into the street and then across it to Union Square, and there we picked up all the games then prevailing. A few years ago, happening to cross the square, I encountered a ma'm in horn-rimmed spectacles teaching a gang of little girls ring-around-a-rosy. The sight filled me suddenly with so black an indignation that I was tempted to grab the ma'm and heave her into the goldfish pond. In the days of my own youth no bossy female on the public payroll was needed to teach games to little girls. They taught one another—as they had been doing since the days of Neanderthal Man.

Nevertheless, there was a constant accretion of novelty, at least in detail. When we boys chased Indians we were only following the Sumerian boys who chased Akkadians, but the use of hatchets was certainly new, and so was the ceremony of scalping; moreover, our fiends in human form, Sitting Bull and Rain-in-the-Face, had been as unknown and unimagined to the Sumerian boys as Henry Ward Beecher or John L. Sullivan. The group songs we sang were mainly of English provenance, but they had all degenerated with the years. Here, precisely, is what we made of "King William" in Hollins Street, *circa* 1885:

King William was King James's son;
Upon a ri' a race he won;
Upon his breast he wore a star,
The which was called the life of war.

What a *ri'* was we never knew and never inquired, nor did we attach any rational concept to *the life of war*. A favorite boys' game, called "Playing Se*bast*apool" (with a heavy accent on the *bast*), must have been no older in its outward form than the Crimean War, for Sebastapool was plainly Sevastopol, but in its essence it no doubt came down from Roman times. It could be played only when building or paving was going on in the neighborhood, and a pile of sand lay conveniently near. We would fashion this sand into circular ramparts in some friendly gutter, and then bristle the ramparts with gaudy tissue-paper flags, always home-made. Their poles were slivers of firewood, and their tissue-paper came from Newton's toy-store at Baltimore and Calhoun Streets, which served the boys and girls of West Baltimore for seventy years, and did not shut down at last until the Spring of 1939. The hired girls of the block cooked flour paste to fasten the paper to the poles.

To the garrison of a Sebastapool all the smaller boys contributed tin soldiers, including Indians. These soldiers stood in close and peaceful ranks, for there was never any attempt at attack or defense. They were taken in at night by their owners, but the flags remained until rain washed the Sebastapool away, or the milkman's early morning horse squashed it. There were sometimes two or three in a block. Girls took a hand in making the flags, but they were not allowed to pat the ramparts into shape, or to touch the tin soldiers. Indeed, for a little girl of that era to show any interest in military affairs would have been as indecorous as for her to play leap-frog or chew tobacco. The older boys also kept rather aloof, though they stood ready to defend a Sebastapool against raiders. Tin soldiers were only for the very young. The more elderly were beyond such inert and puerile simulacra, which ranked with rag dolls and paper boats. These elders fought in person, and went armed.

In the sacred rubbish of the family there is a specimen of my handwriting dated 1883—two signatures on a sheet of paper now turned a dismal brown, the one small and rather neat and the other large and ornamented with flourishes. They seem somehow fraudulent, for I was then but three years old, but there they are, and the date, which is in my mother's hand, is very clear. Maybe she guided my stubby fingers. In the same collection there is another specimen dated January 1, 1887. It shows a beginning ease with the pen, though hardly much elegance. My mother also taught me many other humble crafts—for example, how to drive a nail, how to make paper boats, and how to sharpen a lead pencil. She even taught me how to thread a needle, and for a time I hoped to take over darning my own stockings and patching the seats of my own pants, but I never managed to master the use of the thimble, and so I had to give up. Tying knots was another art that stumped me. To this day I can't tie a bow tie, though I have taken lessons over and over again from eminent masters, including such wizards as Joe Hergesheimer and Paul Patterson. When I go to a party someone has to tie my tie for me. Not infrequently I arrive with the ends hanging, and must appeal to my hostess.

This incapacity for minor dexterities has pursued me all my life, often to my considerable embarrassment. In school I could never learn to hold a pen in the orthodox manner: my handwriting satisfied the professors, but my stance outraged them, and I suffered some rough handling until they finally resigned me to my own devices. In later life I learned bricklaying, and also got some fluency in rough carpentering, but I could never do anything verging upon cabinet-work. Thus I inherited nothing of the skill of my Grandfather Abhau. All my genes in that field came from my father, who was probably the most incompetent man with his hands ever seen on earth. I can't recall him teaching me anything in my infancy, not even marbles. He would sometimes brag of his youthful virtuosity at all the customary boys' games, but he always added that he had grown so old (he was thirty-one when I was six) and suffered so much from dead beats, noisy children and ungrateful cigarmakers, drummers and bookkeepers that he had lost it. Nor could he match the endless stories that my mother told me in the years before I could read, or the many songs. The only song I ever heard him sing was this one:

Rain forty days,
Rain forty nights,
Sauerkraut sticking out the smokestack.

Apparently there were additional words, but if so he never sang them. The only *Märchen* in his répertoire had to do with a man who built a tin bridge. I recall nothing of this tale save the fact that the bridge was of tin, which astonished my brother and me all over again every time we heard of it. We tried to figure out how such a thing was possible, for the mention of tin naturally made us think of tomato-cans. But we never learned.

The Birthday Party

VICTORIA LINCOLN

IT WAS late June, and the air pushed in at the open windows in thick, sweetish puffs. It had rained in the night, and the wet clematis over the side porch drugged the early freshness. In the dining room, the loaded honey-rot breath was rolled back and lost in the smell of fried steak and apple pie. Charles Anson Hollander, his wife, and his two children, were at breakfast.

Mr. Hollander sat erect at the table, his left hand, with its narrow fingers and short, clean nails spread on the starched white cloth. Two generations ago, winter breakfast the year round was part and parcel of substantial living. It was an institution, like Mr. Hollander's black cloth coat, his high collar and heavy satin stock. He took a mouthful of pie, and touched his short beard and shaven upper lip with the big napkin. For him, custom was not subject to season.

As for his wife, she always liked a good breakfast. She was a thin, untidy little woman and she ate voraciously, like a fox fattening for the winter. When she thought that her husband was looking the other way, she took a bite or two with her knife. She wore a loose muslin wrapper over her full petticoats, and her black hair was tumbled roughly into a beaver-tail net at her neck. She had big, work-thickened wrists and knuckles. Under her wedding-ring there was a large half-loop of diamonds and turquoises. She was his second wife, and before her marriage she had worked in the cotton-mill.

The two children sat between them at the right and the left, a boy of six and a little girl of two. The boy, Charlie, was pale with the heat. He had clear blue eyes, a soft, receding chin, and long, thin arms. He would be a tall man like his father. He was not eating. He had a doughnut on his plate, and he was picking off its brown skin and piling the bits into a pyramid. His lips moved silently. He was talking to himself. His half-sister, Lizzie, moist and flushed, was tucking into her bowl of bread and milk with exactly her mother's animal concentration. She was a black brunette like her mother, too, but she would be prettier. She had a short little face and very live eyes.

"Well," said Mrs. Hollander, "today's the little Talbot boy's birthday party. Seems like a lot of foolishness to me, all that taking on just because it's a child's birthday. They never done that way when we was little."

"Well, Mary," Mr. Hollander replied, in his even, amiable voice, "I guess people have more time than they used to. It will be a pleasant little outing for you, won't it?"

"Airs and graces," replied Mrs. Hollander with venom. "Airs and graces. She has to have *two* hired girls, she says, to help with a house as big as hers. And party goings-on for a boy six years old!"

Mr. Hollander did not answer her. Her defensive bitterness left him undisturbed. It was like eating with her knife, he thought, a habit of her class, without personal significance. He turned to his son.

"Well, Charlie," he said, "not very hungry?"

The little boy squirmed around in his seat and looked at his father.

"No, sir," he whispered, "not very."

"Well," said his father. "Suppose you're going to have a fine time at the party?"

The child swallowed and nodded. He was not at all sure that he was going to have a fine time, but he hoped so, desperately.

Mrs. Hollander wiped her mouth on the back of her hand and pushed back her chair.

"So long's he ain't sick," she remarked. "But he will be. Always is, when there's any doings going on."

She pushed back her chair and stood up, shaking her petticoats.

"Gracious, Lizzie, ain't you through yet? Mama's going to the kitchen, going to tell Katie what to do. Want to see Katie? Come on, baby."

Mrs. Hollander and her child went out of the room.

When they were alone together a shyness came between father and son. The boy drew the sugar basket towards him and caressed the fat garlands of roses with his fingertips.

The man pulled out his watch and snapped open the case.

"Time for work," he said. "Time to get down to the shop."

He folded his napkin precisely and slid it through the silver ring. He looked at his son. Good blood on both sides there. Hollander and Channing. Good stock. Times when the boy looked so much like Alethea, it startled you.

He stood up.

"Now, Charlie, be a good boy today," he said. It was not what he wanted to say.

Charlie put a crumb of brown doughnut skin between his lips.

"Do men ever go to parties, Papa?"

"I guess not to fancy tea-parties like yours, Charlie."

"I wish you could come to this party, Papa."

"Do you Charlie?"

"Yes, sir."

There was a pause. Then Mr. Hollander said,

"Well, good-day Charlie," and walked out.

They both felt that they had been unusually demonstrative.

At three o'clock Charlie walked out of the house with his mother and Lizzie. He felt stiff and important in his party kilt and he hoped that his curls did not make him look girly. Lizzie trotted along holding her mother's hand with difficulty over the ballooning of crinoline. Her skirts weighted her about so that she toddled with the dignity of a Velásquez infanta. She crooned as she walked, "Lizzie party, Lizzie party."

The sun was hot, but Mrs. Hollander walked along briskly. She liked to feel dove-gray summer silk swelling about her.

It takes up the room of six men, she thought with satisfaction. I'll say that for Charles. He don't scrimp on his wife's clothes. Not one of them big-feeling devils will look as much like a lady as me.

She thrust out her chin. Two hired girls, she thought again. She didn't feel so big when she was carrying her grandpa's dinner-pail over in Pawtucket.

"Step up, Charlie," she said. "Turn your toes out and step up. This ain't no funeral."

Charlie glanced sidewise at his mama. He thought that she looked pretty and elegant when she was all dressed up, and he was glad to think it, for it hurt his conscience that he did not love her. As they turned up the Talbots' carriage drive he could feel her gait stiffen.

"Now, you try to behave yourself, Charlie," she said.

Charlie only swallowed. He always tried to behave himself. He wanted nothing in the world more than affection and approval. His round, weak little chin quivered.

How beautiful it would be, he thought, if Mrs. Talbot was to say to his papa, "Yes, Mr. Hollander, Charlie was the nicest behaving boy at the party."

He would try as hard as he could to do everything just the way he ought to.

Mrs. Talbot opened the door. In spite of the heat she wore black satin, for Mr. Talbot was dead and she was a widow. She had a red face, a large bust and a positive voice.

"Come right in," she said, "and let me close the door. Every time I open it, it's like a furnace. Terrible day. Little Lottie Davis is sick with the heat and couldn't come."

Charlie stumbled over the threshold behind his mother. He was wondering about the airs and graces. He did not see them. Was two hired girls really an awful lot? It was a very big house.

By that time they were in the parlor and it was too late to make a bow and say, "Good-day, Mrs. Talbot." And all the way he had been wondering if it would be nice to do or if she would think it was sissy, and deciding finally that it would be very nice to do.

The children were the same children that he played with every day, but ill-at-ease in their Sunday clothes they all looked different. They were standing around Frank and staring at him as if he was a stranger.

Mrs. Hollander brought her skirts into the middle of the room and looked at Frank, her disapproval of his estate as the center of attention clear in her shallow bright eyes.

"Well, Frank," she said, "how does it feel to be seven?"

Frank looked down at his tasseled boots and answered cautiously, "It feels all right."

"Ma'am," prompted his mother.

"Ma'am," said Frank.

Charlie was sorry for Frank. He hoped that he would not forget to say Ma'am, or otherwise disgrace himself. He felt a moment's envy of Lizzie, who was still a baby and not expected to behave. He edged his way to the most inconspicuous position that he could find.

They played games, clap in and clap out, going to Jerusalem, and spelling-out. The spelling-out had only easy words, for none of the guests was more than eight, and Charlie came out third from the last. He spelled down Billy David, who was eight years old. He was very glad and he could see that his mama was glad, too. The party strain lightened, and he realized that he was having a good time, just as he had hoped to. He did not even feel as if he were going to be sick any more.

When the time came for refreshments they all marched into the dining room, two and two. All the extension-leaves were in, and the table looked very exciting, set for so many. Some of the children tucked their napkins in their necks, but Charlie put his in his lap and sat up as straight as he could. There was a bowl of frozen custard, and a big layer cake with chocolate frosting. It looked lovely. Charlie's clear blue eyes were round and happy.

The hired girls were not in evidence. Mrs. Talbot served out the saucers of frozen custard, and the children and mothers passed them down the table. Then she cut the cake. It was delicate with butter, but not crumbly. Charlie watched the fresh, heavenly slices lean and topple down as the silver knife bore through.

He thought, I'll eat it slow. I'll have the nicest manners.

Mrs. Talbot stood up and took the plate in her hands. She passed down the table, stopping at each place. Charlie watched her coming. The pieces were not exactly equal in size.

How awful it would be, he thought, if I took a very big piece, and they thought I was greedy. I must take a little piece. The littlest of all.

She had come to his place.

But it was so hard to decide which was the meanest, when they were all so fat, so ample. Charlie stared at the plate and could not lift his hand.

Mrs. Talbot said in her positive voice,

"Come, come, Charlie, they're all alike. Don't try to get the biggest slice."

She set a piece of cake down before him and walked on.

Charlie sat perfectly still. He could feel nothing but the awful quietness of his shame. If he could just go on eating, he thought, and not feel sick. It would look so bad if he just left it there. It would look like he was sulking.

He picked up his ice-cream spoon and stared at it. It was a pretty little spoon, smaller than a teaspoon, the bowl washed in gold. He sat staring at it, as if it were the center of life, the most important thing in the world.

The children had begun to giggle, the little, soft, under-the-breath sniggerings concomitant with party manners. The biggest piece, the biggest piece, Charlie tried to get the biggest piece. And Mama would be mad. She set such store on genteel behavior when they were out, and especially somehow, with people she didn't like much. He could not eat the cake, he could not leave it, he could not become invisible. He could only sit turning the pretty spoon over and over between thumb and finger, knowing that he had come to a blank wall, a complete stop. There was no future beyond the awful insoluble minute that was the present.

Then his mother spoke.

"Charlie," she said, "Charlie, listen here a minute, dearie."

He raised his eyes and looked at her, frightened by her voice which was queer, soft and unsteady, the way it got when she was really, terribly mad; when she was only a little mad, which was often, she screamed and hollered. He had only heard this voice once or twice before, and then she had been speaking to his father, and his father had got up quickly to slam the heavy door of his study shut between them and Charlie.

"Charlie," she said now, in that same low voice that shook a little, "see, now, you'd of done better, dear, to do like I said and speak right up and say you don't like none of that sweet stuff."

Charlie stared at her.

"Ma'am?"

And then he saw her eyes, glancing sidewise at Mrs. Talbot, and he understood. It was not with him that she was mad. Under the crinkly black hair her face was white, and her thin lips were shrewdly tightened. She looked like a weasel watching a rabbit. But if the rabbit is fat enough, and mean enough, there is a definite point at which you can't help siding with the weasel. Charlie was spellbound.

"You ought to listened to Mama, Charlie, just like I said when we come in, out there in the hall. But no, you got to be polite and take a piece if it kills you."

The giggling had stopped. Mrs. Talbot's face was already as flushed as it could be, with the heat and her tight stays, but now it mottled a little. Mama's thick fingers stole to her round collar and caressed the handsome diamond brooch that flashed upon it.

Charlie had never noticed it before, but he did now. For the first time he realized that it must have cost a great deal of money, and he was glad that Papa had given it to her, and glad that he had let her buy the new summer silk that took up the room of six men, and the straw bonnet with the velvet flowers that came from New York.

When I grow up, he thought suddenly, I'll give my wife beautiful clothes. If Mama's still alive, I'll give her something, too. I'll give her a handsome pair of bracelets.

He felt bewildered, still, but not sick at all. He felt as if he were beginning to understand something brand new.

Lizzie, stimulated by the excitement in the air, began to bounce on her chair at her mother's side.

"Why, Mama," she said, high and loud, "why Mama, Charlie never . . ."

The hand at the shining brooch flew up and descended on Lizzie's cheek in a hard smack.

"Lizzie Hollander," she said, "you keep quiet. How often I got to tell you not to talk with your mouth full? Thank goodness, I got one child with good manners."

She picked up her spoon and dug into the last of the frozen custard. The party went on.

Now the candy mottoes were passed, the little lozenges that said *Be true, Sweetheart* and *May I see you home?*

A small, plump girl sitting beside Charlie looked at him seriously.

"I just love cake," she said.

"Do you?" said Charlie. "Then why don't you wrap up my slice in your handkerchief when there isn't anyone looking? You could do it easy, when we're all getting up."

She was a very small, plump girl, but her eyes, grateful and applauding, gave Charlie a lovely feeling.

"Don't you like cake, honest?" she asked. "Does it make you sick?"

Charlie smiled, the superior smile of the older man for the charming, unformed young girl.

"Oh, nothing makes me sick," he said, easily. "Once I ate a ball of tar, right off the roof. Once I swallowed a caterpillar."

The little girl shuddered, but her eyes were wide with love.

"Did you like to?"

"Oh, I just did it to show I could. What I like are bitter things, like coffee and wine and beer."

"My," said the little girl. "Do they let you have them?"

Charlie considered for a second. But his hesitation, in this moment of liberated spirit, was for an aesthetic rather than an ethical consideration. Love for womankind stirred the wellsprings of art in him, and he was determined to handle his material with justice and taste.

"No they don't," he said. "Hardly ever. They think I'm too young."

The children were starting to get up from the table. The little girl, dazzled with her first moment of social success, leaned forward suddenly. In her five-year-old breast welled, quick and heavy, age-old womanly feelings, an aching desire for power, for permanence. She snatched at the simple and ancient weapon of blackmail.

"How do you know," she said, "that I won't tell on you, about the tar and the caterpillar?"

Charlie glanced across the table at his mama, the handsomest dressed woman in the room, wearing the fine things his father had given her. A benign sense of security filled him with wisdom beyond his years.

"Oh, you aren't that *kind*," he said, smiling again. "I guess I know a sneak and a tattle-tale when I see one. I don't tell secrets to just everybody."

The power ebbed from her face. He could see that she was undone. In the generosity of his strength he shoved his heap of sugar mottoes towards her hand.

"Here," he said, casually, "take these, too, why don't you? I can get plenty, any time."

He slid down from the table.

"See, now," he said. "There's the cake. It fits right in your pocket. And nobody saw you."

He had wished, when he first entered the house that he was old enough to wear pants, like Billy Davis, but now he felt no disadvantage in kilts and curls and a gold locket. The suitable time would take care of everything. His parents were not the kind to make a baby of a boy. Everyone his age wore kilts. It wasn't clothes that made you a big boy for your age.

The party ended in quiet comfort.

"Good-bye, Mrs. Talbot," he said with sincerity, "I had a real nice time."

He held the door open for the great billowing of his mother's skirts.

They walked down the path a short distance in silence, for Lizzie, stumbling between them, was too full, too hot, too sleepy even to whine.

His mother spoke sharply, but the shrewd edge of her voice was not turned against him.

"Don't you feel bad about missing that old birthday cake, Charlie," she said. " 'Tweren't much good, anyway. First thing when I get home I'll tell Katie to cook you a Lady Baltimore with a dozen yolks and any kind of frosting you say."

Charlie did not answer her directly. He took her hand, as he had never done before of his own volition.

"You looked the nicest, in that new dress, Mama," he said. "You got the biggest diamond pin of any lady in town."

"You done real good on the spelling, Charlie. I'll tell your papa."

They paused.

" 'Spose I'll have to lug you home, Lizzie," she said. "I hate to get mussed, but you certainly do look tuckered."

She picked the child up in her wiry arms.

"My, what a mess of petticoats! A boy'd be easier to cart. Only boys don't need no cartin', do they, Charlie?"

They hesitated for a minute more, in the hot afternoon, under the dusty trees.

"Charlie," she said suddenly, "trouble with you is, you let folks put on you. You never say a sassy word. Too polite, like all the Hollanders. Don't you be too polite, Charlie. Don't you let folks put on you."

He looked up at his mother, shrewd and unsure in her fine clothes, and for the first time he saw the uneasy bright defense in her eyes.

Why, he thought, she's scared of folks.

He remembered his father's face, clear and assured, the fine hard lips shaven above the short beard. He remembered it with love heightened by a new, profound wave of pride, a conscious identification.

Papa doesn't let folks put on him, he thought. But he doesn't have to be sassy about it, either. Papa's real fond of Mama. He don't give her those things just to show off. He does it because he's fond of her, and he knows she's scared of folks.

He looked up at his mother, the small, wiry woman in the voluminous dress, her arms encircling the huge bundle of starched cambric, of mull and ribbon, that was Lizzie sleeping. They were his women folks, and he took comfort from them; comfort, but not protection, not shelter.

His light-blue eyes regarded them warmly. He reached out one thin arm, to touch his mother's skirt.

"I won't never let anybody sass you, while I'm around," he promised.

He hesitated. Then, in a small voice oddly charged with surprise and the fullness of release, he added, "Mama, I love you."

The Good Night Kiss at Combray

MARCEL PROUST

My sole consolation when I went upstairs for the night was that Mamma would come in and kiss me after I was in bed. But this good night lasted for so short a time: she went down again so soon that the moment in which I heard her climb the stairs, and then caught the sound of her garden dress of blue muslin, from which hung little tassels of plaited straw, rustling along the double-doored corridor, was for me a moment of the keenest sorrow. So much did I love that good night that I reached the stage of hoping that it would come as late as possible, so as to prolong the time of respite during which Mamma would not yet have appeared. Sometimes when, after kissing me, she opened the door to go, I longed to call her back, to say to her "Kiss me just once again," but I knew that then she would at once look displeased, for the concession which she made to my wretchedness and agitation in coming up to me with this kiss of peace always annoyed my father, who thought such ceremonies absurd, and she would have liked to try to induce me to outgrow the need, the custom of having her there at all, which was a very different thing from letting the custom grow up of my asking her for an additional kiss when she was already crossing the threshold. And to see her look displeased destroyed all the sense of tranquillity she had brought me a moment before, when she bent her loving face down over my bed, and held it out to me like a Host, for an act of Communion in which my lips might drink deeply the sense of her real presence, and with it the power to sleep. But those evenings on which Mamma stayed so short a time in my room were sweet indeed compared to those on which we had guests to dinner, and therefore she did not come at all. Our 'guests' were practically limited to M. Swann, who, apart from a few passing strangers, was almost the only person who ever came to the house at Combray, sometimes to a neighbourly dinner (but less frequently since his unfortunate marriage, as my family did not care to receive his wife) and sometimes after dinner, uninvited. On those evenings when, as we sat in front of the house beneath the big chestnut-tree and round the iron table, we heard, from the far end of the garden, not the large and noisy rattle which heralded and deafened as he approached with its ferruginous, interminable, frozen sound any member of the household who had put it out of action by coming in 'without ringing,' but the double peal—timid, oval, gilded—of the visitors' bell, everyone would at once exclaim "A visitor! Who in the world can it be?" but they knew quite well that it could only be M. Swann. My great-aunt, speaking in a loud voice, to set an example, in a tone which she endeavoured to make sound natural, would tell the others not to whisper so; that nothing could be more unpleasant for a stranger coming in, who would be led to think that people were saying things about him which he was not meant to hear; and then my grandmother would be sent out as a scout, always happy to find an excuse for an additional turn in the garden, which she would utilise to remove surreptitiously, as she passed, the stakes of a rose-tree or two, so as to make the roses look a little more natural, as a mother might run her hand through her boy's hair, after the barber had smoothed it down, to make it stick out properly round his head.

And there we would all stay, hanging on the words which would fall from my grandmother's lips when she brought us back her report of the enemy, as though there had been some uncertainty among a vast number of possible invaders, and then, soon after, my grandfather would say: "I can hear Swann's voice." And, indeed, one could tell him only by his voice, for it was difficult to make out his face with its arched nose and green eyes, under a high forehead fringed with fair, almost red hair, dressed in the Bressant style, because in the garden we used as little light as possible, so as not to attract mosquitoes: and I would slip away as though not going for anything in particular, to tell them to bring out the syrups; for my grandmother made a great point, thinking it 'nicer,' of their not being allowed to seem anything out of the ordinary, which we kept for visitors only. Although a far younger man, M. Swann was very much attached to my grandfather, who had been an intimate friend, in his time, of Swann's father, an excellent but an eccentric man in whom the least little thing would, it seemed, often check the flow of his spirits and divert the current of his thoughts. Several times in the course of a year I would hear my grandfather tell at table the story, which never varied, of the behaviour of M. Swann the elder upon the death of his wife, by whose bedside he had watched day and night. My grandfather, who had not seen him for a long time, hastened to join him at the Swanns' family property on the outskirts of Combray, and managed to entice him for a moment, weeping profusely, out of the death-chamber, so that he should not be present when the body was laid in its coffin. They took a turn or two in the park, where there was a little sunshine. Suddenly M. Swann seized my grandfather by the arm and cried, "Oh, my dear old friend, how fortunate we are to be walking here together on such a charming day! Don't you see how pretty they are, all these trees—my hawthorns, and my new pond, on which you have never congratulated me? You look as glum as a night-cap. Don't you feel this little breeze? Ah! whatever you may say, it's good to be alive all the same, my dear Amédée!" And then, abruptly, the memory of his dead wife returned to him, and probably thinking it too complicated to inquire into how, at such a time, he could have allowed himself to be carried away by an impulse of happiness, he confined himself to a gesture which he habitually employed whenever any perplexing question came into his mind: that is, he passed his hand across his forehead, dried his eyes, and wiped his glasses. And he could never be consoled for the loss of his wife, but used to say to my grandfather, during the two years for which he survived her, "It's a funny thing, now; I very often think of my poor wife, but I cannot think of her very much at any one time." "Often, but a little at a time, like poor old Swann," became one of my grandfather's favourite phrases, which he would apply to all kinds of things. And I should have assumed that this father of Swann's had been a monster if my grandfather, whom I regarded as a better judge than myself, and whose word was my law and often led me in the long run to pardon offences which I should have been inclined to condemn, had not gone on to exclaim, "But, after all, he had a heart of gold."

For many years, albeit—and especially before his marriage—M. Swann the younger came often to see them at Combray, my great-aunt and grandparents never suspected that he had entirely ceased to live in the kind of society which his family had frequented, or that, under the sort of incognito which the name of Swann gave him among us, they were harbouring—with the complete innocence of a family of honest innkeepers who have in their midst some distinguished highwayman and never know it—one of the smartest members of the Jockey Club, a particular friend of the Comte de Paris and of the Prince of Wales, and one of the men most sought after in the aristocratic world of the Faubourg Saint-Germain. . . .

The only one of us in whom the prospect of Swann's arrival gave rise to an unhappy foreboding was myself. And that was because on the evenings when there were visitors, or just M. Swann in the house, Mamma did not come up to my room. I did not, at that time, have dinner with the family: I came out to the garden after dinner, and at nine I said good night and went to bed. But on these evenings I used to dine earlier than the others, and to come in afterwards and sit at table until eight o'clock, when it was understood that I must go upstairs; that frail and precious kiss which Mamma used always to leave upon my lips when I was in bed and just going to sleep I had to take with me from the dining-room to my own, and to keep inviolate all the time that it took me to undress, without letting its sweet charm be broken, without letting its volatile essence diffuse itself and evaporate; and just on those very evenings when I must needs take most pains to receive it with due formality, I had to snatch it, to seize it instantly and in public, without even having the time or being properly free to apply to what I was doing the punctiliousness which madmen use who compel themselves to exclude all other thoughts from their minds while they are shutting a door, so that when the sickness of uncertainty sweeps over them again they can triumphantly face and overcome it with the recollection of the precise moment in which the door was shut.

We were all in the garden when the double peal of the gate-bell sounded shyly. Everyone knew that it must be Swann, and yet they looked at one another inquiringly and sent my grandmother scouting.

"See that you thank him intelligibly for the wine," my grandfather warned his two sisters-in-law; "you know how good it is, and it is a huge case."

"Now, don't start whispering!" said my great-aunt. "How would you like to come into a house and find everyone muttering to themselves?"

"Ah! There's M. Swann," cried my father. "Let's ask him if he thinks it will be fine to-morrow."

My mother fancied that a word from her would wipe out all the unpleasantness which my family had contrived to make Swann feel since his marriage. She found an opportunity to draw him aside for a moment. But I followed her: I could not bring myself to let her go out of reach of me while I felt that in a few minutes I should have to leave her in the dining-room and go up to my bed without the consoling thought, as on ordinary evenings, that she would come up, later, to kiss me.

"Now, M. Swann," she said, "do tell me about your daughter; I am sure she shews a taste already for nice things, like her papa."

"Come along and sit down here with us all on the verandah," said my grandfather, coming up to him. My mother had to abandon the quest, but managed to extract from the restriction itself a further refinement of thought, as great poets do when the tyranny of rhyme forces them into the discovery of their finest lines.

"We can talk about her again when we are by ourselves," she said, or rather whispered to Swann. "It is only a mother who can understand. I am sure that hers would agree with me."

And so we all sat down round the iron table. I should have liked not to think of the hours of anguish which I should have to spend, that evening, alone in my room, without the possibility of going to sleep: I tried to convince myself that they were of no importance, really, since I should have forgotten them next morning, and to fix my mind on thoughts of the future which would carry me, as on a bridge, across the terrifying abyss that yawned at my feet. But my mind, strained by this foreboding, distended like the look which I shot at my mother, would not allow any other impression to enter. Thoughts did, indeed, enter it, but only on the condition that they left behind them every element of beauty, or even of quaintness, by which I might have been distracted or beguiled. As a surgical patient, by means of a local anaesthetic, can look on with a clear consciousness while an operation is being performed upon him and yet feel nothing, I could repeat to myself some favourite lines, or watch my grandfather attempting to talk to Swann about the Duc d'Audriffet-Pasquier, without being able to kindle any emotion from one or amusement from the other. . . .

I never took my eyes off my mother. I knew that when they were at table I should not be permitted to stay there for the whole of dinner-time, and that Mamma, for fear of annoying my father, would not allow me to give her in public the series of kisses that she would have had in my room. And so I promised myself that in the dining-room, as they began to eat and drink and as I felt the hour approach, I would put beforehand into this kiss, which was bound to be so brief and stealthy in execution, everything that my own efforts could put into it: would look out very carefully first the exact spot on her cheek where I would imprint it, and would so prepare my thoughts that I might be able, thanks to these mental preliminaries, to consecrate the whole of the minute Mamma would allow me to the sensation of her cheek against my lips, as a painter who can have his subject for short sittings only prepares his palette, and from what he remembers and from rough notes does in advance everything which he possibly can do in the sitter's absence. But to-night, before the dinner-bell had sounded, my grandfather said with unconscious cruelty: "The little man looks tired; he'd better go up to bed. Besides, we are dining late to-night."

And my father, who was less scrupulous than my grandmother or mother in observing the letter of a treaty, went on: "Yes; run along; to bed with you."

I would have kissed Mamma then and there, but at that moment the dinner-bell rang.

"No, no, leave your mother alone. You've said good night quite enough. These exhibitions are absurd. Go on upstairs."

And so I must set forth without viaticum; must climb each step of the staircase 'against my heart,' as the saying is, climbing in opposition to my heart's desire, which was to return to my mother, since she had not, by her kiss, given my heart leave to accompany me forth. That hateful staircase, up which I always passed with such dismay, gave out a smell of varnish which had to some extent absorbed, made definite and fixed the special quality of sorrow that I felt each evening, and made it perhaps even more cruel to my sensibility because, when it assumed this olfactory guise, my intellect was powerless to resist it. When we have gone to sleep with a maddening toothache and are conscious of it only as a little girl whom we attempt, time after time, to pull out of the water, or as a line of Molière which we repeat incessantly to ourselves, it is a great relief to wake up, so that our intelligence can disentangle the idea of toothache from any artificial semblance of heroism or rhythmic cadence. It was the precise converse of this relief which I felt when my anguish at having to go up to my room invaded my consciousness in a manner infinitely more rapid, instantaneous almost, a manner at once insidious and brutal as I breathed in—a far more poisonous thing than any moral penetration—the peculiar smell of the varnish upon that staircase.

Once in my room I had to stop every loophole, to close the shutters, to dig my own grave as I turned down the bedclothes, to wrap myself in the shroud of my nightshirt. But before burying myself in the iron bed which had been placed there because, on summer nights, I was too hot among the rep curtains of the four-poster, I was stirred to revolt, and attempted the desperate stratagem of a condemned prisoner. I wrote to my mother begging her to come upstairs for an important reason which I could not put in writing. My fear was that Françoise, my aunt's cook who used to be put in charge of me when I was at Combray, might refuse to take my note. I had a suspicion that, in her eyes, to carry a message to my mother when there was a stranger in the room would appear flatly inconceivable, just as it would be for the door-keeper of a theatre to hand a letter to an actor upon the stage. For things which might or might not be done she possessed a code at once imperious, abundant, subtle, and uncompromising on points themselves imperceptible or irrelevant, which gave it a resemblance to those ancient laws which combine such cruel ordinances as the massacre of infants at the breast with prohibitions, of exaggerated refinement, against "seething the kid in his mother's milk," or "eating of the sinew which is upon the hollow of the thigh." This code, if one could judge it by the sudden obstinacy which she would put into her refusal to carry out certain of our instructions, seemed to have foreseen such social complications and refinements of fashion as nothing in Françoise's surroundings or in her career as a servant in a village household could have put into her head; and we were obliged to assume that there was latent in her some past existence in the ancient history of France, noble and little understood, just as there is in those manufacturing towns where old mansions still testify to their former courtly days, and chemical workers toil among delicately sculptured scenes of the Miracle of Theophilus or the Quatre Fils Aymon.

In this particular instance, the article of her code which made it highly improbable that—barring an outbreak of fire—Françoise would go down and disturb Mamma when M. Swann was there for so unimportant a person as myself was one embodying the respect she shewed not only for the family (as for the dead, for the clergy, or for royalty), but also for the stranger within our gates; a respect which I should perhaps have found touching in a book, but which never failed to irritate me on her lips, because of the solemn and gentle tones in which she would utter it, and which irritated me more than usual this evening when the sacred character in which she invested the dinner-party might have the effect of making her decline to disturb its ceremonial. But to give myself one chance of success I lied without hesitation, telling her that it was not in the least myself who had wanted to write to Mamma, but Mamma who, on saying good night to me, had begged me not to forget to send her an answer about something she had asked me to find, and that she would certainly be very angry if this note were not taken to her. I think that Françoise disbelieved me, for, like those primitive men whose senses were so much keener than our own, she could immediately detect, by signs imperceptible by the rest of us, the truth or falsehood of anything that we might wish to conceal from her. She studied the envelope for five minutes as though an examination of the paper itself and the look of my handwriting could enlighten her as to the nature of the contents, or tell her to which article of her code she ought to refer the matter. Then she went out with an air of resignation which seemed to imply: "What a dreadful thing for parents to have a child like this!"

A moment later she returned to say that they were still at the ice stage and that it was impossible for the butler to deliver the note at once, in front of everybody; but that when the finger-bowls were put round he would find a way of slipping it into Mamma's hand. At once my anxiety subsided; it was now no longer (as it had been a moment ago) until to-morrow that I had lost my mother, for my little line was going—to annoy her, no doubt, and doubly so because this contrivance would make me ridiculous in Swann's eyes—but was going all the same to admit me, invisibly and by stealth, into the same room as herself, was going to whisper from me into her ear; for that forbidden and unfriendly dining-room, where but a moment ago the ice itself—with burned nuts in it—and the finger-bowls seemed to me to be concealing pleasures that were mischievous and of a mortal sadness because Mamma was tasting of them and I was far away, had opened its doors to me and, like a ripe fruit which bursts through its skin, was going to pour out into my intoxicated heart the gushing sweetness of Mamma's attention while she was reading what I had written. Now I was no longer separated from her; the barriers were down; an exquisite thread was binding us. Besides, that was not all, for surely Mamma would come.

As for the agony through which I had just passed, I imagined that Swann would have laughed heartily at it if he had read my letter and had guessed its purpose; whereas, on the contrary, as I was to learn in due course, a similar anguish had been the bane of his life for many years, and no one perhaps could have understood my feelings at that moment so well as himself; to him, that anguish which lies in knowing that the creature one adores is in some place of enjoyment where oneself is not and cannot follow—to him that anguish came through Love, to which it is in a sense predestined, by which it must be equipped and adapted; but when, as had befallen me, such an anguish possesses one's soul before Love has yet entered into one's life, then it must drift, awaiting Love's coming, vague and free, without precise attachment, at the disposal of one sentiment to-day, of another to-morrow, of filial piety or affection for a comrade. And the joy with which I first bound myself apprentice, when Françoise returned to tell me that my letter would be delivered, Swann, too, had known well that false joy which a friend can give us, or some relative of the woman we love, when on his arrival at the house or theatre where she is to be found, for some ball or party or 'first-night' at which he is to meet her, he sees us wandering outside, desperately awaiting some opportunity of communicating with her. He recognises us, greets us familiarly, and asks what we are doing there. And when we invent a story of having some urgent message to give to his relative or friend, he assures us that nothing could be more simple, takes us in at the door, and promises to send her down to us in five minutes. How much we love him—as at that moment I loved Françoise—the good-natured intermediary who by a single word has made supportable, human, almost propitious the inconceivable, infernal scene of gaiety in the thick of which we had been imagining swarms of enemies, perverse and seductive, beguiling away from us, even making laugh at us, the woman whom we love. If we are to judge of them by him, this relative who has accosted us and who is himself an initiate in those cruel mysteries, then the other guests cannot be so very demoniacal. Those inaccessible and torturing hours into which she had gone to taste of unknown pleasures—behold, a breach in the wall, and we are through it. Behold, one of the moments whose series will go to make up their sum, a moment as genuine as the rest, if not actually more important to ourself because our mistress is more intensely a part of it; we picture it to ourselves, we possess it, we intervene upon it, almost we have created it: namely, the moment in which he goes to tell her that we are waiting there below. And very probably the other moments of the party will not be essentially different, will contain nothing else so exquisite or so well able to make us suffer, since this kind friend has assured us that "Of course, she will be delighted to come down! It will be far more amusing for her to talk to you than to be bored up there." Alas! Swann had learned by experience that the good intentions of a third party are powerless to control a woman who is annoyed to find herself pursued even into a ball-room by a man whom she does not love. Too often, the kind friend comes down again alone.

My mother did not appear, but with no attempt to safeguard my self-respect (which depended upon her keeping up the fiction that she had asked me to let her know the result of my search for something or other) made Françoise tell me, in so many words "There is no answer"—words I have so often, since then, heard the hall-porters in 'mansions' and the flunkeys in gambling-clubs and the like, repeat to some poor girl, who replies in bewilderment: "What! he's said nothing? It's not possible. You did give him my letter, didn't you? Very well, I shall wait a little longer." And just as she invariably protests that she does not need the extra gas which the porter offers to light for her, and sits on there, hearing nothing further, except an occasional remark on the weather which the porter exchanges with a messenger whom he will send off suddenly, when he notices the time, to put some customer's wine on the ice; so, having declined Françoise's offer to make me some tea or to stay beside me, I let her go off again to the servants' hall, and lay down and shut my eyes, and tried not to hear the voices of my family who were drinking their coffee in the garden.

But after a few seconds I realised that, by writing that line to Mamma, by approaching—at the risk of making her angry—so near to her that I felt I could reach out and grasp the moment in which I should see her again, I had cut myself off from the possibility of going to sleep until I actually had seen her, and my heart began to beat more and more painfully as I increased my agitation by ordering myself to keep calm and to acquiesce in my ill-fortune. Then, suddenly, my anxiety subsided, a feeling of intense happiness coursed through me, as when a strong medicine begins to take effect and one's pain vanishes: I had formed a resolution to abandon all attempts to go to sleep without seeing Mamma, and had decided to kiss her at all costs, even with the certainty of being in disgrace with her for long afterwards, when she herself came up to bed. The tranquillity which followed my anguish made me extremely alert, no less than my sense of expectation, my thirst for and my fear of danger.

Noiselessly I opened the window and sat down on the foot of my bed; hardly daring to move in case they should hear me from below. Things outside seemed also fixed in mute expectation, so as not to disturb the moonlight which, duplicating each of them and throwing it back by the extension, forwards, of a shadow denser and more concrete than its substance, had made the whole landscape seem at once thinner and longer, like a map which, after being folded up, is spread out upon the ground. What had to move—a leaf of the chestnut-tree, for instance—moved. But its minute shuddering, complete, finished to the least detail and with utmost delicacy of gesture, made no discord with the rest of the scene, and yet was not merged in it, remaining clearly outlined. Exposed upon this surface of silence, which absorbed nothing from them, the most distant sounds, those which must have come from gardens at the far end of the town, could be distinguished with such exact 'finish' that the impression they gave of coming from a distance seemed due only to their 'pianissimo' execution, like those movements on muted strings so well performed by the orchestra of the Conservatoire that, although one does not lose a single note, one thinks all the same that they are being played somewhere outside, a long way from the concert hall, so that all the old subscribers, and my grandmother's sisters too, when Swann had given them his seats, used to strain their ears as if they had caught the distant approach of an army on the march, which had not yet rounded the corner of the Rue de Trévise.

I was well aware that I had placed myself in a position than which none could be counted upon to involve me in graver consequences at my parents' hands; consequences far graver, indeed, than a stranger would have imagined, and such as (he would have thought) could follow only some really shameful fault. But in the system of education which they had given me faults were not classified in the same order as in that of other children, and I had been taught to place at the head of the list (doubtless because there was no other class of faults from which I needed to be more carefully protected) those in which I can now distinguish the common feature that one succumbs to them by yielding to a nervous impulse. But such words as these last had never been uttered in my hearing; no one had yet accounted for my temptations in a way which might have led me to believe that there was some excuse for my giving in to them, or that I was actually incapable of holding out against them. Yet I could easily recognise this class of transgressions by the anguish of mind which preceded, as well as by the rigour of the punishment which followed them; and I knew that what I had just done was in the same category as certain other sins for which I had been severely chastised, though infinitely more serious than they. When I went out to meet my mother as she herself came up to bed, and when she saw that I had remained up so as to say good night to her again in the passage, I should not be allowed to stay in the house a day longer, I should be packed off to school next morning; so much was certain. Very good: had I been obliged, the next moment, to hurl myself out of the window, I should still have preferred such a fate. For what I wanted now was Mamma, and to say good night to her. I had gone too far along the road which led to the realisation of this desire to be able to retrace my steps.

I could hear my parents' footsteps as they went with Swann; and, when the rattle of the gate assured me that he had really gone, I crept to the window. Mamma was asking my father if he had thought the lobster good, and whether M. Swann had had some more of the coffee-and-pistachio ice. "I thought it rather so-so," she was saying; "next time we shall have to try another flavour."

My father and mother were left alone and sat down for a moment; then my father said: "Well, shall we go up to bed?"

"As you wish, dear, though I don't feel in the least like sleeping. I don't know why; it can't be the coffee-ice—it wasn't strong enough to keep me awake like this. But I see a light in the servants' hall: poor Françoise has been sitting up for me, so I will get her to unhook me while you go and undress."

My mother opened the latticed door which led from the hall to the staircase. Presently I heard her coming upstairs to close her window. I went quietly into the passage; my heart was beating so violently that

I could hardly move, but at least it was throbbing no longer with anxiety, but with terror and with joy. I saw in the well of the stair a light coming upwards, from Mamma's candle. Then I saw Mamma herself: I threw myself upon her. For an instant she looked at me in astonishment, not realising what could have happened. Then her face assumed an expression of anger. She said not a single word to me; and, for that matter, I used to go for days on end without being spoken to, for far less offences than this. A single word from Mamma would have been an admission that further intercourse with me was within the bounds of possibility, and that might perhaps have appeared to me more terrible still, as indicating that, with such a punishment as was in store for me, mere silence, and even anger, were relatively puerile.

A word from her then would have implied the false calm in which one converses with a servant to whom one has just decided to give notice; the kiss one bestows on a son who is being packed off to enlist, which would have been denied him if it had merely been a matter of being angry with him for a few days. But she heard my father coming from the dressing-room, where he had gone to take off his clothes, and, to avoid the 'scene' which he would make if he saw me, she said, in a voice half-stifled by her anger: "Run away at once. Don't let your father see you standing there like a crazy jane!"

But I begged her again to "Come and say good night to me!" terrified as I saw the light from my father's candle already creeping up the wall, but also making use of his approach as a means of blackmail, in the hope that my mother, not wishing him to find me there, as find me he must if she continued to hold out, would give in to me, and say: "Go back to your room. I will come."

Too late: my father was upon us. Instinctively I murmured, though no one heard me, "I am done for!"

I was not, however. My father used constantly to refuse to let me do things which were quite clearly allowed by the more liberal charters granted me by my mother and grandmother, because he paid no heed to 'Principles,' and because in his sight there were no such things as 'Rights of Man.' For some quite irrelevant reason, or for no reason at all, he would at the last moment prevent me from taking some particular walk, one so regular and so consecrated to my use that to deprive me of it was a clear breach of faith; or again, as he had done this evening, long before the appointed hour he would snap out: "Run along up to bed now; no excuses!" But then again, simply because he was devoid of principles (in my grandmother's sense), so he could not, properly speaking, be called inexorable. He looked at me for a moment with an air of annoyance and surprise, and then when Mamma had told him, not without some embarrassment, what had happened, said to her: "Go along with him, then; you said just now that you didn't feel like sleep, so stay in his room for a little. I don't need anything."

"But, dear," my mother answered timidly, "whether or not I feel like sleep is not the point; we must not make the child accustomed . . ."

"There's no question of making him accustomed," said my father, with a shrug of the shoulders; "you can see quite well that the child is unhappy. After all, we aren't gaolers. You'll end by making him ill, and a lot of good that will do. There are two beds in his room; tell Françoise to make up the big one for you, and stay beside him for the rest of the night. I'm off to bed, anyhow; I'm not nervous like you. Good night."

It was impossible for me to thank my father; what he called my sentimentality would have exasperated him. I stood there, not daring to move; he was still confronting us, an immense figure in his white nightshirt, crowned with the pink and violet scarf of Indian cashmere in which, since he had begun to suffer from neuralgia, he used to tie up his head, standing like Abraham in the engraving after Benozzo Gozzoli which M. Swann had given me, telling Sarah that she must tear herself away from Isaac. Many years have passed since that night. The wall of the staircase, up which I had watched the light of his candle gradually climb, was long ago demolished. And in myself, too, many things have perished which, I imagined, would last for ever, and new structures have arisen, giving birth to new sorrows and new joys which in those days I could not have foreseen, just as now the old are difficult of comprehension. It is a long time, too, since my father has been able to tell Mamma to "Go with the child." Never again will such hours be possible for me. But of late I have been increasingly able to catch, if I listen attentively, the sound of the sobs which I had the strength to control in my father's presence, and which broke out only when I found myself alone with Mamma. Actually, their echo has never ceased: it is only because life is now growing more and more quiet round about me that I hear them afresh, like those convent bells which are so effectively drowned during the day by the noises of the streets that one would suppose them to have been stopped for ever, until they sound out again through the silent evening air.

Mamma spent that night in my room: when I had just committed a sin so deadly that I was waiting to be banished from the household, my parents gave me a far greater concession than I should ever have won as the reward of a good action. Even at the moment when it manifested itself in this crowning mercy, my father's conduct towards me was still somewhat arbitrary, and regardless of my deserts, as was characteristic of him and due to the fact that his actions were generally dictated by chance expediencies rather than based on any formal plan. And perhaps even what I called his strictness, when he sent me off to bed, deserved that title less, really, than my mother's or grandmother's attitude, for his nature, which in some respects differed more than theirs from my own, had probably prevented him from guessing, until then, how wretched I was every evening, a thing which my mother and grandmother knew well; but they loved me enough to be unwilling to spare me that suffering, which they hoped to teach me to overcome, so as to reduce my nervous sensibility and to strengthen my will. As for my father, whose affection for me was of another kind, I doubt if he would have shewn so much courage, for as soon as he had grasped the fact that I was unhappy he had said to my mother: "Go and comfort him."

Mamma stayed all night in my room, and it seemed that she did not wish to mar by recrimination those hours, so different from anything that I had had a right to expect; for when Françoise (who guessed that something extraordinary must have happened when she saw Mamma sitting by my side, holding my hand and letting me cry unchecked) said to her: "But, Madame, what is little Master crying for?" she replied: "Why, Françoise, he doesn't know himself: it is his nerves. Make up the big bed for me quickly and then go off to your own." And thus for the first time my unhappiness was regarded no longer as a fault for which I must be punished, but as an involuntary evil which had been officially recognised, a nervous condition for which I was in no way responsible: I had the consolation that I need no longer mingle apprehensive scruples with the bitterness of my tears; I could weep henceforward without sin. I felt no small degree of pride, either, in Françoise's presence at this return to humane conditions which, not an hour after Mamma had refused to come up to my room and had sent the snubbing message that I was to go to sleep, raised me to the dignity of a grown-up person, brought me of a sudden to a sort of puberty of sorrow, to emancipation from tears. I ought then to have been happy; I was not. It struck me that my mother had just made a first concession which must have been painful to her, that it was a first step down from the ideal she had formed for me, and that for the first time she, with all her courage, had to confess herself beaten. It struck me that if I had just scored a victory it was over her; that I had succeeded, as sickness or sorrow or age might have succeeded, in relaxing her will, in altering her judgment; that this evening opened a new era, must remain a black date in the calendar. And if I had dared now, I should have said to Mamma: "No, I don't want you; you mustn't sleep here." But I was conscious of the practical wisdom, of what would be called nowadays the realism with which she tempered the ardent idealism of my grandmother's nature, and I knew that now the mischief was done she would prefer to let me enjoy the soothing pleasure of her company, and not to disturb my father again. Certainly my mother's beautiful features seemed to shine again with youth that evening, as she sat gently holding my hands and trying to check my tears; but, just for that reason, it seemed to me that this should not have happened; her anger would have been less difficult to endure than this new kindness which my childhood had not known; I felt that I had with an impious and secret finger traced a first wrinkle upon her soul and made the first white hair shew upon her head. This thought redoubled my sobs, and then I saw that Mamma, who had never allowed herself to go to any length of tenderness with me, was suddenly overcome by my tears and had to struggle to keep back her own. Then, as she saw that I had noticed this, she said to me, with a smile: "Why, my little buttercup, my little canary-boy, he's going to make Mamma as silly as himself if this goes on. Look, since you can't sleep, and Mamma can't either, we mustn't go on in this stupid way; we must do something; I'll get one of your books." But I had none there. "Would you like me to get out the books now that your grandmother is going to give you for your birthday? Just think it over first, and don't be disappointed if there is nothing new for you then."

I was only too delighted, and Mamma went to find a parcel of books in which I could not distinguish, through the paper in which it was wrapped, any more than its squareness and size, but which, even at this first glimpse, brief and obscure as it was, bade fair to eclipse already the paintbox of last New Year's Day and the silkworms of the year before. It contained *La Mare au Diable, François le Champi, La Petite Fadette,* and *Les Maîtres Sonneurs*. My grandmother, as I learned afterwards, had at first chosen Musset's poems, a volume of Rousseau, and *Indiana;* for while she considered light reading as unwholesome as sweets and cakes, she did not reflect that the strong breath of genius must have upon the very soul of a child an influence at once more dangerous and less quickening than those of fresh air and country breezes upon his body. But when my father had seemed almost to regard her as insane on learning the names of the books she proposed to give me, she had journeyed back by herself to Jouy-le-Vicomte to the bookseller's, so that there should be no fear of my not having my present in time (it was a burning hot day, and she had come home so unwell that the doctor had warned my mother not to allow her again to tire herself in that way), and had there fallen back upon the four pastoral novels of George Sand.

"My dear," she had said to Mamma, "I could not allow myself to give the child anything that was not well written."

The truth was that she could never make up her mind to purchase anything from which no intellectual profit was to be derived, and, above all, that profit which good things bestowed on us by teaching us to seek our pleasures elsewhere than in the barren satisfaction of worldly wealth. Even when she had to make some one a present of the kind called 'useful,' when she had to give an armchair or some table-silver or a walking-stick, she would choose 'antiques,' as though their long desuetude had effaced from them any semblance of utility and fitted them rather to instruct us in the lives of the men of other days than to serve the common requirements of our own. She would have liked me to have in my room photographs of ancient buildings or of beautiful places. But at the moment of buying them, and for all that the subject of the picture had an aesthetic value of its own, she would find that vulgarity and utility had too prominent a part in them, through the mechanical nature of their reproduction by photography. She attempted by a subterfuge, if not to eliminate altogether their commercial banality, at least to minimise it, to substitute for the bulk of it what was art still, to introduce, as it might be, several 'thicknesses' of art; instead of photographs of Chartres Cathedral, of the Fountains of Saint-Cloud, or of Vesuvius she would inquire of Swann whether some great painter had not made pictures of them, and preferred to give me photographs of 'Chartres Cathedral' after Corot, of the 'Fountains of Saint-Cloud' after Hubert Robert, and of 'Vesuvius' after Turner, which were a stage higher in the scale of art. But although the photographer had been prevented from reproducing directly the masterpieces or the beauties of nature, and had there been replaced by a great artist, he resumed his odious position when it came to reproducing the artist's interpretation. Accordingly, having to reckon again with vulgarity, my grandmother would endeavour to postpone the moment of contact still further. She would ask Swann if the picture had not been engraved, preferring, when possible, old engravings with some interest of association apart from themselves, such, for example, as shew us a masterpiece in a state in which we can no longer see it to-day, as Morghen's print of the 'Cenacolo' of Leonardo before it was spoiled by restoration. It must be admitted that the results of this method of interpreting the art of making presents were not always happy. The idea which I formed of

Venice, from a drawing by Titian which is supposed to have the lagoon in the background, was certainly far less accurate than what I have since derived from ordinary photographs. We could no longer keep count in the family (when my great-aunt tried to frame an indictment of my grandmother) of all the armchairs she had presented to married couples, young and old, which on a first attempt to sit down upon them had at once collapsed beneath the weight of their recipient. But my grandmother would have thought it sordid to concern herself too closely with the solidity of any piece of furniture in which could still be discerned a flourish, a smile, a brave conceit of the past. And even what in such pieces supplied a material need, since it did so in a manner to which we are no longer accustomed, was as charming to her as one of those old forms of speech in which we can still see traces of a metaphor whose fine point has been worn away by the rough usage of our modern tongue. In precisely the same way the pastoral novels of George Sand, which she was giving me for my birthday, were regular lumber-rooms of antique furniture, full of expressions that have fallen out of use and returned as imagery, such as one finds now only in country dialects. And my grandmother had bought them in preference to other books, just as she would have preferred to take a house that had a gothic dovecot, or some other such piece of antiquity as would have a pleasant effect on the mind, filling it with a nostalgic longing for impossible journeys through the realms of time.

Mamma sat down by my bed; she had chosen *François le Champi,* whose reddish cover and incomprehensible title gave it a distinct personality in my eyes and a mysterious attraction. I had not then read any real novels. I had heard it said that George Sand was a typical novelist. That prepared me in advance to imagine that *François le Champi* contained something inexpressibly delicious. The course of the narrative, where it tended to arouse curiosity or melt to pity, certain modes of expression which disturb or sadden the reader, and which, with a little experience, he may recognise as 'common form' in novels, seemed to me then distinctive—for to me a new book was not one of a number of similar objects, but was like an individual man, unmatched, and with no cause of existence beyond himself—an intoxicating whiff of the peculiar essence of *François le Champi.* Beneath the everyday incidents, the commonplace thoughts and hackneyed words, I could hear, or overhear, an intonation, a rhythmic utterance fine and strange. The 'action' began: to me it seemed all the more obscure because in those days, when I read to myself, I used often, while I turned the pages, to dream of something quite different. And to the gaps which this habit made in my knowledge of the story more were added by the fact that when it was Mamma who was reading to me aloud she left all the love-scenes out. And so all the odd changes which take place in the relations between the miller's wife and the boy, changes which only the birth and growth of love can explain, seemed to me plunged and steeped in a mystery, the key to which (as I could readily believe) lay in that strange and pleasant-sounding name of *Champi,* which draped the boy who bore it, I knew not why, in its own bright colour, purpurate and charming. If my mother was not a faithful reader, she was, nonetheless, admirable when reading a work in which she found the note of true feeling by the respectful simplicity of her interpretation and by the sound of her sweet and gentle voice. It was the same in her daily life, when it was not works of art but men and women whom she was moved to pity or admire: it was touching to observe with what deference she would banish from her voice, her gestures, from her whole conversation, now the note of joy which might have distressed some mother who had long ago lost a child, now the recollection of an event or anniversary which might have reminded some old gentleman of the burden of his years, now the household topic which might have bored some young man of letters. And so, when she read aloud the prose of George Sand, prose which is everywhere redolent of that generosity and moral distinction which Mamma had learned from my grandmother to place above all other qualities in life, and which I was not to teach her until much later to refrain from placing, in the same way, above all other qualities in literature; taking pains to banish from her voice any weakness or affectation which might have blocked its channel for that powerful stream of language, she supplied all the natural tenderness, all the lavish sweetness which they demanded to phrases which seemed to have been composed for her voice, and which were all, so to speak, within her compass. She came to them with the tone that they required, with the cordial accent which existed before they were, which dictated them, but which is not to be found in the words themselves, and by these means she smoothed away, as she read on, any harshness there might be or discordance in the tenses of verbs, endowing the imperfect and the preterite with all the sweetness which there is in generosity, all the melancholy which there is in love; guided the sentence that was drawing to an end towards that which was waiting to begin, now hastening, now slackening the pace of the syllables so as to bring them, despite their difference of quantity, into a uniformed rhythm, and breathed into this quite ordinary prose a kind of life, continuous and full of feeling.

My agony was soothed; I let myself be borne upon the current of this gentle night on which I had my mother by my side. I knew that such a night could not be repeated; that the strongest desire I had in the world, namely, to keep my mother in my room through the sad hours of darkness, ran too much counter to general requirements and to the wishes of others for such a concession as had been granted me this evening to be anything but a rare and casual exception. To-morrow night I should again be the victim of anguish and Mamma would not stay by my side. But when these storms of anguish grew calm I could no longer realise their existence; besides, to-morrow evening was still a long way off; I reminded myself that I should still have time to think about things, albeit that remission of time could bring me no access of power, albeit the coming event was in no way dependent upon the exercise of my will, and seemed not quite inevitable only because it was still separated from me by this short interval.

Fishermen at Night

ROBERT TRAVER

WE LEFT the camp and cut down the hill into the waving grass of the ancient beaver meadows. My father pointed at a fresh deer track in the soggy trail and kept walking, his long legs swishing the wild grass. He was carrying his fly rod, set up, slowly smoking a briar pipe—an old, caked one with a hole worn through the bit. I drank in the fine smell and it was mixed with smells from the damp earth.

Over the little log bridge at the creek and at the far edge of the meadows, in the young poplars, we flushed two partridges, and we kept raising the rooster, who would fly ahead of us and land, and then turn, ruffling and bobbing like a young prize fighter, until we got too close. Finally it sped in heavy flight over a little hill and we could hear it drumming on the next ridge.

My father could step over most of the charred, weather-worn logs, skeletons of the giant white pines, while I had to climb up on each one and stand there for a little while as tall as my father, and then jump down and run after him, my leader box rattling against my creel.

We came out of the poplars and down below us there was a series of beaver ponds and a big beaver house stood in the reeds. There were no beaver. The sun going down made a reddish color on the water. The water was quiet except for the ripples of the trout rising to the flies. A mist was beginning to spread over the ponds, and it was still, there was no noise, except for the frogs croaking and whistling and the splashing of the water spilling over the beaver dams into the ponds below.

My father stood there and packed and relit his pipe. He said, "Next year, son, I'll put in a system here to furnish electric lights for the camp."

I said, "Yes, sir." Then I said, "Don't you think it's more fun to have kerosene lamps? Honest, Pa, I don't mind tending them. Don't you think machinery and things would sort of spoil it here—it's so pretty-like."

My father laughed and walked ahead and I followed him along the edge of the ponds as we walked up to the big pond at the head of the dams. We worked through a thicket of willows and came out in the reeds at the edge of the big pond. The ground was soft and it shook when we moved. My father touched my arm and pointed across the water. A deer stood looking at us, standing in the tall reeds, its big ears up and forward, then one ear, then the other, sort of moving its head in the air, all the while looking at us. Then my father clapped his hands and the deer blew and wheeled, and I saw its white tail straight up, bouncing and bouncing over the fallen old pine logs, and it was gone.

"A beautiful running shot, son," my father said.

The trout were rising and my father knelt and looked at the water and then tied on a leader and a little black fly. I stood watching him. I watched his easy spiral casts as he worked out the line, straight up and forward to avoid catching the thick willows behind us, and then he placed the fly, and it floated down into the water like a thistle. There was a quick roll, and my father had him, the rod bending like a buggy whip, and I watched my father smile and he smiled so that I could see his teeth closed over his pipe and little lines by his eyes. My father slowly worked him in, smiling that way, until the trout lay still at his feet, and my father, not using the net, reached down and took him with his hand.

"Pretty tired trout, son," my father said.

I could hear a whippoorwill make a noise across the pond.

I found a little black fly, and I fumbled in my hurry to tie it and pricked myself and my father said, "Be deliberate, son."

"Yes, sir," I said.

On my first cast I hooked the willows and snapped the leader, and my little black fly was twenty feet up in a willow. My father laughed and I could feel my cheeks burning as I searched in my kit for another black fly but there were none.

I said, "Have you any more of these black flies, Pa?"

My father said, "Sh—don't talk so much. Work your own flies, son." He cast his fly again, so easily, and just missed a beautiful strike.

I fouled my second cast in the willows and I had to bite my lip to keep the tears back when my father laughed again, showing his strong teeth clenching his pipe.

"You'd better go around and get out on the raft," my father said, pointing across the pond.

In the twilight I saw the logs of an old raft lying in the water amid the reeds. I scrambled through the willows and made my way across the matted arc of the beaver dam. I did not look at my father. It took me a long time to get around the pond and I could hear splashing and my father chuckling and I knew that the fishing was good.

I found a long jack-pine pole. I did not look across at my father, but quickly pushed the raft off into the deep water. Just as I was about to cast, the raft started to sink, over my ankles, my boots, up to my knees. I tried to push it back to shore and the pole caught in the mucky bottom and pulled me into deeper water. It was then that I heard my father laughing and I looked over at him and he was slapping his leg and laughing loudly with his mouth open. I worked hard with the pole, and then I couldn't touch the bottom. I tried to paddle with the pole, and it snapped off, and I held a little piece in my hand. The raft started to tip and the water was over my hips, and I saw that the sun had gone down. And all the time I could hear my father laughing and laughing, roaring with laughter. Then I saw him holding his stomach, laughing, and I began to cry, I could not stop, and I stood looking at him, laughing so that the tears rolled down his cheeks. Suddenly I shouted, "You standing there laughing and watching your own son drown . . . you—*you go to hell!*"

I started striking the water, the tears running down my face, and the raft started to rise and move slowly across the pond toward my father. He stood there holding his stomach with both hands, bending up and down, laughing all the while.

"You go to hell!" I shouted again, crying harder than ever, and then he doubled up and leaned against the willows, shaking like he was crying. As I wildly threshed the water I prayed over and over for a gun so that I could shoot my father.

The raft was across the pond and I stepped off the raft on to the boggy edge of the pond and stood there dripping, looking up at my father, my fists clenched at my side. My father had stopped laughing and he looked at me, and we stood there. I was not crying. Then he smiled a little and said, "That's a hell of a raft for a fisherman, son. We'll have to get us a real boat. Come on, we'll get back to camp and dry out and have a damn nice drink of whiskey—what do you say, John?"

"We'll sure have to get us a boat. That raft's no good. And we'll have a fine drink of whiskey, Pa—a hell of a big drink, you bet."

It was dark on the way back to camp, and the meadow was thick with the mist. I did not mind shivering at all, and I whistled to imitate the frogs. "Tomorrow," I thought as I walked behind my father, "Tomorrow I'll sure in hell get hold of the old man's pipe—and smoke the damn thing right in front of him, you bet."

And These Went Down to Burlington

MACKINLAY KANTOR

ONCE THE trees and poles stood still for a long time; among the trees was a cluster of purple flowers that stretched friendly tongues to her. She climbed up and stood, hammering both hands against the glass and saying, "Pretty, pretty."

In the front seat, Nanna heard her. "Yes, honey-bunch. Pretty. Does baby want a flower?"

"Pretty."

Doddy was out in the road beside the car. He had a funny stick in his hands and he bent over it, making it go up and down steadily. Sometimes he would lift his face and see Gwen looking out at him; if he noticed her he might wink and shake his head briskly. . . . She would chuckle when he did that.

Other cars went past, but Gwen had seen a great many other cars that day and the day before, so she didn't notice them much. Finally one stopped—it was almost like a large chunk of the sky, it was so blue. Gwen almost wished that she was riding in a car like that. But she was very comfortable with Nanna and Doddy. They had a thick, soft cloth thing—it had been taken off the bed at home—and it covered the whole back seat and the mound of suitcases. The baby could crawl around on there without much chance of her getting hurt. . . .

A big man got out of the bright blue car.

"Need any help, brother?"

"Thanks. I'll get it all right."

"Thought maybe you wanted a patch."

"I got one on here I think'll hold."

"Okay. Where you headed for?"

"Burlington."

The big man had yellow hair like Gwen's doll. He walked past the windows of the little car; he smiled at Nanna and tapped on the glass with something bright.

"How old's baby?"

"Nineteen months," said Nanna.

Gwen wasn't watching the big man. For in his car was a Wow. She hadn't noticed it before. The Wow sat up very straight inside the blue car and stared at Gwen. She beat on the glass ecstatically and cried, "Wow—Wow!"

The Wow noticed her. He made a sharp, pleasant noise and lifted his ears higher.

"She sees the dog," said the big man. "Well, so long."

"So long. Sure much obliged."

The big car went away suddenly—man and Wow and all. Gwen scrambled across the soft cushions and gazed out of the rear window. She could see the Wow looking back at her. . . . Maybe it would come again.

Doddy opened the door and slid a lot of sharp, heavy things under the mattress, beside the suitcases. Gwen reached down and tried to get them.

"No, no."

"No?"

"No. . . . Agnes, make her let those tools alone. . . . You'll get all dirty, skeezix."

He climbed into the front seat and sat very quietly for a moment. Gwen crept up behind him and breathed softly against his neck. He had had on a woolly sweater, much like hers, only it was a brighter color and had holes in it. She put her finger into one of the holes; it was enjoyable to put her finger in, and then pull it out quickly, pretending that the hole was hot-boo.

"Well, kid, that's that."

"Oh, Joe. I sure hope we don't have any more punctures."

"So do I."

"Gosh, honey, what'd we do if we had to buy another tire before we got to Burlington?"

"I dunno. . . . Don't worry, kid. That old casing's good for a long ways yet."

Then the trees and fences started off again. The purple flowers brushed the side of the car and began to wave at Gwen. So she waved her hand and called loudly, "Bye. . . ."

"Didja hear that, Joe?"

"What?"

"She was waving bye-bye."

He grinned. "What at?"

"Oh . . . you know. Just waving."

Gwen put her head down on the soft mattress, and watched the trees going past . . . the motion of the car went through her body with a warm, comfortable ripple, and she stretched out in the softness, watching Nanna and Doddy with quiet gray eyes.

"She's getting sleepy, Joe."

"Huh?"

"Sleepy. The baby's getting—"

"Say, she ain't had anything to eat yet. Not since morning."

"I know it. But she'll take her nap first, and feel lots better. Riding makes them sleepy. . . ."

Gwen heard them saying all this: she heard "eat" and wanted to rouse up and ask, "Crackaw?" But the motion of the car kept rippling in her mind; the world was all purple flowers and big blue cars, and filled with nice Wows which made friendly noises. . . . Her eyes were closing. She could hear Nanna and Doddy talking in the front seat; their voices had a warm sound. . . . She thought of crackers, and a round golden orange, and a mug full of milk. But it seemed that she could not open her eyes.

When she awoke, a beautiful red and yellow wall was just outside the window of the car, and it was standing still. On the side of the wall were two babies not much older than Gwen, but many times larger, and they were eating something out of a bowl; but they seemed never to put their spoons into their mouths. Gwen smiled at them and said, "Bay-bee!" She turned to share the glory of their presence with Nanna. But neither Nanna nor Doddy was in the front seat. Doddy was standing out in the road; he had part of the car lifted up in the air; the sun gleamed brightly on the uplifted sheet of metal, and he was prying underneath it with something that glimmered.

Nanna was across the road, standing in front of a little building. The building, too, was beautiful; it had red and white curly-cues all over it, and a delicious odor of things cooking seemed to emanate from it.

Gwen stood up and waved her arms and screamed uproariously, beating a wild tattoo on the glass with her hands. She yelled, "Nanna—Nanna—"

Her mother came back across the road; she waited for a moment until several cars had whizzed past, and then she scurried over the pavement. Gwen giggled at seeing her run. . . . Nanna had two round, papery things in her hand.

"Did you say mustard on yours, Joe?"

He straightened up; his face looked very wrinkly, and Gwen smiled at seeing him. "Yeh. Mustard. . . . Kid, I dunno what it is. Those taps seem to be all right. I dunno; maybe the rocker-arms could use a little oil. Something's sticking."

Nanna opened the door of the car and Gwen fell into her arms, still chuckling. "Here's my big girl! Are you ready for your milk?"

"Eat." Gwen reached for the round, papery things in Nanna's hand. Something smelled very appetizing.

"No, honey-bunch. Baby can't. No, no. . . . Gee, Joe, she's trying to get these hot dogs."

"Put 'em down on the running board—"

"No, *no,* baby. . . . See—here's baby's milk. In this bottle. Here, all nice—"

Gwen sat on Nanna's lap. She had a paper napkin tucked under her chin, and she drank deeply out of her own white mug. The milk filled her mouth with richness; she could have wished that it was a little warmer, but it tasted good anyway. . . . After a time, she pushed the cup from her and demanded, "Crackaw?"

"Joe, where'd you put those crackers?"

"Didn't have them. Yes, I did too. Down next to that straw suitcase. Next to the seat."

Nanna found the red box. Gwen yelled, "Crackaw!"

"Yes, cracker. Isn't that nice? Cracker for baby. Now, sit down there on your mattress. Good girl. Sit down."

Doddy was sitting on the running board. He had taken the paper wrapping from the round object, and he was munching gravely.

"How's your hot dog, Joe?"

"Notsa bad. I've seen better. . . . Makes you thirsty."

"Go across to the stand. They'll give you a drink. That lady's real nice."

"Spose she would?"

"Sure. Go on. . . . Take this cup, honey. Bring me a drink, too."

When he came back, he carried a brown can with a long, pointed spout, and behind him waddled a fat, rosy-faced woman with a gray sweater, and a man's old cap pulled down over her short gray hair. She laughed, "Hello there again, lady. I just hadda come over an' see baby."

Nanna held Gwen up to the open window. Doddy was poking the long spout of his can under the uplifted part of the car. "Squeejee, squeejee, squeejee—" chanted the fat woman, squeezing Gwen's hands.

Gwen grinned at her and said, "Hay-oh."

"Ja hear that?" the fat woman chortled. "She says hello. Ain't that cute? What's her name?"

"Gwendolyn Marie. . . . She's nineteen months."

"She's little," said the fat woman, "but she looks like a awful healthy baby. I got two. The girl's married an' lives over at West Springs."

Gwen sniffed at the fat woman's sleeve. There was a comfortable, sweetish odor about her—the odor of fried meat and hot things in a kitchen. "I bet she smells the hamburg," beamed the visitor. "My land, I get all splashed up with that grease. You going far?"

"Burlington," replied Nanna. "Joe's got a job with the Mid-Ocean Sieve Company. If we ever get there."

"Oh. You'll make it." She muzzled down at Gwen and made a little grunting noise. Gwen laughed. The fat woman turned to Doddy. "Through with that oil, mister?"

"I oiled 'em," nodded Joe. "I'm sure much obliged. Maybe we'll have better luck now." He handed the can to the woman, and climbed into his seat. The car began to whistle and jiggle pleasantly. "By gosh," said Doddy. "That loosened her up, for now anyway. Sure much obliged."

The fat woman waved the oilcan and threw a kiss to Gwen as the car pulled away. Gwen waved, "Bye," until the road was only a narrow slit behind them—until the fat woman was like a gray bug, crossing the slit.

"I bet she thought I was gonna beat it with that oilcan."

"Oh, Joe! She was just being nice to baby."

"Maybe so. . . . That oil loosened it. It don't spit like it did. Maybe we'll make it to Burlington yet."

They drove for an eternity. . . . Gwen sat up on the mattress and played with her zebra. It was a rubber zebra, blown full of air. She called it, "Horshy." She twisted its ears and squealed, "Horshy, horshy!"

"Lookit, Joe."

"What?"

"She was kissing that zebra. Gee. . . ."

He permitted himself a swift glance over his shoulder. "You oughtn't to let her chew that. It's dirty."

"She wasn't chewing it. Was you, mother's precious?"

Gwen sat up and pointed to a field which they were passing. The field was full of Moos; one of the Moos switched its tail and nodded kindly at her. "Horshy!" said Gwen.

"No, baby. That's Cow. A Moo-Cow-Moo. Say Moo."

"Horshy-moo," said Gwen, and fell over upon the mattress, much pleased with herself. She sat up and demanded, "Crackaw."

Nanna fumbled around. "Joe, I can't find that box of crackers."

"Gosh, kid! They're all gone. I ate the last one awhile ago, and threw out the box."

"Crackaw," petitioned Gwen.

"Ain't there any oranges left, Agnes?"

"She had the last orange awhile ago. . . . Oh, Joe, I just guess we'll have to stop and buy something. She didn't have much for her lunch. I bet she's awful hungry."

Tall weeds began to brush the glass; the wheels bounced over hummocks, and the car came to a clattering stop. Doddy felt in his pocket and brought out a handful of bright, round things. Gwen reached for them, but he held them farther away. "Sixty-five, ninety, a dollar fifteen, a dollar twenty, a dollar twenty-two. Kid, you got any money?"

"Fifteen cents left from those hot dogs, Joe."

"That makes one-thirty-seven."

Gwen stood up and rubbed her nose against the glass; the weeds were soft and yellow, just outside. She had forgotten the cracker. She whispered, "Pretty."

"We'll have to buy five more gallons of gas, kid. At least that. And maybe oil. A quart. That'll be one-twenty-eight. That leaves nine cents. Could we get something for baby for nine cents?"

"Joe, what about our supper?"

"If you can wait, we ought to make it by eight o'clock. I'll find Harry Spevak. He'll lend me some dough. And he said he'd have a place all ready for us to step into, till we could get a house. They won't ask for rent tonight. Or maybe he's paid it."

Gwen looked out of the rear window. The sky was broken into scallops of white; they were like flowers, too. She thought of the gold flowers beside the car, the purple flowers she had seen so long before. She thought of the Wow, with its attentive ears. . . . "Pretty-Wow," she said quietly.

"Maybe we could stop at a store. Get crackers—graham crackers—in a sack instead of package. You know, in bulk. Then you and me could have some, too."

A car was coming from behind. Gwen watched it; maybe another Wow, a big yellow Wow, would be riding in it. The car swung from side to side, and came closer with a loud noise, but Gwen was not frightened. Cars did not hurt you; cars were nice; only you must not grab the round wheel in Doddy's hands. . . .

Then there was a great smash; it sounded like the time when Gwen had upset the bread-box and jelly glasses in the pantry, only much louder. . . . Gwen was thrown up into the air and down upon something soft; the rubber zebra struck her in the face. She snatched at its leg and cried indignantly, "Horshy!"

There was a shrill noise, very close at hand. Gwen couldn't see anything but Nanna's old coat just above her head. . . . She lay still and listened.

"You hurt, kid? Agnes, you—"

"No, no. Don't mind— Baby! *Gwendolyn! My honey-bunch—Joe—!*"

Something hard and broken came tinkling down beside Gwen. Maybe more jelly-glasses—

Doddy was lifting her high—higher— She was in the open air; Nanna seized her. Nanna was all dusty, and there was something black and gummy on her hand. Gwen waved the zebra and cried excitedly, "Horshy—"

"Joe! She's all right, Joe! Not even crying— My baby! Baby—"

Gwen was somewhat bewildered. First flowers—and then another car came; was there a Wow in it, after all? She asked, "Crackaw?"

The other car had stopped, on the opposite side of the road somewhat ahead of them. Their own car was on its side in the ditch; yellow flowers grew up, all around it. Gwen smiled, to see it there.

Doddy had a bright red mark on his cheek. He rubbed it, and the mark became wider. He made an odd sound, and shook his head, and began to run toward the other car.

"Joe! Joe! Don't you—"

A man was climbing slowly out of the other car. He was grinning. When he stood up beside the car, he held to the open door beside him. His face was very red—redder than the fat woman's—almost as red as the mark on Doddy's face—

"Well," he said. "That was some bump."

"You almost killed us," said Doddy. "Lookit my car!"

"I see it. I see your—car. Pile of junk."

"You broke the wheel," said Doddy. "Bent that fender. Lookit it!"

"Pile of junk," said the other man. He was still grinning. He pulled a roll of paper out of his pocket. "Buy it for ten dollars."

Doddy said something—Gwen couldn't hear what it was—and began to take off his sweater. "I was clear off the pavement. You'll do time for this, you. Or—"

Gwen giggled. Nanna clutched her tightly and whispered, "Joe."

Doddy didn't turn his head. He started toward the other man. "You think just because you got a big Auburn, you can go around killing other folks—"

"Buy it for ten dollars," repeated the man with the red face. He threw two folded slips of paper down in the road, and turned around. His movements were unsteady; he trembled crazily as he climbed into his car; and Gwen laughed. "Bye," she waved.

The big car moved away from them. It began to sway from side to side. It went up over a hill, out of sight.

"Joe!" cried Nanna. "I bet he'll kill somebody! Why didn't you stop him?"

"The town's right ahead—Baxter. He'll never get through that. They'll pick him up."

"You oughta grabbed him, Joe! Our wheel's busted—"

"He had a gun in the side pocket; I could see it. He was drunk. I wasn't taking no chances." Doddy took a handkerchief out of his pocket and wiped the red mark from his face. "Ten dollars, Agnes. We're sure outa luck. That wheel'll cost—"

He stooped down and picked up the two folded slips of paper. He screamed suddenly and jumped into the air. Gwen began to clap her hands.

"Agnes! These are *fifties*! Two fifties! A hundred bucks—"

Nanna ran to him, carrying Gwen. Gwen reached for the pieces of paper. She said, "Pay-pay—" But Doddy snatched them away and waved them in the air. "We're rich, folks! By gosh—that wheel—I can get another cheap. I—"

Gwen began to sing, a song without words. She stopped and demanded, "Crackaw?"

"Yes, baby! You little skeezix! Right away—"

Other cars stopped, one from each direction. Men came climbing out. There was a little girl in a green coat. She stared at Gwen.

The men were talking with Doddy. "How'd it happen?"

"Fellow hit me. Help me lift her up, will you?"

"Sure." They all grabbed the car and hoisted it slowly up on its wheels. Doddy climbed into his seat; the suitcases and mattress were all tumbled around; but the car began to buzz and quiver. "She's all right. Just that glass and wheel and fender—"

"Did he stop?"

"Sure. He settled right off. A big Auburn."

One of the men nodded. "I saw him. Turned off on Twenty-five. Going like hell; you were lucky."

"Sure was. Thanks a lot. . . . You going to town?" he asked the other man.

"You bet. Give you a ride."

Nanna took Gwen and climbed back into their own car. "I'll wait here, Joe. Wait till you come out with the garage man."

"All right. You wait. I'll bring something to eat." Doddy waved at them; his face was all wrinkled with smiles. Then the cars all made a great noise, and drove away; the little girl in the green coat was gone; and Nanna and Gwen were sitting there alone.

Nanna hummed softly, *"That was plucky Lindy's lucky day—"* Her hands rubbed over Gwen; they were soft, slender and warm. Gwen hugged her zebra and let her eyes go shut. . . . Thinking of the girl in the green coat, of Doddy gone to bring crackers, of the many cars and the man with the bright, red face.

It had, she thought, been very wonderful. She had enjoyed herself. Wow and flowers and milk. And the fat woman who smelled nice, and the odd noise when she had been thrown into the air and down again on something soft. It had been a good day, free from worry of any kind.

The Archangel Michael and Gerald Smith

WILLIAM FIFIELD

THE ARCHANGEL MICHAEL came to Gerald Smith's house on Thursday afternoon when the White Sox were in town. There was no particular reason why he should have picked Gerald's house but that was what happened, and here is how it happened.

Gerald was in the living room. At the same time he was being the announcer for the game between the White Sox and the Yanks. At three o'clock it would be on the air and then he'd sit on the ottoman in front of the radio and listen to Red Barber, but now he was the famous radio announcer Gerald Smith and already in the second inning he had the Yanks ahead four runs. Mike Kreevich was up to bat and he had two strikes on him and one ball that was low and inside, but Gerald thought he would let him hit it—a high one—and Joe DiMaggio would run back and make a one-hand catch of it and retire the side with no hits and no runs. Kreevich connected and Gerald could see the ball way up in the air higher than the top of the stands and Joe DiMaggio getting under it to make the catch, and he was very busy telling all the thousands of fans that were listening-in about it. Just then the doorbell rang.

Gerald went to the door and opened it a little. When his mother had gone out and left him home alone for the afternoon she had told him that if anyone came to the door he must only open it a little bit to look out, and that no matter who it was he was not to unhook the screen door. Now he looked out through the crack of the door and there was a man standing there on the porch. He was a very unusual-looking man in many respects, Gerald thought. He was a short man and a very thin man, except that he had a round stomach that stuck out like a watermelon in the middle of him and his pants were hitched on the underside of it so that it looked like they might fall right off any minute. The coat he had on did not match the pants and it did not match him either, but his stomach was what fascinated Gerald. It was right on the level of his eyes and he had a hard time to make himself look up into the man's face because his stomach was so much more interesting.

"Is your mother at home, my fine young man?" the man asked.

Gerald shook his head no.

"Is your sister at home then, my bucko?"

"I don't have a sister," Gerald said, "and anyway there's nobody home except me."

"Aha!" the man said, "the brave protector of the house, are you? Are you indeed? Well, look what I have to show you." The man took something out of his coat pocket and held it in the palm of his hand. Gerald hung back a moment and then his curiosity got the best of him because whatever the man had in his hand was alive and it moved. Gerald pushed the door open farther and got right up with his nose against the screen so he could see better what it was.

"What is it?" he asked, trying very hard to see.

"Look," the man said, and he held his hand up close to the screen. There was a turtle in the palm of his hand, one of the kind Gerald had seen once when his dad took him to Coney Island, very small and with Coney Island written on its back, only this one didn't have writing on it.

"It's a turtle," Gerald said.

"It *is* a turtle, young man," the man replied, "and were you but to give this starved and weary traveler a bite of food it would be *your* turtle."

Gerald wondered if he ought to do it.

"I have come a long way, a long and bitter way, and I am very hungry," the man said. "I have had no food for twenty days," he said. "Twenty days and twenty nights, my boy."

"Gee," Gerald said. The man was a nice man and he certainly needed something to eat all right and the turtle was nice too, but just the same his mother had told him that he wasn't to open the screen door no matter who came and that he was to tell whoever it was to come back the next day when somebody would be home.

"My mother will be home tomorrow and maybe she will give you something to eat," Gerald said as politely as he knew how, trying not to notice the disappointed way the man hitched up his stomach with his hands when he said it.

"My fine lad," the man said solemnly, "tomorrow will be too late and I shall have died of hunger. Before tomorrow comes I will lie on the street dead with my soul up in heaven, my boy." The man leaned down and looked right into Gerald's eyes. "You will save a life if you feed this weak and stricken creature. You will save a soul," he said impressively, and his funny red eyebrows came almost together over his long nose because he said it so intensely.

Gerald knew that to save a soul was something very proper to do and certainly even his mother wouldn't want to punish him for that; so he unhooked the screen door and let the man come in.

"Which way is the kitchen?" the man asked as soon as he got inside.

Gerald pointed down the hall toward the kitchen door and the man started right off without any urging whatsoever.

"Now my true little Christian," he said, seating himself at the kitchen table and adjusting his stomach, "let us not trouble ourselves with formalities. What good things does the larder provide?"

Gerald found some cold ham in the icebox and two bananas, and he climbed up onto the drainboard and got down the cookies that he knew were hidden behind the boxes of cereal in the cupboard. He put the ham on a plate and the cookies on another plate and poured a glass of milk for the man. On second thought he poured another glass of milk and set it in front of the other place at the kitchen table. Then he sat down and began reflectively to munch on one of his mother's good ginger cookies and watch the man eat.

The man ate very fast and Gerald noticed he didn't have particularly good table manners. In fact he had terrible table manners. He put a bite of ham in his mouth and then a bite of banana and then some milk and chewed it all at once with his cheeks puffed out like he had the mumps. When he swallowed, his Adam's apple went up and down in his throat and Gerald could not help watching it because it was so big and the man's throat was so scrawny.

He wanted to ask about the turtle but he didn't dare because the man was so busy eating and he didn't want to interrupt him. After a while the man leaned back in his chair and wiped his mouth with the back of his hand. He had eaten everything Gerald had got out for him and now he put an old cigar in his mouth. It was already half smoked.

"Is there a match on the premises, my lad?" the man asked.

Gerald got up from the table and went over to the stove. There was a box of matches on top of the stove and he climbed up and got it and brought it over to the man. The man took one of the matches and lit his cigar with it and then he shut the box and put it in the big pocket of his coat.

"Thank you, my lad," he said.

"You said I could have the turtle," Gerald said timidly.

"Ah, Mister O'Connor. So I did. I'd forgotten for the moment, and it's quite right of you to remind me, my boy. Quite right indeed."

The man reached down into his pocket and brought out the turtle.

"What's your name, boy?" he asked Gerald.

"Gerald," Gerald said. "Gerald Smith."

"Mister O'Connor, meet Gerald Smith," the man said to the turtle and put him down on the white tabletop.

"Is that the turtle's name?" Gerald asked. The man nodded. Mister O'Connor began to move sedately across the table in the opposite direction from Gerald. The man reached out with his left hand and picked up Mister O'Connor. He closed his hand, moved it around in the air a minute, and then he said presto and opened up his hand. Mister O'Connor was gone. Gerald was very surprised. He was so surprised he didn't say anything at all.

Then the man put his right hand on the top of Gerald's head and said presto again and took something right out of Gerald's hair, and it was Mister O'Connor.

Gerald thought that that was a very good trick and he said, "That was a good trick," whereupon the man looked at him with a sad expression. "That was not a trick," he said solemnly. "It was a miracle."

Gerald knew about miracles. Only God and Jesus did miracles, they said at Sunday School. He looked up at the man not knowing whether to believe him or not and the man said, "A miracle, my boy! A miracle! And do you know why? Do you know why I can make miracles?"

Gerald shook his head no.

"Because I am God's representative here on earth," the man said looking right into Gerald's eyes. "Because I am the Archangel Michael come plump right down from Heaven dressed up like an ordinary man to find out who are the good people and who are the bad people," he said. "Watch me make another miracle."

He took out his handkerchief and put a match in it and wrapped it all up tight around the match. Then he held it out to Gerald. "Break the match," he said. Gerald broke the match. He broke it up into little bits inside the handkerchief. Then the man said presto and opened up the handkerchief and there wasn't anything in it at all. And then he said presto again and waved the handkerchief in the air and then spread it out on the table and there right in the middle of it was the match, but it wasn't broken at all. "What do you think of that, my young friend?" the man asked.

Gerald didn't answer. He was staring at the match lying on the handkerchief and it must have been a miracle all right because he had personally broken the match up into little pieces himself. The big fellows said it was sissy, the things they learned in Sunday School, and they whammed the stuffings out of Jeep Lanning who sat across from Gerald in the second grade because once at recess they tried to make him say Mr. Peabody, the Sunday School teacher, was an old horse and he wouldn't. But just the same it certainly was a miracle.

"Watch this," the man said. He clapped his hands together and then reached into Gerald's front pocket and, sure enough, he brought Mister O'Connor right out of his pocket. "How's that?" he said.

Gerald nodded his head up and down vigorously and watched Mister O'Connor walk slowly along the enamel tabletop. He guessed the man wasn't fooling him and he really was that angel he said.

"Am I deceived, or is that apple pie I see?" the man asked and Gerald looked over and there was some apple pie in a tin on top of the breadbox.

"It's the pie we had for lunch," he said.

"Since I have given you Mister O'Connor," the man said, "and passed three miracles for your sole and solitary entertainment the least you could do in return would be to give me what remains of that lovely apple pie."

Gerald went over and got the apple pie for him and the man took a piece of newspaper out of his pocket and wrapped the pie up in it and put it in his pocket.

"Now I must be on my way," the man said, "but one final word. You are not to tell anyone I was here."

"Why not?" Gerald asked.

"Do you think for a minute an angel who has just come bang down from Heaven can go around letting everyone know who he is? Do you?" he asked indignantly, shoving out his chin that had red whiskers on it.

Gerald shook his head dubiously. "Huh uh. I guess not."

"Well, I should say not! I should just say not! Why everybody would be coming around and wanting me to do a miracle for them. And how would that be, young man?"

Gerald could see that that would be pretty bad.

"So don't you tell anybody I was here," the man finished. Then he got up and started out of the kitchen. Gerald followed along behind and opened the front door for him. As the man went out of the door his stomach passed right in front of Gerald's face and it looked bigger than ever.

On the porch the man stopped and he turned around and put his hand on Gerald's head. "I will do one more miracle for you since you have been kind and good and it won't be much bother," he said. "What is the thing you want to be most of all when you grow up?"

"An announcer on the radio like Red Barber," Gerald said right away not having to stop and think even for a minute.

"Then you will be," the man said, and he looked so solemn when he said it that he looked more like the Archangel Michael that he really was than the ordinary man he was pretending to be for the time being. "I say you will be even better than Red Barber," he said. "I say it. And what I say goes."

The man went down the steps and up the street and Gerald hooked the screen door again and went in the kitchen and cleaned up the mess. He wiped off the plates and put them back where they belonged and he took the cigar butt the man had left and hid it under the big potato sack in the pantry. If his mother missed the food he would say that he had eaten it himself and he would get a licking from his dad, but that wouldn't be very much to pay for the miracle that had been passed on him. Then he went into the living room and turned on the radio. Red Barber was announcing the game and it would be Gerald Smith in only a few more years when he was grown up. He put Mister O'Connor down on the carpet and Mister O'Connor cautiously stuck out his head and his legs. The Yanks were ahead of the White Sox and there was a man on second with only one out and Joe DiMaggio was up to bat. It was a very lovely Thursday afternoon.

Camp Nomopo

LUDWIG BEMELMANS

AFTER HER first walk through the city, Barbara came back to the Hotel Metropolitano in Quito with her lips blue and her little fists clenched. Mimi put her to bed and I went out to look for a garment that would shield her against the cold wind that blows down from Pichincha. There was no snow suit to be had; it's not cold enough for that, and the coats for little girls which I found and brought back to the hotel Barbara waved away. Four and a half years old, she knew exactly what she wanted. She sat up in bed with the first measles spots on her chest and said she would rather freeze to death than wear anything like the samples she had seen.

During the next weeks while she was in bed, I had to design coats for her. I exhausted myself making a stack of fashion drawings, designs of dramatic coats, and hats to go with them, and I cut paper dolls out of old fashion magazines and pasted my coats on them. The design that found favor with Barbara was a three-storied kind of pelerine, a garment such as Viennese fiacre drivers of the time of Franz Josef used to wear.

"This is it," she said. "That's the bestest good one."

As soon as Barbara was well, we went to a tailor with the design. The shop of Señor Pablo Duque Arias faces the square of San Francisco. It is like an indoor farm. Chickens run around among the sewing machines and over the low podium on which Mr. Arias's chief cutter sits with crossed legs; a cat, a dog with offspring, and a parrot complete the fauna; the flora consist of artificial paper roses stuck in a dry vase that stands on a small shelf between an oil print of the Madonna and a picture of the Temptation of St. Anthony.

Barbara eyed this *salon de couture* with alarm and suspicion, but she let Señor Arias measure her. He studied my design and then we went to the store of Don Alfonso Pérez Pallares to buy the cloth—the tailor, Barbara, Madame, and myself. We found something that looked like the lining of a good English traveling bag. It was made in Ecuador and it was agreeable to everyone.

The coat was in work for a week, and on each day we inspected progress of the garment. At the end, Barbara looked into a mirror and was delighted with the results. It cost $7.50, not counting my time and talent. The coat was a very warm and useful garment on the return trip to New York in February.

Barbara is one of the seventy-five or a hundred over-privileged children who are allowed to play inside the cast-iron confines of Gramercy Park. Another little girl, equally well fixed, is an earnest, dark-haired, five-year-old whose name is Ruthie. Ruthie played with Barbara one day and they became friends—and at their third meeting, on a day in March, when Barbara was dressed in my creation, little Ruthie said to Barbara, "You look like Oliver Twister in that coat. That's a coat like orphans wear. I think it's terrible. I don't see how you can wear it."

On a visit to Ruthie's house that afternoon, Barbara inspected Ruthie's wardrobe. She did not wear the "Oliver Twister" coat when she came back, but carried it in her arms and hid it in the closet of her room.

She succeeded by a week of ceaseless cajolery and little-girl appeal in wangling a new winter outfit from me when it was already spring and all the Gramercy Park trees were breaking out with small green buds. Of course, it was an outfit exactly like something that Ruthie had, only newer.

Barbara and Ruthie were now bosom friends. They sat together on a bench facing a stone urn, to the left of the statue of Mr. Booth, and there they hatched another plot. The plan was to go to a summer camp together. Little Ruthie had been at this camp the year before and she described the sylvan, rugged beauty of that life to Barbara. Barbara said to Ruthie that she'd love to go but that she was afraid she would be lonesome, that she never had gone anywhere without her parents.

"Oh," said Ruthie, "after the third day you forget you ever had a father or mother."

Barbara came home with this bit of grim wisdom.

The camp we chose took care of a hundred girls. It was in the upper Adirondacks. The water came from artesian wells, the children slept in semi-bungalows and washed themselves at ten taps that spouted cold artesian water. The taps were conveniently located in front of the bungalows, the prospectus said, and the children got up to the sound of a bugle at 7:30 a.m. and did their own housework.

When I came to this part of the booklet I was convinced that nothing was better for our darling than to rise in the upper Adirondacks at seven-thirty and scrub herself at a cold-water tap.

Barbara hopped on one foot and on the other and clasped her hands with joy when I told her that she would be one of the lucky members of Camp Nomopo, which in the language of the Indians means Land That Is Bright. The equipment needed for this simple life had to be marked with the name of the child and was as follows:

Bathing suits, 2
Bathing sandals, 1 pair
Heavy bathing caps, 2
Cotton ankle socks, 4 pairs
Cotton underwear, 4 suits
Pajamas, 3 pairs
Bathrobe, 1
Tennis sneakers, 1 pair
Handkerchiefs, 6
Play suits, 2
Bedroom slippers, 1 pair
Rubbers, 1 pair
Tennis racquet, 1
Tennis balls, 3
Toilet articles
Poncho, 1
Rain hat, 1
Riding breeches, 1 pair
Bed sheets, 3
Pillow cases, 3
Dark blankets, 3
Bath towels, 3
Face towels, 3
Mattress protector, 1
Laundry bag, 1
Duffle bag, 1
Folding knife and spoon, 1 each
Drinking cup with handle, 1
Sewing material
Bible, 1

In addition, there was this special equipment:

1 pair Nomopo gabardine shorts
1 pair Nomopo brown oxfords
2 white Nomopo shirts
2 Nomopo suits
1 Nomopo green tie
1 Nomopo green sweater
2 pairs Nomopo ankle socks

The whole thing went into a green army trunk and was stowed in the back seat of the car.

The cost of going to the camp for two months was a healthy figure, about what it would take to stay at a good hotel for that time. There was a canteen. There were, besides, provisions for pocket money to buy extra things at the canteen and an additional charge for the materials used in the arts and crafts building of Camp Nomopo.

The camp was full of cheer and gladness when we arrived. The Madame who ran it received her guests with the intense charm and cordiality of a Howard Johnson hostess; the counselors hopped around, and little Ruthie, who had arrived the day before, took Barbara by the hand and led her down to their semi-bungalow, Number 5. I checked on the waterspout which was right next to it. The cabin was a loose shelter built on stilts, open to the north and south, with no windows, but large shutters that were held up by pieces of wood. In it stood six little cast-iron cots such as you see in orphanages; birds sang outside and the branches of the trees were the curtains.

In this room the floor was a row of unpainted boards through which, here and there, you could see the good earth. We also inspected the Mess Hall and the Infirmary. The counselor that had Barbara in charge showed her how to make her bed, how to sweep the floor, and how to empty the rubbish bin—three duties that were her part of the housekeeping. Barbara did it all with gusto.

The Madame came around at about 3 p.m. and said, "Please leave before it gets dark. It's easier for the child that way."

So we said good-by to Barbara. She was brave. She said, "Good-by," and walked away with her back to the car waving as she walked. Halfway down to shack Number 5, at the cold-water tap, she suddenly turned. The small face was streaked with tears and she came back and got a grip on her mother and announced that she would not stay in the camp.

I don't know where I got the courage because my heart was breaking, but I took Barbara, handed her to the Madame, who pressed her to her ample bosom. I got Mimi into the car, and drove off. We called the camp an hour later on the phone and the Madame announced that Barbara's grief had lasted for a quarter of an hour. "Now she's in the recreation hall having the time of her life, the little darling. She's sitting in front of the big fire with little Ruthie, listening to 'Peter and the Wolf.' Don't you worry a minute about her—and please, please don't come visiting her until ten days from now."

The next day, while staying at a hotel, I reflected what a wonderful racket a children's camp is, how much better it is than owning a hotel, for example.

Imagine if the guests of a hotel like the Savoy-Plaza arrived bringing their own three dark blankets and sheets, towels, and pillow cases, made their own beds, emptied their garbage, went down to the cold-water taps in Central Park to scrub themselves, and without murmur ate the healthy, strength-giving diet you put before them! If instead of going out in the evening and spending their money in rival establishments, they would quietly sit around the bar listening to "Peter and the Wolf" or do arty-crafty things in the ballroom—all of them dressed in hats, shoes, and sweaters marked Savoy-Plaza!

We came back after ten days in which we wrote nine letters and received four cards written by Barbara's counselor. After a glowing report on how glad and happy and what a fine girl she was, the Madame sent for her.

She came in the rain, between the wet dripping trees, in the Nomopo rain hat, the Nomopo green sweater and poncho, alone and much sadder looking than "Oliver Twister" ever was. She broke out in streams of tears when she saw us and she kept crying even after it stopped raining outside. She blinked red-eyed in the sun that shone above rays of floating mist.

We went out to a play field, and, at one moment when we stepped aside to discuss what to do, Barbara found herself surrounded by her comrades. Madame looked down at her with reproach and her counselor, a maiden from whose Nomopo sweater I could hardly take my eyes, said, "You're not going to be a sissy now, are you, and run away from us?"

Barbara was the most complete portrait of misery I have ever seen, not excepting the work of El Greco. She cried, "I don't like it here. I want to go home with Mummy and Pappy. I want to go home; I don't like it here. I want to go home."

We took her into the car with us and I said in French to Mimi that I thought under the circumstances it would be the best thing to take her home with us. While I spoke, she took hold of the leather straps that are attached to the convertible top of the car as if to anchor herself, and said, "You don't have to speak French, I know what you were saying. You said, 'Let's start the car and push Barbara out and drive away like the last time' "—and then she continued, "I dream about you at night and when I wake up you're not there, and in the morning, another little girl next to me cries and that makes me cry too.

"Ruthie said she cried too the first time last year, but her mother just left her there and never came to see her and now she's used to it, but I won't get used to it because I dream of you every night. And it's so cold in the morning, and I have to empty the pail and sweep."

The washing at the tap she had got around, apparently. She was streaked with dirt and her hair was a mess. She said, "We take a bath twice a week, down at the lake, and the water is cold. I want to go home. I don't like it here. I want to go home with Mummy and Pappy."

A man came to the car and smiled and said, "I'm only the husband of Mrs. Van Cortland who runs the camp and I can assure you that Barbara's the happiest little girl when you're not here. She sings and plays all day long. I think it would be a great mistake for you to take her away."

I told him that we would take her away. Barbara let go of the straps and the man said, "Well, all I can say is that in my twenty-seven years this has happened only once before."

Barbara smelled of garlic and unwashed hair. They had had meat loaf for lunch. It was dark by the time we had made the decision and we stayed for supper. It began to rain again and there is nothing more wet and desolate than Adirondack camps in the rain. The meal was served on a drafty porch, a piece of canvas blew in with every gust of wind. The menu consisted of melted cheese poured over toast and a lukewarm rice pudding that tasted like glue; a glass of milk was served to each diner.

We left poor Ruthie behind, and the Madame and her husband assured us again that it was only the second time in twenty-seven years that such a thing had happened.

A Day's Wait

ERNEST HEMINGWAY

He came into the room to shut the windows while we were still in bed and I saw he looked ill. He was shivering, his face was white, and he walked slowly as though it ached to move.

"What's the matter, Schatz?"

"I've got a headache."

"You better go back to bed."

"No. I'm all right."

"You go to bed. I'll see you when I'm dressed."

But when I came downstairs he was dressed, sitting by the fire, looking a very sick and miserable boy of nine years. When I put my hand on his forehead I knew he had a fever.

"You go up to bed," I said, "you're sick."

"I'm all right," he said.

When the doctor came he took the boy's temperature.

"What is it?" I asked him.

"One hundred and two."

Downstairs, the doctor left three different medicines in different colored capsules with instructions for giving them. One was to bring down the fever, another a purgative, the third to overcome an acid condition. The germs of influenza can only exist in an acid condition, he explained. He seemed to know all about influenza and said there was nothing to worry about if the fever did not go above one hundred and four degrees. This was a light epidemic of flu and there was no danger if you avoided pneumonia.

Back in the room I wrote the boy's temperature down and made a note of the time to give the various capsules.

"Do you want me to read to you?"

"All right. If you want to," said the boy. His face was very white and there were dark areas under his eyes. He lay still in the bed and seemed very detached from what was going on.

I read aloud from Howard Pyle's *Book of Pirates;* but I could see he was not following what I was reading.

"How do you feel, Schatz?" I asked him.

"Just the same, so far," he said.

I sat at the foot of the bed and read to myself while I waited for it to be time to give another capsule. It would have been natural for him to go to sleep, but when I looked up he was looking at the foot of the bed, looking very strangely.

"Why don't you try to go to sleep? I'll wake you up for the medicine."

"I'd rather stay awake."

After a while he said to me, "You don't have to stay in here with me, Papa, if it bothers you."

"It doesn't bother me."

"No, I mean you don't have to stay if it's going to bother you."

I thought perhaps he was a little lightheaded and after giving him the prescribed capsules at eleven o'clock I went out for a while.

It was a bright, cold day, the ground covered with a sleet that had frozen so that it seemed as if all the bare trees, the bushes, the cut brush and all the grass and the bare ground had been varnished with ice. I took the young Irish setter for a little walk up the road and along a frozen creek, but it was difficult to stand or walk on the glassy surface and the red dog slipped and slithered and I fell twice, hard, once dropping my gun and having it slide away over the ice.

We flushed a covey of quail under a high clay bank with overhanging brush and I killed two as they went out of sight over the top of the bank. Some of the covey lit in trees, but most of them scattered into brush piles and it was necessary to jump on the ice-coated mounds of brush several times before they would flush. Coming out while you were poised unsteadily on the icy, springy brush they made difficult shooting and I killed two, missed five, and started back pleased to have found a covey close to the house and happy there were so many left to find on another day.

At the house they said the boy had refused to let anyone come into the room.

"You can't come in," he said. "You mustn't get what I have."

I went up to him and found him in exactly the position I had left him, white-faced, but with the tops of his cheeks flushed by the fever, staring still, as he had stared, at the foot of the bed.

I took his temperature.

"What is it?"

"Something like a hundred," I said. It was one hundred and two and four tenths.

"It was a hundred and two," he said.

"Who said so?"

"The doctor."

"Your temperature is all right," I said. "It's nothing to worry about."

"I don't worry," he said, "but I can't keep from thinking."

"Don't think," I said. "Just take it easy."

"I'm taking it easy," he said and looked straight ahead. He was evidently holding tight onto himself about something.

"Take this with water."

"Do you think it will do any good?"

"Of course it will."

I sat down and opened the *Pirate* book and commenced to read, but I could see he was not following, so I stopped.

"About what time do you think I'm going to die?" he asked.

"What?"

"About how long will it be before I die?"

"You aren't going to die. What's the matter with you?"

"Oh, yes, I am. I heard him say a hundred and two."

"People don't die with a fever of one hundred and two. That's a silly way to talk."

"I know they do. At school in France the boys told me you can't live with forty-four degrees. I've got a hundred and two."

He had been waiting to die all day, ever since nine o'clock in the morning.

"You poor Schatz," I said. "Poor old Schatz. It's like miles and kilometers. You aren't going to die. That's a different thermometer. On that thermometer thirty-seven is normal. On this kind it's ninety-eight."

"Are you sure?"

"Absolutely," I said. "It's like miles and kilometers. You know, like how many kilometers we make when we do seventy miles in the car?"

"Oh," he said.

But his gaze at the foot of the bed relaxed slowly. The hold over himself relaxed too, finally, and the next day it was very slack and he cried very easily at little things that were of no importance.

The Word, Love and Speech

HELEN KELLER

THE MOST important day I remember in all my life is the one on which my teacher, Anne Mansfield Sullivan, came to me. I am filled with wonder when I consider the immeasurable contrasts between the two lives which it connects. It was the third of March, 1887, three months before I was seven years old.

On the afternoon of that eventful day, I stood on the porch, dumb, expectant. I guessed vaguely from my mother's signs and from the hurrying to and fro in the house that something unusual was about to happen, so I went to the door and waited on the steps. The afternoon sun penetrated the mass of honeysuckle that covered the porch, and fell on my upturned face. My fingers lingered almost unconsciously on the familiar leaves and blossoms which had just come forth to greet the sweet southern spring. I did not know what the future held of marvel or surprise for me. Anger and bitterness had preyed upon me continually for weeks and a deep languor had succeeded this passionate struggle.

Have you ever been at sea in a dense fog, when it seemed as if a tangible white darkness shut you in, and the great ship, tense and anxious, groped her way toward the shore with plummet and sounding-line, and you waited with beating heart for something to happen? I was like that ship before my education began, only I was without compass or sounding-line, and had no way of knowing how near the harbour was. "Light! give me light!" was the wordless cry of my soul, and the light of love shone on me in that very hour.

I felt approaching footsteps. I stretched out my hand as I supposed to my mother. Someone took it, and I was caught up and held close in the arms of her who had come to reveal all things to me, and, more than all things else, to love me.

The morning after my teacher came she led me into her room and gave me a doll. The little blind children at the Perkins Institution had sent it and Laura Bridgman had dressed it; but I did not know this until afterward. When I had played with it a little while, Miss Sullivan slowly spelled into my hand the word "d-o-l-l." I was at once interested in this finger play and tried to imitate it. When I finally succeeded in making the letters correctly I was flushed with childish pleasure and pride. Running downstairs to my mother I held up my hand and made the letters for doll. I did not know that I was spelling a word or even that words existed; I was simply making my fingers go in monkey-like imitation. In the days that followed I learned to spell in this uncomprehending way a great many words, among them *pin, hat, cup* and a few verbs like *sit, stand* and *walk*. But my teacher had been with me several weeks before I understood that everything has a name.

One day, while I was playing with my new doll, Miss Sullivan put my big rag doll into my lap also, spelled "d-o-l-l" and tried to make me understand that "d-o-l-l" applied to both. Earlier in the day we had had a tussle over the words "m-u-g" and "w-a-t-e-r." Miss Sullivan had tried to impress it upon me that "m-u-g" is *mug* and that "w-a-t-e-r" is *water,* but I persisted in confounding the two. In despair she had dropped the subject for the time, only to renew it at the first opportunity. I became impatient at her repeated attempts and, seizing the new doll, I dashed it upon the floor. I was keenly delighted when I felt the fragments of the broken doll at my feet. Neither sorrow nor regret followed my passionate outburst. I had not loved the doll. In the still, dark world in which I lived there was no strong sentiment or tenderness. I felt my teacher sweep the fragments to one side of the hearth, and I had a sense of satisfaction that the cause of my discomfort was removed. She brought me my hat, and I knew I was going out into the warm sunshine. This thought, if a wordless sensation may be called a thought, made me hop and skip with pleasure.

We walked down the path to the well-house, attracted by the fragrance of the honeysuckle with which it was covered. Someone was drawing water and my teacher placed my hand under the spout. As the cool stream gushed over one hand she spelled into the other the word *water,* first slowly, then rapidly. I stood still, my whole attention fixed upon the motions of her fingers. Suddenly I felt a misty consciousness as of something forgotten—a thrill of returning thought; and somehow the mystery of language was revealed to me. I knew then that "w-a-t-e-r" meant the wonderful cool something that was flowing over my hand. That living word awakened my soul, gave it light, hope, joy, set it free! There were barriers still, it it true, but barriers that could in time be swept away.

I left the well-house eager to learn. Everything had a name, and each name gave birth to a new thought. As we returned to the house every object which I touched seemed to quiver with life. That was because I saw everything with the strange, new sight that had come to me. On entering the door I remembered the doll I had broken. I felt my way to the hearth and picked up the pieces. I tried vainly to put them together. Then my eyes filled with tears; for I realized what I had done, and for the first time I felt repentance and sorrow.

I learned a great many new words that day. I do not remember what they all were; but I do know that *mother, father, sister, teacher* were among them —words that were to make the world blossom for me, "like Aaron's rod, with flowers." It would have been difficult to find a happier child than I was as I lay in my crib at the close of that eventful day and lived over the joys it had brought me, and for the first time longed for a new day to come.

I had now the key to all language, and I was eager to learn to use it. Children who hear acquire language without any particular effort; the words that fall from others' lips they catch on the wing, as it were, delightedly, while the little deaf child must trap them by a slow and often painful process. But whatever the process, the result is wonderful. Gradually from naming an object we advance step by step until we have traversed the vast distance between our first stammered syllable and the sweep of thought in a line of Shakespeare.

At first, when my teacher told me about a new thing I asked very few questions. My ideas were vague, and my vocabulary was inadequate; but as my knowledge of things grew, and I learned more and more words, my field of inquiry broadened, and I would return again and again to the same subject, eager for further information. Sometimes a new word revived an image that some earlier experience had engraved on my brain.

I remember the morning that I first asked the meaning of the word "love." This was before I knew many words. I had found a few early violets in the garden and brought them to my teacher. She tried to kiss me; but at that time I did not like to have anyone kiss me except my mother. Miss Sullivan put her arm gently round me and spelled into my hand, "I love Helen."

"What is love?" I asked.

She drew me closer to her and said, "It is here," pointing to my heart, whose beats I was conscious of for the first time. Her words puzzled me very much because I did not then understand anything unless I touched it.

I smelt the violets in her hand and asked, half in words, half in signs, a question which meant, "Is love the sweetness of flowers?"

"No," said my teacher.

Again I thought. The warm sun was shining on us.

"Is this not love?" I asked, pointing in the direction from which the heat came, "Is this not love?"

It seemed to me that there could be nothing more beautiful than the sun, whose warmth makes all things grow. But Miss Sullivan shook her head, and I was greatly puzzled and disappointed. I thought it strange that my teacher could not show me love.

A day or two afterward I was stringing beads of different sizes in symmetrical groups—two large beads, three small ones, and so on. I had made many mistakes, and Miss Sullivan had pointed them out again and again with gentle patience. Finally I noticed a very obvious error in the sequence and for an instant I concentrated my attention on the lesson and tried to think how I should have arranged the beads. Miss Sullivan touched my forehead and spelled with decided emphasis, "Think."

In a flash I knew that the word was the name of the process that was going on in my head. This was my first conscious perception of an abstract idea.

For a long time I was still—I was not thinking of the beads in my lap, but trying to find a meaning for "love" in the light of this new idea. The sun had been under a cloud all day, and there had been brief showers; but suddenly the sun broke forth in all its southern splendour.

Again I asked my teacher, "Is this not love?"

"Love is something like the clouds that were in the sky before the sun came out," she replied. Then in simpler words than these, which at that time I could not have understood, she explained: "You cannot touch the clouds, you know; but you feel the rain and know how glad the flowers and the thirsty earth are to have it after a hot day. You cannot touch love either; but you feel the sweetness that it pours into everything. Without love you would not be happy or want to play."

The beautiful truth burst upon my mind—I felt that there were invisible lines stretched between my spirit and the spirits of others.

From the beginning of my education Miss Sullivan made it a practice to speak to me as she would speak to any hearing child; the only difference was that she spelled the sentences into my hand instead of speaking them. If I did not know the words and idioms necessary to express my thoughts, she supplied them, even suggesting conversation when I was unable to keep up my end of the dialogue.

This process was continued for several years; for the deaf child does not learn in a month, or even in two or three years, the numberless idioms and expressions used in the simplest daily intercourse. The little hearing child learns these from constant repetition and imitation. The conversation he hears in his home stimulates his mind and suggests topics and calls forth the spontaneous expression of his own thoughts. This natural exchange of ideas is denied to the deaf child. My teacher, realizing this, determined to supply the kinds of stimulus I lacked. This she did by repeating to me as far as possible, verbatim, what she heard, and by showing me how I could take part in the conversation. But it was a long time before I ventured to take the initiative, and still longer before I could find something appropriate to say at the right time.

The deaf and the blind find it very difficult to acquire the amenities of conversation. How much more this difficulty must be augmented in the case of those who are both deaf and blind! They cannot distinguish the tone of the voice or, without assistance, go up and down the gamut of tones that give significance to words; nor can they watch the expression of the speaker's face, and a look is often the very soul of what one says.

It was in the spring of 1890 that I learned to speak. The impulse to utter audible sounds had always been strong within me. I used to make noises, keeping one hand on my throat while the other hand felt the movements of my lips. I was pleased with anything that made a noise and liked to feel the cat purr and the dog bark. I also liked to keep my hand on a singer's throat, or on a piano when it was being played. Before I lost my sight and hearing, I was fast learning to talk, but after my illness it was found that I had ceased to speak because I could not hear. I used to sit in my mother's lap all day long and keep my hands on her face because it amused me to feel the motions of her lips; and I moved my lips, too, although I had forgotten what talking was. My friends say that I laughed and cried naturally, and for a while I made many sounds and word-elements, not because they were a means of communications, but because the need of exercising my vocal organs was imperative. There was, however, one word the meaning of which I still remembered, *water*. I pronounced it "wa-wa." Even this became less and less intelligible until the time when Miss Sullivan began to teach me. I stopped using it only after I had learned to spell the word on my fingers.

I had known for a long time that the people about me used a method of communication different from mine; and even before I knew that a deaf child could be taught to speak, I was conscious of dissatisfaction with the means of communication I already possessed. One who is entirely dependent upon the manual alphabet has always a sense of restraint, of narrowness. This feeling began to agitate me with a vexing, forward-reaching sense of a lack that should be filled. My thoughts would often rise and beat up like birds against the wind; and I persisted in using my lips and voice. Friends tried to discourage this tendency, fearing lest it would lead to disappointment. But I persisted, and an accident soon occurred which resulted in the breaking down of this great barrier—I heard the story of Ragnhild Kaata.

In 1890 Mrs. Lamson, who had been one of Laura Bridgman's teachers, and who had just returned from a visit to Norway and Sweden, came to see me, and told me of Ragnhild Kaata, a deaf and blind girl in Norway who had actually been taught to speak. Mrs. Lamson had scarcely finished telling me about this girl's success before I was on fire with eagerness. I resolved that I, too, would learn to speak. I would not rest satisfied until my teacher took me, for advice and assistance, to Miss Sarah Fuller, principal of the Horace Mann School. This lovely, sweet-natured lady offered to teach me herself, and we began the twenty-sixth of March, 1890.

Miss Fuller's method was this: she passed my hand lightly over her face, and let me feel the position of her tongue and lips when she made a sound. I was eager to imitate every motion and in an hour had learned six elements of speech: M, P, A, S, T, I. Miss Fuller gave me eleven lessons in all. I shall never forget the surprise and delight I felt when I uttered my first connected sentence, "It is warm." True, they were broken and stammering syllables; but they were human speech. My soul, conscious of new strength, came out of bondage, and was reaching through those broken symbols of speech to all knowledge and all faith.

No deaf child who has earnestly tried to speak the words which he has never heard—to come out of the prison of silence, where no tone of love, no song of bird, no strain of music ever pierces the stillness—can forget the thrill of surprise, the joy of discovery which came over him when he uttered his first word. Only such a one can appreciate the eagerness with which I talked to my toys, to stones, trees, birds and dumb animals, or the delight I felt when at my call Mildred ran to me or my dogs obeyed my commands. It is an unspeakable boon to me to be able to speak in winged words that need no interpretation. As I talked, happy thoughts fluttered up out of my words that might perhaps have struggled in vain to escape my fingers.

But it must not be supposed that I could really talk in this short time. I had learned only the elements of speech. Miss Fuller and Miss Sullivan could understand me, but most people would not have understood one word in a hundred. Nor is it true that, after I had learned these elements, I did the rest of the work myself. But for Miss Sullivan's genius, untiring perseverance and devotion, I could not have progressed as far as I have toward natural speech. In the first place, I laboured night and day before I could be understood even by my most intimate friends; in the second place, I needed Miss Sullivan's assistance constantly in my efforts to articulate each sound clearly and to combine all sounds in a thousand ways. Even now she calls my attention every day to mispronounced words.

All teachers of the deaf know what this means, and only they can at all appreciate the peculiar difficulties with which I had to contend. In reading my teacher's lips I was wholly dependent on my fingers: I had to use the sense of touch in catching the vibrations of the throat, the movements of the mouth and the expression of the face; and often this sense was at fault. In such cases I was forced to repeat the words or sentences, sometimes for hours, until I felt the proper ring in my own voice. My work was practice, practice, practice. Discouragement and weariness cast me down frequently; but the next moment the thought that I should soon be at home and show my loved ones what I had accomplished, spurred me on, and I eagerly looked forward to their pleasure in my achievement.

"My little sister will understand me now," was a thought stronger than all obstacles. I used to repeat ecstatically, "I am not dumb now." I could not be despondent while I anticipated the delight of talking to my mother and reading her responses from her lips. It astonished me to find how much easier it is to talk than to spell with the fingers, and I discarded the manual alphabet as a medium of communication on my part; but Miss Sullivan and a few friends still use it in speaking to me, for it is more convenient and more rapid than lip-reading.

Just here, perhaps, I had better explain our use of the manual alphabet, which seems to puzzle people who do not know us. One who reads or talks to me spells with his hand, using the single-hand manual alphabet generally employed by the deaf. I place my hand on the hand of the speaker so lightly as not to impede its movements. The position of the hand is as easy to feel as it is to see. I do not feel each letter any more than you see each letter separately when you read. Constant practice makes the fingers very flexible, and some of my friends spell rapidly—about as fast as an expert writes on a typewriter. The mere spelling is, of course, no more a conscious act than it is in writing.

When I had made speech my own, I could not wait to go home. At last the happiest of happy moments arrived. I had made my homeward journey, talking constantly to Miss Sullivan, not for the sake of talking, but determined to improve to the last minute. Almost before I knew it, the train stopped at the Tuscumbia station, and there on the platform stood the whole family. My eyes fill with tears now as I think how my mother pressed me close to her, speechless and trembling with delight, taking in every syllable that I spoke, while little Mildred seized my free hand and kissed it and danced, and my father expressed his pride and affection in a big silence. It was as if Isaiah's prophecy had been fulfilled in me, "The mountains and the hills shall break forth before you into singing, and all the trees of the field shall clap their hands!"

The Knife

BRENDAN GILL

MICHAEL THREW himself down, locked his hands over one of his father's knees, and began, in a loud whisper, " 'Our Father, who art in heaven, hallowed be thy name, kingdom come, will be done, earth as it is in heaven, give us this day—' "

Carroll folded his newspaper. Michael should have been in bed an hour ago. "Take it easy, kid," he said. "Let's try it again, slow."

Michael repeated distinctly, " 'Our Father, who art in heaven, hallowed . . .' " The boy's pajamas, Carroll saw, were dirty at the cuffs; probably he had not brushed his teeth. " '. . . as we forgive them, who trespass against us'—what does 'trespass' mean, Dad?"

"Why, hurting anybody."

"Do I trespass anybody?"

"Not much, I guess. Finish it up."

Michael drew a breath. " 'And lead us not into temptation, but deliver us from evil. Amen.' "

"Now," his father said, brushing back Michael's tangled hair, "what about a good 'Hail, Mary'?"

"All right," Michael said. " 'Hail, Mary, full of grace, the Lord is with thee, blessed art thou among women, and blessed is the fruit of thy womb, Jesus.' " Michael lifted his head to ask if a womb got fruit like a tree, but thought better of it. His father never answered questions seriously, the way his mother used to. Michael decided to wait and ask Mrs. Nolan. "Is Mrs. Nolan coming tomorrow?" he asked.

"She'll be here, all right," Carroll said. "I give you ten seconds to finish the prayer."

Michael grinned at the ultimatum. "I thought you wanted me to go slow. 'Holy Mary, Mother of God, pray for us sinners, now and at the hour of our death. Amen.' " He unlocked his fingers. "Will she?"

"Will she what?"

"Will she now and at the hour of our death, A-men?"

The words of Michael's prayer caught in Carroll's mind and stayed there, a long way beyond his smiling face. "Yes," he said, and set his pipe in the broken dish on the table beside him. He had not emptied the dish of ashes in two days. Mrs. Nolan would give him a piece of her mind tomorrow morning, as she did each week when she came in to give the apartment a general cleaning and to do the laundry.

"What good can she do?" Michael asked.

"Climb into bed, young ragamuffin," Carroll said sternly. "It's past nine."

"What *good* can she do?"

"She'll help you get anything you want. I suppose she'll help you climb up into heaven when the time comes. You know all about heaven, don't you?"

Michael felt himself on the defensive. "Of course."

"Well, then, get along with you."

But Michael had something difficult to say. "You mean she'll ask God for anything I want and He'll give it to her for me?"

"She's His mother."

Michael stood up and kissed his father carefully on the cheek. Then he walked from the room, and Carroll could hear his bare feet crossing the hall. The bed creaked as Michael lay down on it. Carroll opened the newspaper, read a paragraph, then dropped it in a white heap on the rug. He felt tired; perhaps tonight he might be able to get some sleep. He got up, slipped his suspenders from his shoulders, unknotted his tie, kicked off his shoes. He had learned to undress quickly in the last six months, since his wife had died.

His pajamas were hanging inside out in the bathroom, where he had left them that morning. When he had undressed he felt Michael's toothbrush with his thumb; it was dry. He should have explained to the child what happened to a person's teeth when he forgot to clean them every night and morning.

Carroll stared at his face in the mirror above the basin. He tried smiling. No one could honestly tell what a man was thinking by the way he smiled. Even Michael, who was like a puppy about sensing moods, could not tell. He entered the bedroom on tiptoe. Feeling the sheets bunched at the foot of the mattress, he remembered that he had made the beds in a hurry. The sheets felt fresh and cool only on Saturdays, when Mrs. Nolan changed them.

Michael was not asleep. "Dad?" he whispered.

"Go to sleep."

"I been asking Hail Mary for something."

"Tomorrow."

"No, I been asking her right now."

Carroll lay on his back with his hands over his eyes. "What've you been asking her for, Mickey?"

Michael hesitated. "I thought I'd better make it something easy first. To see what happened." He sat up in bed. "A jackknife."

A few blocks away the clock in the Metropolitan Life tower was striking ten. Michael was deep in the noisy middle of a dream. Carroll listened to his breathing. He tried matching his own breath to Michael's, to make sleep come, but it was no use. Every night Carroll pretended to himself he was just at the brink of falling off to sleep, but his eyes always widened with wakefulness in the dark. Now, as the clock stopped striking, Carroll got up and walked into the bathroom and dressed. Then he went into the living room, unlocked the outside door of the apartment, and then locked it again before he walked down the two flights of stairs to the sidewalk. Shops reached out of sight down both sides of Lexington Avenue. Carroll walked uptown as he always did. He stopped in front of each bright shop window, studying its contents for the fifth or sixth time. He knew by now the day on which each window was changed and by whom. Certain plaster models, certain fringed crêpe papers were old friends.

At the top of a long slope Carroll waited for the lights to change. On his left was a bar; on his right, across the street, a drugstore. Carroll waited a moment outside the bar. Between the slats of its cheap orange Venetian blinds he could see the gleaming mahogany counter, the stacked glasses, the barman slicing foam from a mug of beer. A man and a girl were sitting at a table by the window, a foot under Carroll's eyes. They did not seem to be speaking. The man's hands lay halfway across the table and the girl's black dress made her throat look soft and white. Carroll turned away and crossed the street to the drugstore. The owner, Sam Ramatsky, stood sniffing the night air under the painted sign bearing his name.

"Well, Mr. Carroll, nice night for March."

"Yes." Carroll wanted only to hear a voice. "How's business?" he asked.

"Can't complain." Sam grinned, shaking his head. "I take that back. It's *lousy*. I got to break myself of this old 'Can't complain.' I got to remember how serious it is. Business is lousy."

Carroll leaned back against Sam's window, which was crammed with hot-water bottles, perfumes, toys, and two cardboard girls in shorts and sandals. The girls had been there for two months. There was dust on their

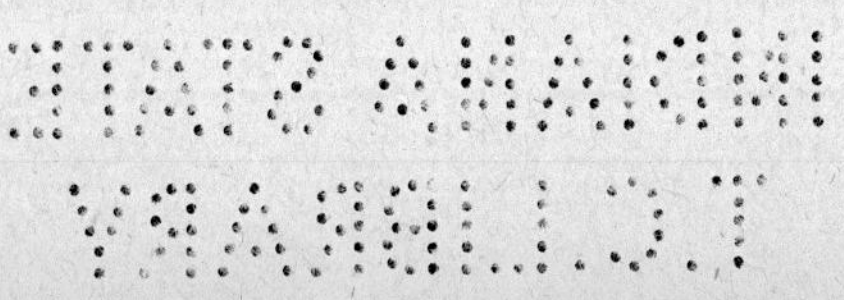

teeth and on their smooth brown legs. "You ought to brush their teeth, Sam," Carroll said, "and run your hand down their legs now and then."

"You walk a lot," Sam said. "I figure on you, ten or eleven, every night."

"I guess I do," Carroll said.

Sam patted his hard belly. "Nothing like exercise to keep a man in shape."

Carroll nodded impatiently. It was not Sam's voice he wanted to hear, after all. "Give me a milk shake, Sam."

They walked into the store. Carroll sat down on one of the round stools at the fountain and watched Sam pouring milk into the shaker. "Nothing like milk," Sam said, "keep a man's system clean." Carroll watched the hands of the electric clock above the door. Ten-forty-five. He could not go to bed before twelve. He glanced at the packed counters behind him. "Sell any jackknives, Sam?"

"Sure. I sell everything. That's what keeps me broke. Nothing like keeping a thing in stock to kill demand." Sam lifted a tray of jackknives from a counter, brought it over, and set it down on the fountain. "Beauties," Sam said. "Fifty cents up."

Carroll looked at several of them and finally picked up the biggest and shiniest one. "I'll take this one," he said.

"Such expensive taste! One buck."

Carroll paid for the milk shake and the knife, said "Good night, Sam," and walked out into the street. In another hour and a half he should have walked six miles. By that time his body would be tired enough so that he could sleep. By that time, he hoped, no voice could rouse him.

It was morning when Carroll awoke. He lay with his face on his hands, listening to the sound of the March rain against the windows. He remembered suddenly the absurd song that everyone used to sing: "Though April showers may come your way, they bring the flowers that bloom in May." March rains brought you nothing. March rains only shut you in your room without any hope of escape.

Michael and Mrs. Nolan were talking together in the kitchen. Michael's voice was high with excitement. "Look at it, Mrs. Nolan, look at it! Isn't it beautiful?"

"It is that," Mrs. Nolan said in her deep voice. Carroll sat up in bed. It was too late to give Mrs. Nolan warning.

"Do you ask for things when you say your prayers, Mrs. Nolan?" Michael demanded.

"I do." A pan clattered to the floor. "I've seen many a nice clean sty I'd swap for this dirty kitchen," Mrs. Nolan said. "You live like a couple of savages from week to week. God love you."

"Do you always get what you ask for?" Michael said.

"It all depends. I sort of try to guess what the good Lord wants to give me, and I ask for that."

"That's how I got this knife," Michael said. "It's got a big blade and a little blade and a screwdriver and a thing to punch holes in leather with and a file."

"You must have said yourself a fine prayer," Mrs. Nolan said. There was no hint of surprise in her voice.

"It was only a 'Hail, Mary,'" Michael said, "but I did it very slow, the way Dad told me to." Michael was silent for a moment. "But I'm asking for the real thing tonight. The knife was just to see. Someone's going to be here when you come next week."

Mrs. Nolan made a clucking sound in her mouth. "Someone instead of me?"

"She was here with Dad and me before you came," Michael said, his voice thin with its burden, "and she's coming back."

"Michael!" Carroll shouted.

Michael ran to the doorway. The knife gleamed in his fist. "Look what I got," he said. "I was showing Mrs. Nolan."

"Come here," Carroll said. When Michael reached the edge of the bed Carroll bent over and fastened his arms behind the child's back. There was only one thing to say, and one way to say it, and that was fast. "I'm glad you like it," he said. "I bought it for you at Ramatsky's last night. The biggest and shiniest one he had."

The Downward Path to Wisdom

KATHERINE ANNE PORTER

IN THE square bedroom with the big window Mama and Papa were lolling back on their pillows handing each other things from the wide black tray on the small table with crossed legs. They were smiling and they smiled even more when the little boy, with the feeling of sleep still in his skin and hair, came in and walked up to the bed. Leaning against it, his bare toes wriggling in the white fur rug, he went on eating peanuts which he took from his pajama pocket. He was four years old.

"Here's my baby," said Mama. "Lift him up, will you?"

He went limp as a rag for Papa to take him under the arms and swing him up over a broad, tough chest. He sank between his parents like a bear cub in a warm litter, and lay there comfortably. He took another peanut between his teeth, cracked the shell, picked out the nut whole and ate it.

"Running around without his slippers again," said Mama. "His feet are like icicles."

"He crunches like a horse," said Papa. "Eating peanuts before breakfast will ruin his stomach. Where did he get them?"

"You brought them yesterday," said Mama, with exact memory, "in a grisly little cellophane sack. I have asked you dozens of times not to bring him things to eat. Put him out, will you? He's spilling shells all over me."

Almost at once the little boy found himself on the floor again. He moved around to Mama's side of the bed and leaned confidingly near her and began another peanut. As he chewed he gazed solemnly in her eyes.

"Brighter-looking specimen, isn't he?" asked Papa, stretching his long legs and reaching for his bathrobe. "I suppose you'll say it's my fault he's dumb as an ox."

"He's my little baby, my only baby," said Mama richly, hugging him, "and he's a dear lamb." His neck and shoulders were quite boneless in her firm embrace. He stopped chewing long enough to receive a kiss on his crumby chin. "He's sweet as clover," said Mama. The baby went on chewing.

"Look at him staring like an owl," said Papa.

Mama said, "He's an angel and I'll never get used to having him."

"We'd be better off if we never *had* had him," said Papa. He was walking about the room and his back was turned when he said that. There was silence for a moment. The little boy stopped eating, and stared deeply at his Mama. She was looking at the back of Papa's head, and her eyes were almost black. "You're going to say that just once too often," she told him in a low voice. "I hate you when you say that."

Papa said, "You spoil him to death. You never correct him for anything. And you don't take care of him. You let him run around eating peanuts before breakfast."

"You gave him the peanuts, remember that," said Mama. She sat up and hugged her only baby once more. He nuzzled softly in the pit of her arm. "Run along, my darling," she told him in her gentlest voice, smiling at him straight in the eyes. "Run along," she said, her arms falling away from him. "Get your breakfast."

The little boy had to pass his father on the way to the door. He shrank into himself when he saw the big hand raised above him. "Yes, get out of here and stay out," said Papa, giving him a little shove toward the door. It was not a hard shove, but it hurt the little boy. He slunk out, and trotted down the hall trying not to look back. He was afraid something was coming after him, he could not imagine what. Something hurt him all over, he did not know why.

He did not want his breakfast; he would not have it. He sat and stirred it round in the yellow bowl, letting it stream off the spoon and spill on the table, on his front, on the chair. He liked seeing it spill. It was hateful stuff, but it looked funny running in white rivulets down his pajamas.

"Now look what you're doing, dirty boy," said Marjory. "You dirty little old boy."

The little boy opened his mouth to speak for the first time. "You're dirty yourself," he told her.

"That's right," said Marjory, leaning over him and speaking so her voice would not carry. "That's right, just like your papa. Mean," she whispered, "mean."

The little boy took up his yellow bowl full of cream and oatmeal and sugar with both hands and brought it down with a crash on the table. It burst and some of the wreck lay in chunks and some of it ran all over everything. He felt better.

"You see?" said Marjory, dragging him out of the chair and scrubbing him with a napkin. She scrubbed him as roughly as she dared until he cried out. "That's just what I said. That's exactly it." Through his tears he saw her face terribly near, red and frowning under a stiff white band, looking like the face of somebody who came at night and stood over him and scolded him when he could not move or get away. "Just like your papa, *mean*."

The little boy went out into the garden and sat on a green bench dangling his legs. He was clean. His hair was wet and his blue woolly pull-over made his nose itch. His face felt stiff from the soap. He saw Marjory going past a window with the black tray. The curtains were still closed at the window he knew opened into Mama's room. Papa's room. Mommanpoppasroom, the word was pleasant, it made a mumbling snapping noise between his lips; it ran in his mind while his eyes wandered about looking for something to do, something to play with.

Mommanpoppas' voices kept attracting his attention. Mama was being cross with Papa again. He could tell by the sound. That was what Marjory always said when their voices rose and fell and shot up to a point and crashed and rolled like the two tomcats who fought at night. Papa was being cross, too, much crosser than Mama this time. He grew cold and disturbed and sat very still, wanting to go to the bathroom, but it was just next to Mommanpoppasroom; he didn't dare think of it. As the voices grew louder he could hardly hear them any more, he wanted so badly to go to the bathroom. The kitchen door opened suddenly and Marjory ran out, making the motion with her hand that meant he was to come to her. He didn't move. She came to him, her face still red and frowning, but she was not angry; she was scared just as he was. She said, "Come on, honey, we've got to go to your gran'ma's again." She took his hand and pulled him. "Come on quick, your gran'ma is waiting for you." He slid off the bench. His mother's voice rose in a terrible scream, screaming something he could not understand, but she was furious; he had seen her clenching her fists and stamping in one spot, screaming with her eyes shut; he knew how she looked. She was screaming in a tantrum, just as he remembered having heard himself. He stood still, doubled over, and all his body seemed to dissolve, sickly, from the pit of his stomach.

"Oh, my God," said Marjory. "Oh, my God. Now look at you. Oh, my God. I can't stop to clean you up."

He did not know how he got to his grandma's house, but he was there at last, wet and soiled, being handled with disgust in the big bathtub. His grandma was there in long black skirts saying, "Maybe he's sick; maybe we should send for the doctor."

"I don't think so, m'am," said Marjory. "He hasn't et anything; he's just scared."

The little boy couldn't raise his eyes, he was so heavy with shame. "Take this note to his mother," said Grandma.

She sat in a wide chair and ran her hands over his head, combing his hair with her fingers; she lifted his chin and kissed him. "Poor little fellow," she said. "Never you mind. You always have a good time at your grandma's, don't you? You're going to have a nice little visit, just like the last time."

The little boy leaned against the stiff, dry-smelling clothes and felt horribly grieved about something. He began to whimper and said, "I'm hungry. I want something to eat." This reminded him. He began to bellow at the top of his voice; he threw himself upon the carpet and rubbed his nose in a dusty woolly bouquet of roses. "I want my peanuts," he howled. "Somebody took my peanuts."

His grandma knelt beside him and gathered him up so tightly he could hardly move. She called in a calm voice above his howls to Old Janet in the doorway, "Bring me some bread and butter with strawberry jam."

"I want peanuts," yelled the little boy desperately.

"No, you don't, darling," said his grandma. "You don't want horrid old peanuts to make you sick. You're going to have some of grandma's nice fresh bread with good strawberries on it. That's what you're going to have." He sat afterward very quietly and ate and ate. His grandma sat near him and Old Janet stood by, near a tray with a loaf and a glass bowl of jam upon the table at the window. Outside there was a trellis with tube-shaped red flowers clinging all over it, and brown bees singing.

"I hardly know what to do," said Grandma, "it's very . . ."

"Yes, m'am," said Old Janet, "it certainly is . . ."

Grandma said, "I can't possibly see the end of it. It's a terrible . . ."

"It certainly is bad," said Old Janet, "all this upset all the time and him such a baby."

Their voices ran on soothingly. The little boy ate and forgot to listen. He did not know these women, except by name. He could not understand what they were talking about; their hands and their clothes and their voices were dry and far away; they examined him with crinkled eyes without any expression that he could see. He sat there waiting for whatever they would do next with him. He hoped they would let him go out and play in the yard. The room was full of flowers and dark red curtains and big soft chairs, and the windows were open, but it was still dark in there somehow; dark, and a place he did not know, or trust.

"Now drink your milk," said Old Janet, holding out a silver cup.

"I don't want any milk," he said, turning his head away.

"Very well, Janet, he doesn't have to drink it," said Grandma quickly. "Now run out in the garden and play, darling. Janet, get his hoop."

A big strange man came home in the evenings who treated the little boy very confusingly. "Say 'please,' and 'thank you,' young man," he would roar, terrifyingly, when he gave any smallest object to the little boy. "Well, fellow, are you ready for a fight?" he would say, again, doubling up huge, hairy fists and making passes at him. "Come on now, you must learn to box." After the first few times this was fun.

"Don't teach him to be rough," said Grandma. "Time enough for all that."

"Now, Mother, we don't want him to be a sissy," said the big man. "He's got to toughen up early. Come on now, fellow, put up your mitts." The little boy liked this new word for hands. He learned to throw himself upon the strange big man, whose name was Uncle David, and hit him on the chest as hard as he could; the big man would laugh and hit him back with his huge, loose fists. Sometimes, but not often, Uncle David came home in the middle of the day. The little boy missed him on the other days, and would hang on the gate looking down the street for him. One evening he brought a large square package under his arm.

"Come over here, fellow, and see what I've got," he said, pulling off quantities of green paper and string from the box which was full of flat, folded colors. He put something in the little boy's hand. It was limp and silky and bright green with a tube on the end. "Thank you," said the little boy nicely, but not knowing what to do with it.

"Balloons," said Uncle David in triumph. "Now just put your mouth here and blow hard." The little boy blew hard and the green thing began to grow round and thin and silvery.

"Good for your chest," said Uncle David. "Blow some more." The little boy went on blowing and the balloon swelled steadily.

"Stop," said Uncle David, "that's enough." He twisted the tube to keep the air in. "That's the way," he said. "Now I'll blow one, and you blow one, and let's see who can blow up a big balloon the fastest."

They blew and blew, especially Uncle David. He puffed and panted and blew with all his might, but the little boy won. His balloon was perfectly round before Uncle David could even get started. The little boy was so proud he began to dance and shout, "I beat, I beat," and blew in his balloon again. It burst in his face and frightened him so he felt sick. "Ha ha, ho ho ho," whooped Uncle David. "That's the boy. I bet I can't do that. Now let's see." He blew until the beautiful bubble grew and wavered and burst into thin air, and there was only a small colored rag in his hand. This was a fine game. They went on with it, until Grandma came in and said, "Time for supper now. No, you can't blow balloons at the table. Tomorrow maybe." And it was all over.

The next day, instead of being given balloons, he was hustled out of bed early, bathed in warm soapy water and given a big breakfast of soft-boiled eggs with toast and jam and milk. His grandma came in to kiss him good morning. "And I hope you'll be a good boy and obey your teacher," she told him.

"What's teacher?" asked the little boy.

"Teacher is at school," said Grandma. "She'll tell you all sorts of things and you must do as she says."

Mama and Papa had talked a great deal about School, and how they must send him there. They had told him it was a fine place with all kinds of toys and other children to play with. He felt he knew about School. "I didn't know it was time, Grandma," he said. "Is it today?"

"It's this very minute," said Grandma. "I told you a week ago."

Old Janet came in with her bonnet on. It was a prickly looking bundle held with a black rubber band under her back hair. "Come on," she said. "This is my busy day." She wore a dead cat slung around her neck, its sharp ears bent over under her baggy chin.

The little boy was excited and wanted to run ahead. "Hold to my hand like I told you," said Old Janet. "Don't go running off like that and get yourself killed."

"I'm going to get killed, I'm going to get killed," sang the little boy, making a tune of his own.

"Don't say that, you give me the creeps," said Old Janet. "Hold to my hand now." She bent over and looked at him, not at his face but at something on his clothes. His eyes followed hers.

"I declare," said Old Janet, "I did forget. I was going to sew it up. I might have known. I *told* your grandma it would be that way from now on."

"What?" asked the little boy.

"Just look at yourself," said Old Janet crossly. He looked at himself. There was a little end of him showing through the slit in his short blue flannel trousers. The trousers came halfway to his knees above, and his socks came halfway to his knees below, and all winter long his knees were cold. He remembered now how cold his knees were in cold weather. And how sometimes he would have to put the part of him that came through the slit back again, because he was cold there too. He saw at once what was wrong, and tried to arrange himself, but his mittens got in the way. Janet said,

"Stop that, you bad boy," and with a firm thumb she set him in order, at the same time reaching under his belt to pull down and fold his knit undershirt over his front.

"There now," she said, "try not to disgrace yourself today." He felt guilty and red all over, because he had something that showed when he was dressed that was not supposed to show then. The different women who bathed him always wrapped him quickly in towels and hurried him into his clothes, because they saw something about him he could not see for himself. They hurried him so he never had a chance to see whatever it was they saw, and though he looked at himself when his clothes were off, he could not find out what was wrong with him. Outside, in his clothes, he knew he looked like everybody else, but inside his clothes there was something bad the matter with him. It worried him and confused him and he wondered about it. The only people who never seemed to notice there was something wrong with him were Mommanpoppa. They never called him a bad boy, and all summer long they had taken all his clothes off and let him run in the sand beside a big ocean.

"Look at him, isn't he a love?" Mama would say and Papa would look, and say, "He's got a back like a prize fighter." Uncle David was a prize fighter when he doubled up his mitts and said, "Come on, fellow."

Old Janet held him firmly and took long steps under her big rustling skirts. He did not like Old Janet's smell. It made him a little quivery in the stomach; it was just like wet chicken feathers.

School was easy. Teacher was a square-shaped woman with square short hair and short skirts. She got in the way sometimes, but not often. The people around him were his size; he didn't have always to be stretching his neck up to faces bent over him, and he could sit on the chairs without having to climb. All the children had names, like Frances and Evelyn and Agatha and Edward and Martin, and his own name was Stephen. He was not Mama's "Baby," nor Papa's "Old Man"; he was not Uncle David's "Fellow" or Grandma's "Darling," or even Old Janet's "Bad Boy." He was Stephen. He was learning to read, and to sing a tune to some strange-looking letters or marks written in chalk on a blackboard. You talked one kind of lettering, and you sang another. All the children talked and sang in turn, and then all together. Stephen thought it a fine game. He felt awake and happy. They had soft clay and paper and wires and squares of colors in tin boxes to play with, colored blocks to build houses with. Afterward they all danced in a big ring, and then they danced in pairs, boys with girls. Stephen danced with Frances, and Frances kept saying, "Now you just follow me." She was a little taller than he was, and her hair stood up in short, shiny curls, the color of an ash tray on Papa's desk. She would say, "You can't dance." "I can dance too," said Stephen, jumping around holding her hands, "I can, too, dance." He was certain of it. "*You* can't dance," he told Frances, "you can't dance at all."

Then they had to change partners, and when they came round again, Frances said, "I don't *like* the way you dance." This was different. He felt uneasy about it. He didn't jump quite so high when the phonograph record started going dumdiddy dumdiddy again. "Go ahead, Stephen, you're doing fine," said Teacher, waving her hands together very fast. The dance ended, and they all played "relaxing" for five minutes. They relaxed by swinging their arms back and forth, then rolling their heads round and round. When Old Janet came for him he didn't want to go home. At lunch his grandma told him twice to keep his face out of his plate. "Is that what they teach you at school?" she asked. Uncle David was at home. "Here you are, fellow," he said and gave Stephen two balloons. "Thank you," said Stephen. He put the balloons in his pocket and forgot about them. "I told you that boy could learn something," said Uncle David to Grandma. "Hear him say 'thank you'?"

In the afternoon at school Teacher handed out big wads of clay and told the children to make something out of it. Anything they liked. Stephen decided to make a cat, like Mama's Meeow at home. He did not like Meeow, but he thought it would be easy to make a cat. He could not get the clay to work at all. It simply fell into one lump after another. So he stopped, wiped his hands on his pull-over, remembered his balloons and began blowing one.

"Look at Stephen's horse," said Frances. "Just look at it."

"It's not a horse, it's a cat," said Stephen. The other children gathered around. "It looks like a horse, a little," said Martin.

"It is a cat," said Stephen, stamping his foot, feeling his face turning hot. The other children all laughed and exclaimed over Stephen's cat that looked like a horse. Teacher came down among them. She sat usually at the top of the room before a big table covered with papers and playthings. She picked up Stephen's lump of clay and turned it round and examined it with her kind eyes. "Now, children," she said, "everybody has the right to make anything the way he pleases. If Stephen says this is a cat, it *is* a cat. Maybe you were thinking about a horse, Stephen?"

"It's a *cat*," said Stephen. He was aching all over. He knew then he should have said at first, "Yes, it's a horse." Then they would have let him alone. They would never have known he was trying to make a cat. "It's Meeow," he said in a trembling voice, "but I forgot how she looks."

His balloon was perfectly flat. He started blowing it up again, trying not to cry. Then it was time to go home, and Old Janet came looking for him. While Teacher was talking to other grown-up people who came to take other children home, Frances said, "Give me your balloon; I haven't got a balloon." Stephen handed it to her. He was happy to give it. He reached in his pocket and took out the other. Happily, he gave her that one too. Frances took it, then handed it back. "Now you blow up one and I'll blow up the other, and let's have a race," she said. When their balloons were only half filled Old Janet took Stephen by the arm and said, "Come on here, this is my busy day."

Frances ran after them, calling, "Stephen, you give me back my balloon," and snatched it away. Stephen did not know whether he was surprised to find himself going away with Frances' balloon, or whether he was surprised to see her snatching it as if it really belonged to her. He was badly mixed up in his mind, and Old Janet was hauling him along. One thing he knew, he liked Frances, he was going to see her again tomorrow, and he was going to bring her more balloons.

That evening Stephen boxed awhile with his uncle David, and Uncle David gave him a beautiful orange. "Eat that," he said, "it's good for your health."

"Uncle David, may I have some more balloons?" asked Stephen.

"Well, what do you say first?" asked Uncle David, reaching for the box on the top bookshelf.

"Please," said Stephen.

"That's the word," said Uncle David. He brought out two balloons, a red and a yellow one. Stephen noticed for the first time they had letters on them, very small letters that grew taller and wider as the balloon grew rounder. "Now that's all, fellow," said Uncle David. "Don't ask for any more because that's all." He put the box back on the bookshelf, but not before Stephen had seen that the box was almost full of balloons. He didn't say a word, but went on blowing, and Uncle David blew also. Stephen thought it was the nicest game he had ever known.

He had only one left, the next day, but he took it to school and gave it to Frances. "There are a lot," he said, feeling very proud and warm; "I'll bring you a lot of them."

Frances blew it up until it made a beautiful bubble, and said, "Look, I want to show you something." She took a sharp-pointed stick they used in working the clay; she poked the balloon, and it exploded. "Look at that," she said.

"That's nothing," said Stephen, "I'll bring you some more."

After school, before Uncle David came home, while Grandma was resting, when Old Janet had given him his milk and told him to run away and not bother her, Stephen dragged a chair to the bookshelf, stood upon it and reached into the box. He did not take three or four as he believed he intended; once his hands were upon them he seized what they could hold and jumped off the chair, hugging them to him. He stuffed them into his reefer pocket where they folded down and hardly made a lump.

He gave them all to Frances. There were so many, Frances gave most of them away to the other children. Stephen, flushed with his new joy, the lavish pleasure of giving presents, found almost at once still another happiness. Suddenly he was popular among the children; they invited him specially to join whatever games were up; they fell in at once with his own notions for play, and asked him what he would like to do next. They had festivals of blowing up the beautiful globes, fuller and rounder and thinner, changing as they went from deep color to lighter, paler tones, growing glassy thin, bubbly thin, then bursting with a thrilling loud noise like a toy pistol.

For the first time in his life Stephen had almost too much of something he wanted, and his head was so turned he forgot how this fullness came about, and no longer thought of it as a secret. The next day was Saturday, and Frances came to visit him with her nurse. The nurse and Old Janet sat in Old Janet's room drinking coffee and gossiping, and the children sat on the side porch blowing balloons. Stephen chose an apple-colored one and Frances a pale green one. Between them on the bench lay a tumbled heap of delights still to come.

"I once had a silver balloon," said Frances, "a beyootiful silver one, not round like these; it was a long one. But these are even nicer, I think," she added quickly, for she did want to be polite.

"When you get through with that one," said Stephen, gazing at her with the pure bliss of giving added to loving, "you can blow up a blue one and then a pink one and a yellow one and a purple one." He pushed the heap of limp objects toward her. Her clear-looking eyes, with fine little rays of brown in them like the spokes of a wheel, were full of approval for Stephen. "I wouldn't want to be greedy, though, and blow up all your balloons."

"There'll be plenty more left," said Stephen, and his heart rose under his thin ribs. He felt his ribs with his fingers and discovered with some surprise that they stopped somewhere in front, while Frances sat blowing balloons rather halfheartedly. The truth was, she was tired of balloons. After you blow six or seven your chest gets hollow and your lips feel puckery. She had been blowing balloons steadily for three days now. She had begun to hope they were giving out. "There's boxes and boxes more of them, Frances," said Stephen happily. "Millions more. I guess they'd last and last if we didn't blow too many every day."

Frances said somewhat timidly, "I tell you what. Let's rest awhile and fix some liquish water. Do you like liquish?"

"Yes, I do," said Stephen, "but I haven't got any."

"Couldn't we buy some?" asked Frances. "It's only a cent a stick, the nice rubbery, twisty kind. We can put it in a bottle with some water, and shake it and shake it, and it makes foam on top like soda pop and we can drink it. I'm kind of thirsty," she said in a small, weak voice. "Blowing balloons all the time makes you thirsty, I think."

Stephen, in silence, realized a dreadful truth and a numb feeling crept over him. He did not have a cent to buy licorice for Frances and she was tired of his balloons. This was the first real dismay of his whole life, and he aged at least a year in the next minute, huddled, with his deep, serious blue eyes focused down his nose in intense speculation. What could he do to please Frances that would not cost money? Only yesterday Uncle David had given him a nickel, and he had thrown it away on gumdrops. He regretted that nickel so bitterly his neck and forehead were damp. He was thirsty too.

"I tell you what," he said, brightening with a splendid idea, lamely trailing off on second thought, "I know something we can do, I'll—I . . ."

"I *am* thirsty," said Frances with gentle persistence. "I think I'm so thirsty maybe I'll have to go home." She did not leave the bench, though, but sat, turning her grieved mouth toward Stephen.

Stephen quivered with the terrors of the adventure before him, but he said boldly, "I'll make some lemonade. I'll get sugar and lemon and some ice and we'll have lemonade."

"Oh, I love lemonade," cried Frances. "I'd rather have lemonade than liquish."

"You stay right there," said Stephen, "and I'll get everything."

He ran around the house, and under Old Janet's window he heard the dry, chattering voices of the two old women whom he must outwit. He sneaked on tiptoe to the pantry, took a lemon lying there by itself, a handful of lump sugar and a china teapot, smooth, round, with flowers and leaves all over it. These he left on the kitchen table while he broke a piece of ice with a sharp metal pick he had been forbidden to touch. He put the ice in the pot, cut the lemon and squeezed it as well as he could—a lemon was tougher and more slippery than he had thought—and mixed sugar and water. He decided there was not enough sugar so he sneaked back and took another handful. He was back on the porch in an astonishingly short time, his face tight, his knees trembling, carrying iced lemonade to thirsty Frances with both his devoted hands.

A pace distant from her he stopped, literally stabbed through with a thought. Here he stood in broad daylight carrying a teapot with lemonade in it, and his grandma or Old Janet might walk through the door at any moment.

"Come on, Frances," he whispered loudly. "Let's go round to the back behind the rosebushes where it's shady." Frances leaped up and ran like a deer beside him, her face wise with knowledge of why they ran; Stephen ran stiffly, cherishing his teapot with clenched hands.

It was shady behind the rosebushes, and much safer. They sat side by side on the dampish ground, legs doubled under, drinking in turn from the slender spout. Stephen took his just share in large, cool, delicious swallows. When Frances drank she set her round pink mouth daintily to the spout and her throat beat steadily as a heart. Stephen was thinking he had really done something pretty nice for Frances. He did not know where his own happiness was; it was mixed with the sweet-sour taste in his mouth and a cool feeling in his bosom because Frances was there drinking his lemonade which he had got for her with great danger.

Frances said, "My, what big swallows you take," when his turn came next.

"No bigger than yours," he told her downrightly. "You take awfully big swallows."

"Well," said Frances, turning this criticism into an argument for her rightness about things, "that's the way to drink lemonade anyway." She peered into the teapot. There was quite a lot of lemonade left and she was beginning to feel she had enough. "Let's make up a game and see who can take the biggest swallows."

This was such a wonderful notion they grew reckless, tipping the spout into their opened mouths above their heads until lemonade welled up and ran over their chins in rills down their fronts. When they tired of this there was still lemonade left in the pot. They played first at giving the rosebush a drink and ended by baptizing it. "Name father son holygoat," shouted Stephen, pouring. At this sound Old Janet's face appeared over the low hedge, with the tan, disgusted-looking face of Frances' nurse hanging over her shoulder.

"Well, just as I thought," said Old Janet. "Just as I expected." The bag under her chin waggled.

"We were thirsty," he said; "we were awfully thirsty." Frances said nothing, but she gazed steadily at the toes of her shoes.

"Give me that teapot," said Old Janet, taking it with a rude snatch. "Just because you're thirsty is no reason," said Old Janet. "You can ask for things. You don't have to steal."

"We didn't steal," cried Frances suddenly. "We didn't. We didn't!"

"That's enough from you, missy," said her nurse. "Come straight out of there. You have nothing to do with this."

"Oh, I don't know," said Old Janet with a hard stare at Frances' nurse. "*He* never did such a thing before, by himself."

"Come on," said the nurse to Frances, "this is no place for you." She held Frances by the wrist and started walking away so fast Frances had to run to keep up. "Nobody can call *us* thieves and get away with it."

"You don't have to steal, even if others do," said Old Janet to Stephen, in a high carrying voice. "If you so much as pick up a lemon in somebody else's house you're a little thief." She lowered her voice then and said, "Now I'm going to tell your grandma and you'll see what you get."

"He went in the icebox and left it open," Janet told Grandma, "and he got into the lump sugar and spilt it all over the floor. Lumps everywhere underfoot. He dribbled water all over the clean kitchen floor, and he baptized the rosebush, blaspheming. And he took your spode teapot."

"I didn't either," said Stephen loudly, trying to free his hand from Old Janet's big hard fist.

"Don't tell fibs," said Old Janet; "that's the last straw."

"Oh, dear," said Grandma. "He's not a baby any more." She shut the book she was reading and pulled the wet front of his pull-over toward her. "What's this sticky stuff on him?" she asked and straightened her glasses.

"Lemonade," said Old Janet. "He took the last lemon."

They were in the big dark room with the red curtains. Uncle David walked in from the room with the bookcases, holding a box in his uplifted hand. "Look here," he said to Stephen. "What's become of all my balloons?"

Stephen knew well that Uncle David was not really asking a question.

Stephen, sitting on a footstool at his grandma's knee, felt sleepy. He leaned heavily and wished he could put his head on her lap, but he might go to sleep, and it would be wrong to go to sleep while Uncle David was still talking. Uncle David walked about the room with his hands in his pockets, talking to Grandma. Now and then he would walk over to a lamp and, leaning, peer into the top of the shade, winking in the light, as if he expected to find something there.

"It's simply in the blood, I told her," said Uncle David. "I told her she would simply have to come and get him, and keep him. She asked me if I meant to call him a thief and I said if she could think of a more exact word I'd be glad to hear it."

"You shouldn't have said that," commented Grandma calmly.

"Why not? She might as well know the facts. . . . I suppose he can't help it," said Uncle David, stopping now in front of Stephen and dropping his chin into his collar, "I shouldn't expect too much of him, but you can't begin too early—"

"The trouble is," said Grandma, and while she spoke she took Stephen by the chin and held it up so that he had to meet her eye; she talked steadily in a mournful tone, but Stephen could not understand. She ended, "It's not just about the balloons, of course."

"It *is* about the balloons," said Uncle David angrily, "because balloons now mean something worse later. But what can you expect? His father—well, it's in the blood. He—"

"That's your sister's husband you're talking about," said Grandma, "and there is no use making things worse. Besides, you don't really *know*."

"I *do* know," said Uncle David. And he talked again very fast, walking up and down. Stephen tried to understand, but the sounds were strange and floating just over his head. They were talking about his father, and they did not like him. Uncle David came over and stood above Stephen and Grandma. He hunched over them with a frowning face, a long, crooked shadow from him falling across them to the wall. To Stephen he looked like his father, and he shrank against his grandma's skirts.

"The question is, what to do with him now?" asked Uncle David. "If we keep him here, he'd just be a—I won't be bothered with him. Why can't they take care of their own child? That house is crazy. Too far gone already, I'm afraid. No training. No example."

"You're right, they must take him and keep him," said Grandma. She ran her hands over Stephen's head; tenderly she pinched the nape of his neck between thumb and forefinger. "You're your Grandma's darling," she told him, "and you've had a nice long visit, and now you're going home. Mama is coming for you in a few minutes. Won't that be nice?"

"I want my mama," said Stephen, whimpering, for his grandma's face frightened him. There was something wrong with her smile.

Uncle David sat down. "Come over here, fellow," he said, wagging a forefinger at Stephen. Stephen went over slowly, and Uncle David drew him between his wide knees in their loose, rough clothes. "You ought to be ashamed of yourself," he said, "stealing Uncle David's balloons when he had already given you so many."

"It wasn't that," said Grandma quickly. "Don't say that. It will make an impression—"

"I hope it does," said Uncle David in a louder voice; "I hope he remembers it all his life. If he belonged to me I'd give him a good thrashing."

Stephen felt his mouth, his chin, his whole face jerking. He opened his mouth to take a breath, and tears and noise burst from him. "Stop that, fellow, stop that," said Uncle David, shaking him gently by the shoulders, but Stephen could not stop. He drew his breath again and it came back in a howl. Old Janet came to the door.

"Bring me some cold water," called Grandma. There was a flurry, a commotion, a breath of cool air from the hall, the door slammed, and Stephen heard his mother's voice. His howl died away, his breath sobbed and fluttered, he turned his dimmed eyes and saw her standing there. His heart turned over within him and he bleated like a lamb, "Maaaaama," running toward her. Uncle David stood back as Mama swooped in and fell on her knees beside Stephen. She gathered him to her and stood up with him in her arms.

"What are you doing to my baby?" she asked Uncle David in a thickened voice. "I should never have let him come here. I should have known better—"

"You always should know better," said Uncle David, "and you never do. And you never will. You haven't got it here," he told her, tapping his forehead.

"David," said Grandma, "that's your—"

"Yes, I know, she's my sister," said Uncle David. "I know it. But if she must run away and marry a—"

"Shut up," said Mama.

"And bring more like him into the world, let her keep them at home. I say let her keep—"

Mama set Stephen on the floor and, holding him by the hand, she said to Grandma all in a rush as if she were reading something, "Good-by, Mother. This is the last time, really the last. I can't bear it any longer. Say good-by to Stephen; you'll never see him again. You let this happen. It's your fault. You know David was a coward and a bully and a self-righteous little beast all his life and you never crossed him in anything. You let him bully me all my life and you let him slander my husband and call my baby a thief, and now this is the end. . . . He calls my baby a thief over a few horrible little balloons because he doesn't like my husband. . . ."

She was panting and staring about from one to the other. They were all standing. Now Grandma said, "Go home, daughter. Go away, David. I'm sick of your quarreling. I've never had a day's peace or comfort from either of you. I'm sick of you both. Now let me alone and stop this noise. Go away," said Grandma in a wavering voice. She took out her handkerchief and wiped first one eye and then the other and said, "All this hate, hate—what is it for? . . . So this is the way it turns out. Well, let me alone."

"You and your little advertising balloons," said Mama to Uncle David. "The big honest businessman advertises with balloons and if he loses one he'll be ruined. And your beastly little moral notions . . ."

Grandma went to the door to meet Old Janet, who handed her a glass of water. Grandma drank it all, standing there.

"Is your husband coming for you, or are you going home by yourself?" she asked Mama.

"I'm driving myself," said Mama in a far-away voice as if her mind had wandered. "You know he wouldn't set foot in this house."

"I should think not," said Uncle David.

"Come on, Stephen darling," said Mama. "It's far past his bedtime," she said, to no one in particular. "Imagine keeping a baby up to torture him about a few miserable little bits of colored rubber." She smiled at Uncle David with both rows of teeth as she passed him on the way to the door, keeping between him and Stephen. "Ah, where would we be without high moral standards," she said, and then to Grandma, "Good night, Mother," in quite her usual voice. "I'll see you in a day or so."

"Yes, indeed," said Grandma cheerfully, coming out into the hall with Stephen and Mama. "Let me hear from you. Ring me up tomorrow. I hope you'll be feeling better."

"I feel very well now," said Mama brightly, laughing. She bent down and kissed Stephen. "Sleepy, darling? Papa's waiting to see you. Don't go to sleep until you've kissed your papa good night."

Stephen woke with a sharp jerk. He raised his head and put out his chin a little. "I don't want to go home," he said; "I want to go to school. I don't want to see Papa, I don't like him."

Mama laid her palm over his mouth softly. "Darling, don't."

Uncle David put his head out with a kind of snort. "There you are," he said. "There you've got a statement from headquarters."

Mama opened the door and ran, almost carrying Stephen. She ran across the sidewalk, jerking open the car door and dragging Stephen in after her. She spun the car around and dashed forward so sharply Stephen was almost flung out of the seat. He sat braced then with all his might, hands digging into the cushions. The car speeded up and the trees and houses whizzed by all flattened out. Stephen began suddenly to sing to himself, a quiet, inside song so Mama would not hear. He sang his new secret; it was a comfortable, sleepy song: "I hate Papa, I hate Mama, I hate Grandma, I hate Uncle David, I hate Old Janet, I hate Marjory, I hate Papa, I hate Mama . . ."

His head bobbed, leaned, came to rest on Mama's knee, eyes closed. Mama drew him closer and slowed down, driving with one hand.

The Secret Drawer

KENNETH GRAHAME

IT MUST surely have served as a boudoir for the ladies of old time, this little used, rarely entered chamber where the neglected old bureau stood. There was something very feminine in the faint hues of its faded brocades, in the rose and blue of such bits of china as yet remained, and in the delicate old-world fragrance of potpourri from the great bowl—blue and white, with funny holes in its cover—that stood on the bureau's flat top. Modern aunts disdained this out-of-the-way backwater, upstairs room, preferring to do their accounts and grapple with their correspondence in some central position more in the whirl of things, whence one eye could be kept on the carriage-drive, while the other was alert for malingering servants and marauding children. Those aunts of a former generation—I sometimes felt—would have suited our habits better. But even by us children, to whom few places were private or reserved, the room was visited but rarely. To be sure, there was nothing particular in it that we coveted or required. Only a few spindle-legged, gilt-backed chairs,—an old harp on which, so that legend ran, Aunt Eliza herself used once to play, in years remote, unchronicled; a corner-cupboard with a few pieces of china; and the old bureau. But one other thing the room possessed, peculiar to itself; a certain sense of privacy—a power of making the intruder feel that he *was* intruding—perhaps a faculty of hinting that some one might have been sitting on those chairs, writing at the bureau or fingering the china, just a second before one entered. No such violent word as "haunted" could possibly apply to this pleasant old-fashioned chamber, which indeed we all rather liked; but there was no doubt it was reserved and stand-offish, keeping itself to itself.

Uncle Thomas was the first to draw my attention to the possibilities of the old bureau. He was pottering about the house one afternoon, having ordered me to keep at his heels for company—he was a man who hated to be left one minute alone,—when his eye fell on it. "H'm! Sheraton!" he remarked. (He had a smattering of most things, this uncle, especially the vocabularies.) Then he let down the flap, and examined the empty pigeon-holes and the dusty paneling. "Fine bit of inlay," he went on: "good work, all of it. I know the sort. There's a secret drawer in there somewhere." Then as I breathlessly drew near, he suddenly exclaimed: "By Jove, I do want to smoke!" And, wheeling round, he abruptly fled for the garden, leaving me with the cup dashed from my lips. What a strange thing, I mused, was this smoking, that takes a man suddenly, be he in the court, the camp or the grove, grips him like an Afreet, and whirls him off to do its imperious behests! Would it be even so with myself, I wondered, in those unknown grown-up years to come?

But I had no time to waste in vain speculations. My whole being was still vibrating to those magic syllables "secret drawer"; and that particular chord had been touched that never fails to thrill responsive to such words as *cave, trap-door, sliding-panel, bullion, ingots,* or *Spanish dollars.* For, besides its own special bliss, who ever heard of a secret drawer with nothing in it? And O I did want money so badly! I mentally ran over the list of demands which were pressing me the most imperiously.

First, there was the pipe I wanted to give George Jannaway. George, who was Martha's young man, was a shepherd, and a great ally of mine; and the last fair he was at, when he bought his sweetheart fairings, as a right-minded shepherd should, he had purchased a lovely snake expressly for me; one of the wooden sort, with joints, waggling deliciously in the hand; with yellow spots on a green ground, sticky and strong-smelling, as a fresh-painted snake ought to be; and with a red-flannel tongue pasted cunningly into its jaws. I loved it much, and took it to bed with me every night, till what time its spinal cord was loosed and it fell apart, and went the way of all mortal joys. I thought it very nice of George to think of me at the fair, and that's why I wanted to give him a pipe. When the young year was chill and lambing-time was on, George inhabited a little wooden house on wheels, far out on the wintry downs, and saw no faces but such as were sheepish and woolly and mute; and when he and Martha were married, she was going to carry his dinner out to him every day, two miles; and after it, perhaps he would smoke my pipe. It seemed an idyllic sort of existence, for both the parties concerned; but a pipe of quality, a pipe fitted to be part of a life such as this, could not be procured (so Martha informed me) for a smaller sum than eighteenpence. And meantime—!

Then there was the fourpence I owed Edward; not that he was bothering me for it, but I knew he was in need of it himself, to pay back Selina, who wanted it to make up a sum of two shillings, to buy Harold an ironclad for his approaching birthday,—*H.M.S. Majestic,* now lying uselessly careened in the toyshop window, just when her country had such sore need of her.

And then there was that boy in the village who had caught a young squirrel, and I had never yet possessed one, and he wanted a shilling for it, but I knew that for ninepence in cash—but what was the good of these sorry threadbare reflections? I had wants enough to exhaust any possible find of bullion, even if it amounted to half a sovereign. My only hope now lay in the magic drawer, and here I was, standing and letting the precious minutes slip by! Whether "findings" of this sort could, morally speaking, be considered "keepings," was a point that did not occur to me.

The room was very still as I approached the bureau; possessed, it seemed to be, by a sort of hush of expectation. The faint odour of orris-root that floated forth as I let down the flap, seemed to identify itself with the yellows and browns of the old wood, till hue and scent were of one quality and interchangeable. Even so, ere this, the potpourri had mixed itself with the tints of the old brocade, and brocade and potpourri had long been one. With expectant fingers I explored the empty pigeon-holes and sounded the depths of the softly sliding drawers. No books that I knew of gave any general recipe for a quest like this; but the glory, should I succeed unaided, would be all the greater.

To him, who is destined to arrive, the fates never fail to afford, on the way, their small encouragements. In less than two minutes, I had come across a rusty button-hook. This was truly magnificent. In the nursery there existed, indeed, a general button-hook, common to either sex; but none of us possessed a private and special button-hook, to lend or to refuse as suited the high humour of the moment. I pocketed the treasure carefully, and proceeded. At the back of another drawer, three old foreign stamps told me I was surely on the high-road to fortune.

Following on these bracing incentives, came a dull, blank period of unrewarding search. In vain, I removed all the drawers and felt over every inch of the smooth surfaces from front to back. Never a knob, spring or projection met the thrilling fingertips; unyielding the old bureau stood, stoutly guarding its secret, if secret it really had. I began to grow weary and disheartened. This was not the first time that Uncle Thomas had proved shallow, uninformed, a guide into blind alleys where the echoes mocked you. Was it any good persisting longer? Was anything any good whatever? In my mind I began to review past disappointments, and life seemed one long record of failure and of non-arrival. Disillusioned and depressed, I left my work and went to the window. The light was ebbing from the room, and seemed outside to be collecting itself on the horizon for its concentrated effort of sunset. Far down the garden, Uncle Thomas was holding Edward in the air reversed, and smacking him. Edward, gurgling hysterically, was striking blind fists in the direction where he judged his stomach should rightly be; the contents of his pockets—a motley show—were strewing the lawn. Somehow, though I had been put through a similar performance myself an hour or two ago, it all seemed very far away and cut off from me.

Westwards the clouds were massing themselves in a low violet bank; below them, to north and south, as far round as eye could reach, a narrow streak of gold ran out and stretched away, straight along the horizon. Somewhere very far off, a horn was blowing, clear and thin; it sounded like the golden streak grown audible, while the gold seemed the visible sound. It prickled my ebbing courage, this blended strain of music and colour. I turned for a last effort; and Fortune thereupon, as if half-ashamed of the unworthy game she had been playing with me, relented, opening her clenched fist. Hardly had I put my hand once more to the obdurate wood when with a sort of small sigh, almost a sob—as it were—of relief, the secret drawer sprang open.

I drew it out and carried it to the window, to examine it in the failing light. Too hopeless had I gradually grown, in my dispiriting search, to expect very much; and yet at a glance I saw that my basket of grass lay in shivers at my feet. No ingots nor dollars were here to crown me the little Monte Cristo of a week. Outside, the distant horn had ceased its gnat-song, the gold was paling to primrose and everything was lonely and still. Within, my confident little castles were tumbling down like so many card-houses, leaving me stripped of estate, both real and personal, and dominated by the depressing reaction.

And yet—as I looked again at the small collection that lay within that drawer of disillusions, some warmth crept back to my heart as I recognised that a kindred spirit to my own had been at the making of it. Two tarnished gilt buttons—naval, apparently—a portrait of a monarch unknown to me, cut from some antique print and deftly coloured by hand in much my own bold style of brush-work—some foreign copper coins, thicker and clumsier of make than those I hoarded myself—and a list of birds' eggs with names of the places where they had been found. Also, a ferret's muzzle, and a twist of tarry string, still faintly aromatic! It was a real boy's hoard, then, that I had happened on. He too had found out the secret drawer, this happy-starred young person; and here he had stowed away his treasures, one by one, and had cherished them secretly awhile; and then—what? Well, one would never know now the reason why these priceless possessions still lay there unclaimed; but across the void stretch of years I seemed to touch hands a moment with my little comrade of seasons—how many seasons?—long since dead.

I restored the drawer, with its contents, to the trusty bureau, and heard the spring click with a certain satisfaction. Some other boy, perhaps, would some day release that spring again. I trusted he would be equally appreciative. As I opened the door to go, I could hear, from the nursery at the end of the passage, shouts and yells, telling that the hunt was up. Bears, apparently, or bandits, were on the evening bill of fare, judging by the character of the noises. In another minute I would be in the thick of it all, in all the warmth and light and laughter. And yet—what a long way off it all seemed, both in space and time, to me yet lingering on the threshold of that old-world chamber!

Early Memories

GEORGE SANTAYANA

OF EARLY childhood I have some stray images, detached and undatable, called up occasionally for no reason, after the fashion of dreams. Indeed, sometimes I suspect that they may be fragments of old dreams, and not genuine recollections; but in that case, where did the old dreams come from? For autobiography it might be no less pertinent, and even more telling, to report them if they were dreams than if they were true memories, because they would show how my young mind grew, what objects impressed it, and on what themes it played its first variations.

These images are all visual. I remember the *sota de copas* or knave of cups in the Spanish cards, with which I was playing on the floor, when I got entangled in my little frock, which had a pattern of white and blue checks; and I can see the corner of the room, our *antesala,* where I was crawling, and the nurse who helped me up. I also remember sitting in my mother's lap, rather sleepy, and playing with a clasp that could run up and down the two strands of her long gold chain, made of flexible scales; she wore a large lace collar, and had on a silk gown which she called *el vestido de los seis colores,* because the black background was sprinkled with minute six-petalled flowers, each petal of a different color, white, green, yellow, brown, red and blue. Clothes and colors evidently had a great fascination for me: the emphasis may have been partly borrowed and verbal, because I heard the women constantly talking *chiffons;* but the interest was congenial. I have always been attentive to clothes, and careful about my own; and in those days of innocence, it was by no means indifferent to me whether with my white summer dress I wore the plain everyday blue sash, which I despised, or the glossy and fresh silk tartan, that made me feel more like myself. Yet I retain a memory, that must have been much earlier, of quite another kind. One evening, before putting me to bed, my mother carried me to the window, sitting on her arm, and pulled back the *visillo* or lace curtain that hung close to the glass. Above the tower of the Oñate house opposite, one bright steady star was shining. My mother pointed it out to me, and said: *"Detrás de ese lucero está Pepín."* Pepín, her lamented first-born, was behind that star. At the time, this announcement neither surprised nor impressed me; but something about my mother's tone and manner must have fixed her words mechanically in my memory. She seldom spoke unnecessarily, and was never emotional; but here was some profound association with her past that, for a moment, had spread its aura about me.

Another set of memories can be dated as not later than my third year, because they introduce my brother Robert, who left Avila when I was three and he was twelve. We occupied the same little room behind our mother's and next to the schoolroom; and I remember our pillow fights, or rather games, because Robert had a tender heart and was nice to his baby brother. He was forbidden to purloin any part of my food, but might stick out his tongue in the hope, not always disappointed, that with my fork I might delicately place a morsel upon it. It was a feat of equilibrium on my part, as well as of magnanimity, and I remember it for both reasons. Also the crisp potato omelette, fried in oil, that I had for supper, and that I still pine for and seldom obtain; and the napkin, white on the black and red table cover, on which the feast was spread. The first toy I can remember was also in Robert's time at Avila, for it was given me by his Alsatian tutor, Herr Schmidt: a velvety gray mouse that could be wound up to run across the floor. And finally I can remember distinctly the occasion of Robert's departure. We all went to the station to see him off; for my father was taking him as far as London, from where his cousin Russell Sturgis (the Evangelical major with the side-whiskers and shapely calves) was to convey him to America to be put to school. But it is not any emotion connected with leave-taking for an indefinite absence that remains in my mind: only the image of young Robert's back, walking before me at a particular corner where we had to go in single file. He wore a long gray coat with a braided mantlet or short cape covering the shoulders; above which I can still see his gray cap and the tightly curling brown hair escaping and bulging out under it. Whether I was actually walking too or was being carried does not appear from the picture. The self in these clear and fixed intuitions remains wholly transcendental and out of sight. It is doing its duty too well to be aware that it is doing it.

That Robert should have had an Alsatian tutor in Avila (who also taught the girls) may seem odd. It was one of those unstable and unsatisfactory compromises that were involved in the circumstances of my parents' marriage. For a time they lived in Madrid, in the flat where I was born: but Madrid has a bad climate, with great heat in summer and cold winds in winter; it made a second residence necessary for the hot months, and was expensive and, for my mother, socially distasteful. Moreover, she had to go back to Boston; my father knew it, but kept finding reasons for putting the thing off. Finally, very characteristically, my mother took the law into her own hands, secretly made all the arrangements and one afternoon escaped with all of us, save my father, in the express train for Paris. There my father's remonstrances reached her. They were so eloquent, or backed by such threats of action (since he had a right at least to retain *me*), that we all finally returned. It had been agreed that we should live in Avila. But what education could Robert or the girls receive there? None! Therefore a private tutor was imperative, and somehow a young Alsatian was found who seemed to possess all the requirements. French and German were native languages for him, he spoke a little English, and would soon learn Spanish. His demands were modest and his character apparently excellent. So Herr Schmidt was installed as a boarder with a poor widow who lived on the ground floor, and there were daily lessons in the sunny little room at the back of the house which became the schoolroom. I don't know what idealistic cobwebs the German Minerva might have spun there had not her labors been interrupted; but presently a German Cupid had flown in over the flowerpots in the open window and tangled those learned threads. For although this was before the Franco-Prussian War, young Schmidt showed all the sentimentality and push of a pure German; he believed in discipline and thoroughness, and the duty of founding all instruction on German geography, in the native language; so that between the difficult and most clearly articulated names of *Harzgebirge* and *Riesengebirge* he would whisper in Susana's ear: "*Je vous aime avec rage.*" She was hardly sixteen, and he had to be sent away, which no doubt he thought a great injustice; for he wrote a long letter explaining his worthiness to be Susana's husband, and his willingness to go to America and establish himself there—on nothing a year.

It was this collapse of superior international education at home that had made it urgent to send at least Robert at once to school in America, and that separated me from my elder brother for the next five years. Two more years elapsed before my mother and sisters also departed. I remember nothing of that interval; but after they went my uncle Santiago, with his wife María Josefa and his daughter Antoñita, came to live with us, and a new and distinct chapter begins in my experience. The scene, the persons, the events are still present to me most vividly. I didn't feel deeply or understand what was going on, but somehow the force of it impressed my young mind and established there a sort of criterion or standard of reality. That crowded, strained, disunited, and tragic family life remains for me the type of what life really is: something confused, hideous, and useless. I do not hate it or rebel against it, as people do who think they have been wronged. It caused me no suffering; I was a child carried along as in a baby-carriage through the crowd of strangers; I was neither much bothered nor seriously neglected; and my eyes and ears became accustomed to the unvarnished truth of the world, neither selected for my instruction nor hidden from me for my benefit.

My aunt María Josefa was frankly a woman of the people. She was most at home in her kitchen, in a large blue apron that covered most of her skirt; and I shall never forget the genuine fresh taste of the fried peppers and eggs, and the great soft cake or *torta* that came from her hands. She was a native of Jaen, with a strong but pleasant Andalusian accent and exaggerated rhetoric. Her every word was a diminutive or an augmentative, and her every passion flowed out in endless unrestrained litanies of sorrow or endearment. She could hardly read or write, and her simplicity or humility was so great that she would casually observe that her daughter Antoñita had been a *siete mesina* or seven-months child; from which any one could gather the reason for her marriage. For my uncle this marriage had been unintended and undesirable; he was much too young and she was much too common; but having got the poor girl into trouble he nobly made the *amende honorable;* and terrible as the sacrifice would have been if he had had much ability or ambition, as things were it rendered poverty perhaps easier to bear. Poverty was not the only misfortune they had to put up with. But when the worst was over, I found my aunt living in Granada with a brother who was a tanner. This was in the summer of 1893, when I had reached Spain via Gibraltar. My mother and I were in the habit of sending María Josefa a small allowance so that she was well received and respected in her brother's household. The tannery occupied the court of an old, possibly a Moorish, house; the skins hung drying from the gallery; and my aunt's brother, in order to do the honors of the city (as I had not been there before, or had no guidebook), took me to see the University, which indeed it would not have occurred to me to visit. In the library there was a large globe; and in order to make talk, which rather ran dry between us, I said I would show him the voyage I had just made from America. I was doing so when he asked, "But which is Spain?—What, that little spot? I thought it was this," and he pointed to Africa. It occurred to me that some great wits before him had seen no difference between Africa and Spain. But I didn't go into the intricacies of that opinion. As to my aunt, of course she was then old, fat, and broken, but calm and strangely silent. She had protested enough, and this was the fifth act of her tragedy, all storms subdued and equalized in resignation. Yet one more trial awaited her. Her brother died before her, and she had to retire to her native village near Jaen, from which soon no more answers reached us to our letters.

Not the person, *tía María Josefa,* in whose hands my mother could have wished to leave me at the age of five! But my mother's mind was made up and inflexible; it was made up abstractly, in scorn of particulars and of consequences. She had put off her departure only too long, and now she *must* go. Besides, strange as it may seem, she was well disposed towards my father's relations, as they were not towards her. She seldom spoke of them, but when she did it was amiably, even sympathetically. She seems to have trusted María Josefa, as one might a devoted old nurse; and this trust was observed, because in relation to me María Josefa behaved perfectly. Moreover there was Antoñita, who but for her love-affairs and marriage would have looked after me more playfully than her mother. Antoñita was a nice girl, a friend of Susana's, pretty and with a latent depth of feeling which made people think her not insignificant, in spite of her simplicity and lack of education. My mother had liked her, and helped her to get prettier clothes. But she was ripening into womanhood and preoccupied with love. I remember her first *novio,* or acknowledged lover, the youngest of the Paz brothers, who were among the leading bourgeois families of Avila; and I think there was more between him and Antoñita than the local conventions allowed to *novios*. He came to the house, which is contrary to the rules: *novios* should meet only in public places, in sight of their elders, or talk together at the window, the girl sitting inside the *reja,* or in the balcony, and the young man standing in the street. This was called *pelando la pava,* plucking the turkey, or conjugating the verb *amo,* I love. There was a great attic over a part of the house, accessible from my father's room or studio, where he painted; and from one of the big beams of the roof hung a trapeze, arranged, I suppose, for my benefit. Into that attic the lovers would wander alone, whether to admire my performance, or not suspecting that I might be swinging there, I didn't know. That something was brewing became evident on another occasion. We were sitting one evening or late afternoon in the *café del Inglés* (for the lamps were lighted) when suddenly my aunt got up, evidently very angry, bundled Antoñita and me out of a side door; and once in the adjoining *portal* or *porte cochère,* began violently beating Antoñita with fists and claws, with such a flood of imprecations as only my aunt was capable of. All I could gather was that the poor girl had been looking at somebody; no doubt, as I now conjecture, at young Paz, at another table, making love to another girl. Anyhow, my aunt had worked herself up to such a rage that, being subject to fits, she fell full length with a loud bang on the stone floor. She fell exactly as *prima donnas* and murdered heroes fall on the stage; and apparently as harmlessly, for I heard no more of the whole affair. Relations with Paz were evidently broken off; there were no more trips to the attic, where I did my swinging undisturbed; and presently a very different *novio,* this time meaning business, appeared on the scene.

What brought him to Avila I do not know; probably some great lawsuit, for he was a lawyer, and ostensibly an important person, *bellâtre,* with well-oiled curly black locks and silken side-whiskers and the beginnings of a paunch, on which a conspicuous gold chain with dangling seals marked the equator. He was a widower with two little girls, but still young, not over forty; for people spoke of his brilliant prospects rather than of his brilliant past, and he had a still beautiful mother whom my father and I once visited in Madrid. She received us in her boudoir, or rather in the alcove attached to it, for she was still in bed, but elaborately prepared to receive callers. There were great lace flounces to her sheets, over a red damask coverlet, and she wore a lovely fresh peignoir and little cap, from which two great black braids hung down over her two shoulders, ending in coquettish knots of blue ribbon. What she and my father were talking about I didn't understand, but I felt I had never been in such a luxurious nest before, so much carpeted, so much curtained, so softly upholstered, and so full of religious and other bric-a-brac.

With such a mother, Rafael Vegas must have begun life convinced that he was a distinguished and fashionable person, and that his clients, when he had them, should pay him handsome fees. Nor could he have helped being a ladykiller, having not only the requisite presence and airs, but the requisite temperament; for he was no vulgar libertine, but a genuine lover of the fair sex, who demanded to conquer and to possess his conquests exclusively. He might have liked a harem, but he despised a brothel. His success with the ladies, young and old, was immense and in one sense deserved, since his admiration for them was sincere. That he was truly subject to the tender passion was proved by his courting and marrying two of my pretty and penniless cousins, beginning with Antoñita. Nothing but love could have prompted him in these cases; but to them it seemed a dazzling match, that meant initiation into a higher social sphere, as well as into all the mysteries of untried passion.

The wedding took place secretly in the small hours of the night, because a rowdy custom subjected widowers, on their new bridal night, to a *cencerrada,* or derisive serenade of cowbells, if the date and place of those mysteries could be discovered. Everything was therefore kept as dark as possible; only the immediate family was summoned, and they at the last moment, and only a cup of chocolate offered afterwards to the sleepy company before the newly married pair vanished to some unknown hiding place. I was of course present, and impressed by the strangeness of going out at night into a dark street and a dark empty church, with a knot of people whispering and hastening, with much trepidation, as if on some criminal errand. We were in our ordinary clothes, the bride in black, with a lace mantilla. It was all over in a moment. I was bundled to bed again, and might have thought it a dream, but for the talk afterwards about everything. Rafael's emphatic personal dignity would have suffered sadly had he not escaped the *cencerrada;* and he managed it cleverly, by not going on any wedding trip (he may also have been short of money) but establishing himself at once in our house, with his two daughters, in the best front rooms left vacant by my mother and sisters, who were in America. For a day or two, however, bride and bridegroom occupied my bedroom, because it looked out on a tangle of little courts and walled gardens, quite shut off from any street. On the first morning I followed the housemaid there—after all, it was my room—when she took in their breakfast to the happy pair. The two cups of chocolate were on a particularly fresh and well-filled tray, with *azucarillos;* there was a bright brass bed, wholly unknown to me, and a gorgeous red damask coverlet, and great lace flounces to the sheets, like those, or the very same, that on that other occasion, in Madrid, I saw setting off the charms of Rafael's black-browed mother. Rafael and Antoñita lay smiling and rosy on quite separate pillows; they said good morning to the servant and me with unusual good humor, and people all day indulged in witticisms and veiled expressions which I didn't quite understand.

I now had playmates in the house, two well-dressed little girls about my own age; but we didn't like one another. It was made clear in every direction that our house and our standard of living were not such as the Vegas expected, and they bore us a grudge for causing them to be lodged and fed so badly. Yet our double or triple *ménage* was kept up for a year or more until an event supervened that brought disaster to my uncle's family and eventually sent my father and me to America.

Antoñita was soon quite obviously in what was called an interesting condition. The place that children come from was no mystery to me, although I was only seven or eight years old. I was already a calm materialist; not that in another direction I was less knowing in theology; and if any one had made the mistake of telling me that babies came in bandboxes from Paris, I am sure I should have scornfully replied that God and not milliners had made me; and that as God was everywhere, it was just as easy for him to make babies in Madrid or even in Avila as in Paris. Yet Antoñita's baby, that God was undoubtedly making in Avila, was very long in coming to light. She continued more and more strangely to enlarge, until her haggard and unseemly condition, and murmurs and consultations in the family, began to suggest that something was wrong. Perhaps the date for the expected event had been miscalculated; or perhaps some complication prevented nature from bringing it about. At last one evening there was much agitation in the house, with strangers coming in, and long consultations; and I began to hear from Antoñita's room (which was my mother's room back to back with mine, but with no communication) piercing cries and weeping invocations of all the heavenly powers. This presumably lasted all night, since it was still going on when I woke up in the morning; and then there were more consultations with strange doctors and exhibition of surgical instruments. At one moment I remember my aunt bursting into the passage, with a bundle of bloodstained linen in her hands and floods of joyful tears, crying, "She is saved, she is saved!" Yet later we children were taken to our neighbor's on the second floor, where we didn't know the people; and on the way out I saw, in a small wooden box that might have held soap or candles, a dead child lying naked, pale yellowish green. Most beautiful, I thought him, and as large and perfectly formed as the Child Jesus in the pictures; except that where the navel ought to be he had a little mound like an acorn, with a long string hanging out of it.

The image of that child, as if made of green alabaster, has remained clear all my life, not as a ghastly object that ought to have been hidden from me, but as the most beautiful of statues, something too beautiful to be alive. And it has suggested to me a theory, doubtless fanciful, yet which I can't think wholly insignificant, concerning the formation of living things. They are all formed in the dark, automatically, protected from interference by what is called experience: experience which indeed would be impossible if there were not first a definite creature to receive it and to react upon it in ways consonant with its inherited nature. This nature has asserted itself in a seed, in an egg, in a womb, where the world couldn't disturb its perfect evolution. Flowers and butterflies come perfect to the light, and many animals are never more beautiful, pure, and courageous than when they first confront the world. But man, and other unhappy mammals, are born helpless and half-shapeless, like unbaked dough; they have not yet become what they meant to be. The receptacle that held them could not feed them long enough, or allow them to attain their full size and strength. They must therefore be cast out into the glare and the cold, to be defeated by a thousand accidents, derailed, distorted, taught and trained to be enemies to themselves, and to prevent themselves from ever existing. No doubt they manage to survive for a time, halt, blind, and mis-shapen; and sometimes these suppressions or mutilations of what they meant to be adapt them to special environments and give them technical knowledge of many a thing that, if they had been free, they might never have noticed, or observed only poetically, in a careless and lordly way. But every living creature remains miserable and vicious, so long as in serving other things it has to suppress itself: and if that alien world must need be served, the only happy solution and one that nature often finds, would be for the unfit species to perish outright—there is nothing ignoble in perishing—and for a different species to appear whose freedom and happiness would lie in contact with those particular circumstances and mastery over them. I say to myself, therefore, that Antoñita's child was so exceptionally beautiful, and would doubtless have been exceptionally brave and intelligent, because he had profited longer than is usual by the opportunity to grow undisturbed, as all children grow in their sleep; but this advantage, allowed to butterflies and flowers, and to some wild animals, is forbidden to mankind, and he paid for it by his life and by that of his mother.

For she had not really been saved; only a false hope made my aunt think so for a moment; and on Antoñita's death, it would have seemed natural that Rafael and his two little girls should have left us and gone to live elsewhere in their own more luxurious way. But not at all. Primitive human nature in my aunt María Josefa yielded absolutely to every passion in turn, put up with every trial, but survived and clung no less passionately to whatever was left. Her grief on this occasion was violent, but violent only by fits, as when each new visitor came to condole with her, and she had to repeat the whole story, with appropriate floods of tears, sobs and lamentations. She even said at times that now she knew there was no God, because, with all her prayers and vows, no God could have allowed her poor innocent daughter to suffer so horribly to no purpose. Her heart thus unburdened, however, she couldn't but take comfort in that splendid man, her son-in-law, and devote herself to his service and care for his little girls. Rafael therefore not only remained in our house, but became all-important in it, as if my father had not existed. Nor could I be looked after exclusively, when after all I had my own mother to love me, even if a thousand leagues away, and there were those two darlings to rescue from the shock of having lost their second Mama as well as their first one. Moreover my uncle

Santiago, though he said little, was beginning to go daft. Not on account of his daughter's death. He used to say, when people expressed their sympathy, that his real loss had come when she was married. I don't think this observation in itself a sign of dementia; but it indicated a general despair and passivity that went with his taking refuge in drink, and finally in idiocy. For idiocy may begin by being partly acted, like Hamlet's madness, in order to mock the facts, until the mockery becomes an automatism, and the facts are lost altogether. Years afterwards, when he was at his worst, he would walk ceaselessly round and round the house, half singing, half moaning, always repeating the same sounds, and crushing a piece of paper in his hand. He had recovered the animal capacity—such an insult to the world!—of still doing his old trick, no matter what might be going on. The marvel is how many individuals and how many governments are able to survive on this system. Perhaps the universe is nothing but an equilibrium of idiocies.

My father was mildness itself on ordinary occasions, but sometimes could be aroused to reveal his hidden and unusually clear mind, when all his command of terse language and his contempt for the world would flow out in a surprising and devastating manner. I was not present, but I gathered from stray comments overheard afterwards, that he had had an explanation of this sort with Rafael and María Josefa. At any rate, they suddenly left us. My father and I remained in what seemed that vast house alone with one little maidservant. Such an arrangement could not be permanent and doubtless was not meant to be so; and presently we too said farewell to that house forever and to Avila, as far as I was concerned, for eleven years.

During the three years that I was separated from my mother I went more or less to school. It was a large darkish room on the ground floor in the public building directly opposite our house; but the entrance was not in our street, and I had to go round the Oñate tower into the lane at the back, where the school door was. We children stood in *corros* or circles round the teacher—I think sometimes only an older lad—and recited the lesson after him. I don't remember any individual questions or answers, nor any reading or writing, yet we did learn somehow to read and write. I had two books: the *cartilla,* with the alphabet and the different syllables, with easy words following; and the catechism, perhaps in a later year. This was itself divided into two parts, one Sacred History, with pictures in it, of which I remember only Moses striking the rock from which water gushed; and Christian Doctrine, of which I remember a great deal, virtually everything, because it was evidently an excellent catechism, so that after learning it I have been able all my life to distinguish at the first hearing the *sapor haereticus* of any dangerous doctrine. Especially present to me is the very philosophic dogma that God is everywhere, by his essence, by his presence and by his power: of which, however, the first clause has always remained obscure to me; for if God is everywhere by his essence, it would seem to follow that everything is essentially divine—a vulgar pantheism; so that the meaning must be something very recondite and highly qualified, which escapes me. But the other two clauses are luminous, and have taught me from the first to conceive omnificent power and eternal truth: inescapable conceptions in any case, quite apart from any doctrines of historical Judaism or Christianity. I have reasserted them, in my mature philosophy, in my notions of the realm of matter and the realm of truth: notions which I am happy to have imbibed in childhood by rote in the language of antiquity, and not to have set them up for myself in the Babel of modern speculation. They belong to human sanity, to human orthodoxy; I wish to cling to that, no matter from what source its expression may come, or encumbered with what myths. The myths dissolve: the presuppositions of intelligence remain and are necessarily confirmed by experience, since intelligence awoke precisely when sensibility began to grow relevant to external things.

II. THE GREAT MOUNTAINS

A Heavenly Place for a Boy

MARK TWAIN

IT WAS a heavenly place for a boy, that farm of my uncle John's. The house was a double log one, with a spacious floor (roofed in) connecting it with the kitchen. In the summer the table was set in the middle of that shady and breezy floor, and the sumptuous meals—well, it makes me cry to think of them. Fried chicken, roast pig; wild and tame turkeys, ducks, and geese; venison just killed; squirrels, rabbits, pheasants, partridges, prairie-chickens; biscuits, hot batter cakes, hot buckwheat cakes, hot "wheat bread," hot rolls, hot corn pone; fresh corn boiled on the ear, succotash, butter-beans, stringbeans, tomatoes, peas, Irish potatoes, sweet potatoes; buttermilk, sweet milk, "clabber"; watermelons, muskmelons, cantaloupes—all fresh from the garden; apple pie, peach pie, pumpkin pie, apple dumplings, peach cobbler—I can't remember the rest. The way that the things were cooked was perhaps the main splendor—particularly a certain few of the dishes. For instance, the corn bread, the hot biscuits and wheat bread, and the fried chicken. These things have never been properly cooked in the North—in fact, no one there is able to learn the art, so far as my experience goes. The North thinks it knows how to make corn bread, but this is mere superstition. Perhaps no bread in the world is quite so good as Southern corn bread, and perhaps no bread in the world is quite so bad as the Northern imitation of it. The North seldom tries to fry chicken, and this is well; the art cannot be learned north of the line of Mason and Dixon, nor anywhere in Europe. This is not hearsay; it is experience that is speaking. In Europe it is imagined that the custom of serving various kinds of bread blazing hot is "American," but that is too broad a spread; it is custom in the South, but is much less than that in the North. In the North and in Europe hot bread is considered unhealthy. This is probably another fussy superstition, like the European superstition that ice-water is unhealthy. Europe does not need ice-water and does not drink it; and yet, notwithstanding this, its word for it is better than ours, because it describes it, whereas ours doesn't. Europe calls it "iced" water. Our word describes water made from melted ice—a drink which has a characterless taste and which we have but little acquaintance with.

It seems a pity that the world should throw away so many good things merely because they are unwholesome. I doubt if God has given us any refreshment which, taken in moderation, is unwholesome, except microbes. Yet there are people who strictly deprive themselves of each and every eatable, drinkable, and smokable which has in any way acquired a shady reputation. They pay this price for health. And health is all they get for it. How strange it is! It is like paying out your whole fortune for a cow that has gone dry.

The farmhouse stood in the middle of a very large yard, and the yard was fenced on three sides with rails and on the rear side with high palings; against these stood the smoke-house; beyond the palings was the orchard; beyond the orchard were the negro quarters and the tobacco fields. The front yard was entered over a stile made of sawed-off logs of graduated heights; I do not remember any gate. In a corner of the front yard were a dozen lofty hickory trees and a dozen black walnuts, and in the nutting season riches were to be gathered there.

Down a piece, abreast the house, stood a little log cabin against the rail fence; and there the woody hill fell sharply away, past the barns, the corn-crib, the stables, and the tobacco-curing house, to a limpid brook which sang along over its gravelly bed and curved and frisked in and out and here and there and yonder in the deep shade of overhanging foliage and vines—a divine place for wading, and it had swimming pools, too, which were forbidden to us and therefore much frequented by us. For we were little Christian children and had early been taught the value of forbidden fruit.

In the little log cabin lived a bedridden white-headed slave woman whom we visited daily and looked upon with awe, for we believed she was upward of a thousand years old and had talked with Moses. The younger negroes credited these statistics and had furnished them to us in good faith. We accommodated all the details which came to us about her; and so we believed that she had lost her health in the long desert trip coming out of Egypt, and had never been able to get it back again. She had a round bald place on the crown of her head, and we used to creep around and gaze at it in reverent silence, and reflect that it was caused by fright through seeing Pharaoh drowned. We called her "Aunt" Hannah, Southern fashion. She was superstitious, like the other negroes; also, like them, she was deeply religious. Like them, she had great faith in prayer and employed it in all ordinary exigencies, but not in cases where a dead certainty of result was urgent. Whenever witches were around she tied up the remnant of her wool in little tufts, with white thread, and this promptly made the witches impotent.

All the negroes were friends of ours, and with those of our own age we were in effect comrades. I say in effect, using the phrase as a modification. We were comrades, and yet not comrades; color and condition interposed a subtle line which both parties were conscious of and which rendered complete fusion impossible. We had a faithful and affectionate good friend, ally, and adviser in "Uncle Dan'l," a middle-aged slave whose head was the best one in the negro quarter, whose sympathies were wide and warm, and whose heart was honest and simple and knew no guile. He has served me well these many, many years. I have not seen him for more than half a century, and yet spiritually I have had his welcome company a good part of that time, and have staged him in books under his own name and as "Jim," and carted him all around—to Hannibal, down the Mississippi on a raft, and even across the Desert of Sahara in a balloon—and he has endured it all with the patience and friendliness and loyalty which were his birthright. It was on the farm that I got my strong liking for his race and my appreciation of certain of its fine qualities. This feeling and this estimate have stood the test of sixty years and more, and have suffered no impairment. The black face is as welcome to me now as it was then.

In my schoolboy days I had no aversion to slavery. I was not aware that there was anything wrong about it. No one arraigned it in my hearing; the local papers said nothing against it; the local pulpit taught us that God approved it, that it was a holy thing, and that the doubter need only look in the Bible if he wished to settle his mind—and then the texts were read aloud to us to make the matter sure; if the slaves themselves had an aversion to slavery, they were wise and said nothing. In Hannibal we seldom saw a slave misused; on the farm, never.

There was, however, one small incident of my boyhood days which touched this matter, and it must have meant a good deal to me or it would not have stayed in my memory, clear and sharp, vivid and shadowless, all these slow-drifting years. We had a little slave boy whom we had hired from someone, there in Hannibal. He was from the eastern shore of Maryland, and had been brought away from his family and his friends, halfway across the American continent, and sold. He was a cheery spirit, innocent and gentle, and the noisiest creature that ever was, perhaps. All day long he was singing, whistling, yelling, whooping, laughing—it was maddening, devastating, unendurable. At last, one day, I lost all my temper, and went raging to my mother and said Sandy had been singing for an hour without a single break, and I couldn't stand it, and *wouldn't* she please shut him up. The tears came into her eyes and her lip trembled, and she said something like this:

"Poor thing, when he sings it shows that he is not remembering, and that comforts me; but when he is still I am afraid he is thinking, and I cannot bear it. He will never see his mother again; if he can sing, I must not hinder it, but be thankful for it. If you were older, you would understand me; then that friendless child's noise would make you glad."

It was a simple speech and made up of small words, but it went home, and Sandy's noise was not a trouble to me any more. She never used large words, but she had a natural gift for making small ones do effective work. She lived to reach the neighborhood of ninety years and was capable with her tongue to the last—especially when a meanness or an injustice roused her spirit. She has come handy to me several times in my books, where she figures as Tom Sawyer's Aunt Polly. I fitted her out with a dialect and tried to think up other improvements for her, but did not find any. I used Sandy once, also; it was in *Tom Sawyer*. I tried to get him to whitewash the fence, but it did not work. I do not remember what name I called him by in the book.

I can see the farm yet, with perfect clearness. I can see all its belongings, all its details; the family room of the house, with a "trundle" bed in one corner and a spinning-wheel in another—a wheel whose rising and falling wail, heard from a distance, was the mournfulest of all sounds to me, and made me homesick and low spirited, and filled my atmosphere with the wandering spirits of the dead; the vast fireplace, piled high, on winter nights, with flaming hickory logs from whose ends a sugary sap bubbled out, but did not go to waste, for we scraped it off and ate it; the lazy cat spread out on the rough hearthstones; the drowsy dogs braced against the jambs and blinking; my aunt in one chimney corner, knitting; my uncle in the other, smoking his corn-cob pipe; the slick and carpetless oak floor faintly mirroring the dancing flame tongues and freckled with black indentations where fire coals had popped out and died a leisurely death; half a dozen children romping in the background twilight; "split"-bottomed chairs here and there, some with rockers; a cradle—out of service, but waiting, with confidence; in the early cold mornings a snuggle of children, in shirts and chemises, occupying the hearthstone and procrastinating—they could not bear to leave that comfortable place and go out on the wind-swept floor space between the house and kitchen where the general tin basin stood, and wash.

Along outside of the front fence ran the country road, dusty in the summertime, and a good place for snakes—they liked to lie in it and sun themselves; when they were rattlesnakes or puff adders, we killed them; when they were black snakes, or racers, or belonged to the fabled "hoop" breed, we fled, without shame; when they were "house snakes," or "garters," we carried them home and put them in Aunt Patsy's workbasket for a surprise; for she was prejudiced against snakes, and always when she took the basket in her lap and they began to climb out of it it disordered her mind. She never could seem to get used to them; her opportunities went for nothing. And she was always cold toward bats, too, and could not bear them; and yet I think a bat is as friendly a bird as there is. My mother was Aunt Patsy's sister and had the same wild superstitions. A bat is beautifully soft and silky; I do not know any creature that is pleasanter to the touch or is more grateful for caressings, if offered in the right spirit. I know all about these coleoptera, because our great cave, three miles below Hannibal, was multitudinously stocked with them, and often I brought them home to amuse my mother with. It was easy to manage if it was a school day, because then I had ostensibly been to school and hadn't any bats. She was not a suspicious person, but full of trust and confidence; and when I said, "There's something in my coat pocket for you," she would put her hand in. But she always took it out again, herself; I didn't have to tell her. It was remarkable, the way she couldn't learn to like private bats. The more experience she had, the more she could not change her views.

I think she was never in the cave in her life; but everybody else went there. Many excursion parties came from considerable distances up and down the river to visit the cave. It was miles in extent and was a tangled wilderness of narrow and lofty clefts and passages. It was an easy place to get lost in; anybody could do it—including the bats. I got lost in it myself, along with a lady, and our last candle burned down to almost nothing before we glimpsed the search party's lights winding about in the distance.

"Injun Joe," the half-breed, got lost in there once, and would have starved to death if the bats had run short. But there was no chance of that; there were myriads of them. He told me all his story. In the book called *Tom Sawyer* I starved him entirely to death in the cave, but that was in the interest of art; it never happened. "General" Gaines, who was our first town drunkard before Jimmy Finn got the place, was lost in there for the space of a week, and finally pushed his handkerchief out of a hole in a hilltop near Saverton, several miles down the river from the cave's mouth, and somebody saw it and dug him out. There is nothing the matter with his statistics except the handkerchief. I knew him for years and he hadn't any. But it could have been his nose. That would attract attention.

The cave was an uncanny place, for it contained a corpse—the corpse of a young girl of fourteen. It was in a glass cylinder inclosed in a copper one which was suspended from a rail which bridged a narrow passage. The body was preserved in alcohol, and it was said that loafers and rowdies used to drag it up by the hair and look at the dead face. The girl was the daughter of a St. Louis surgeon of extraordinary ability and wide celebrity. He was an eccentric man and did many strange things. He put the poor thing in that forlorn place himself.

Beyond the road where the snakes sunned themselves was a dense young thicket, and through it a dim-lighted path led a quarter of a mile; then out of the dimness one emerged abruptly upon a level great prairie which was covered with wild strawberry plants, vividly starred with prairie pinks, and walled in on all sides by forests. The strawberries were fragrant and fine, and in the season we were generally there in the crisp freshness of the early morning, while the dew beads still sparkled upon the grass and the woods were ringing with the first songs of the birds.

Down the forest slopes to the left were the swings. They were made of bark stripped from hickory saplings. When they became dry they were dangerous. They usually broke when a child was forty feet in the air, and this was why so many bones had to be mended every year. I had no ill luck myself, but none of my cousins escaped. There were eight of them, and at one time and another they broke fourteen arms among them. But it cost next to nothing, for the doctor worked by the year—twenty-five dollars for the whole family. I remember two of the Florida doctors, Chowning and Meredith. They not only tended an entire family for twenty-five dollars a year, but furnished the medicines themselves. Good measure, too. Only the largest persons could hold a whole dose. Castor oil was the principal beverage. The dose was half a dipperful, with half a dipperful of New Orleans molasses added to help it down and make it taste good, which it never did. The next standby was calomel; the next, rhubarb; and the next, jalap. Then they bled the patient, and put mustard plasters on him. It was a dreadful system, and yet the death rate was not heavy. The calomel was nearly sure to salivate the patient and cost him some of his teeth. There were no dentists. When teeth became touched with decay or were otherwise ailing, the doctor knew of but one thing to do—he fetched his tongs and dragged them out. If the jaw remained, it was not his fault. Doctors were not called in cases of ordinary illness; the family grandmother attended to those. Every old woman was a doctor, and gathered her own medicines in the woods, and knew how to compound doses that would stir the vitals of a cast-iron dog. And then there was the "Indian doctor";

a grave savage, remnant of his tribe, deeply read in the mysteries of nature and the secret properties of herbs; and most backwoodsmen had high faith in his powers and could tell of wonderful cures achieved by him. In Mauritius, away off yonder in the solitudes of the Indian Ocean, there is a person who answers to our Indian doctor of the old times. He is a negro, and has had no teaching as a doctor, yet there is one disease which he is master of and can cure and the doctors can't. They send for him when they have a case. It is a child's disease of a strange and deadly sort, and the negro cures it with a herb medicine which he makes, himself, from a prescription which has come down to him from his father and grandfather. He will not let anyone see it. He keeps the secret of its components to himself, and it is feared that he will die without divulging it; then there will be consternation in Mauritius. I was told these things by the people there, in 1896.

We had the "faith doctor," too, in those early days—a woman. Her specialty was toothache. She was a farmer's old wife and lived five miles from Hannibal. She would lay her hand on the patient's jaw and say, "Believe!" and the cure was prompt. Mrs. Utterback. I remember her very well. Twice I rode out there behind my mother, horseback, and saw the cure performed. My mother was the patient.

Doctor Meredith removed to Hannibal, by and by, and was our family physician there, and saved my life several times. Still, he was a good man and meant well. Let it go.

I was always told that I was a sickly and precarious and tiresome and uncertain child, and lived mainly on allopathic medicines during the first seven years of my life. I asked my mother about this, in her old age—she was in her eighty-eighth year—and said:

"I suppose that during all that time you were uneasy about me?"

"Yes, the whole time."

"Afraid I wouldn't live?"

After a reflective pause—ostensibly to think out the facts—"No—afraid you would."

The country schoolhouse was three miles from my uncle's farm. It stood in a clearing in the woods and would hold about twenty-five boys and girls. We attended the school with more or less regularity once or twice a week, in summer, walking to it in the cool of the morning by the forest paths, and back in the gloaming at the end of the day. All the pupils brought their dinners in baskets—corn dodger, buttermilk, and other good things—and sat in the shade of the trees at noon and ate them. It is the part of my education which I look back upon with the most satisfaction. My first visit to the school was when I was seven. A strapping girl of fifteen, in the customary sunbonnet and calico dress, asked me if I "used tobacco"—meaning did I chew it. I said no. It roused her scorn. She reported me to all the crowd, and said:

"Here is a boy seven years old who can't chew tobacco."

By the looks and comments which this produced I realized that I was a degraded object, and was cruelly ashamed of myself. I determined to reform. But I only made myself sick; I was not able to learn to chew tobacco. I learned to smoke fairly well, but that did not conciliate anybody and I remained a poor thing, and characterless. I longed to be respected, but I never was able to rise. Children have but little charity for one another's defects.

As I have said, I spent some part of every year at the farm until I was twelve or thirteen years old. The life which I led there with my cousins was full of charm, and so is the memory of it yet. I can call back the solemn twilight and mystery of the deep woods, the earthy smells, the faint odors of the wild flowers, the sheen of rain-washed foliage, the rattling clatter of drops when the wind shook the trees, the far-off hammering of woodpeckers and the muffled drumming of wood pheasants in the remoteness of the forest, the snapshot glimpses of disturbed wild creatures scurrying through the grass—I can call it all back and make it as real as it ever was, and as blessed. I can call back the prairie, and its loneliness and peace, and a vast hawk hanging motionless in the sky, with his wings spread wide and the blue of the vault showing through the fringe of their end feathers. I can see the woods in their autumn dress, the oaks purple, the hickories washed with gold, the maples and the sumachs luminous with crimson fires, and I can hear the rustle made by the fallen leaves as we plowed through them. I can see the blue clusters of wild grapes hanging among the foliage of the saplings, and I remember the taste of them and the smell. I know how the wild blackberries looked, and how they tasted, and the same with the pawpaws, the hazelnuts, and the persimmons; and I can feel the thumping rain, upon my head, of hickory nuts and walnuts when we were out in the frosty dawn to scramble for them with the pigs, and the gusts of wind loosed them and sent them down. I know the stain of blackberries, and how pretty it is, and I know the stain of walnut hulls, and how little it minds soap and water, also what grudged experience it had of either of them. I know the taste of maple sap, and when to gather it, and how to arrange the troughs and the delivery tubes, and how to boil down the juice, and how to hook the sugar after it is made, also how much better hooked sugar tastes than any that is honestly come by, let bigots say what they will. I know how a prize watermelon looks when it is sunning its fat rotundity among pumpkin vines and "simblins"; I know how to tell when it is ripe without "plugging" it; I know how inviting it looks when it is cooling itself in a tub of water under the bed, waiting; I know how it looks when it lies on the table in the sheltered great floor space between house and kitchen, and the children gathered for the sacrifice and their mouths watering; I know the crackling sound it makes when the carving knife enters its end, and I can see the split fly along in front of the blade as the knife cleaves its way to the other end; I can see its halves fall apart and display the rich red meat and the black seeds, and the heart standing up, a luxury fit for the elect; I know how a boy looks behind a yard-long slice of that melon, and I know how he feels; for I have been there. I know the taste of the watermelon which has been honestly come by, and I know the taste of the watermelon which has been acquired by art. Both taste good, but the experienced know which tastes best. I know the look of green apples and peaches and pears on the trees, and I know how entertaining they are when they are inside of a person. I know how ripe ones look when they are piled in pyramids under the trees, and how pretty they are and how vivid their colors. I know how a frozen apple looks, in a barrel down cellar in the wintertime, and how hard it is to bite, and how the frost makes the teeth ache, and yet how good it is, notwithstanding. I know the disposition of elderly people to select the specked apples for the children, and I once knew ways to beat the game. I know the look of an apple that is roasting and sizzling on a hearth on a winter's evening, and I know the comfort that comes of eating it hot, along with some sugar and a drench of cream. I know the delicate art and mystery of so cracking hickory nuts and walnuts on a flatiron with a hammer that the kernels will be delivered whole, and I know how the nuts, taken in conjunction with winter apples, cider, and doughnuts, make old people's old tales and old jokes sound fresh and crisp and enchanting, and juggle an evening away before you know what went with the time. I know the look of Uncle Dan'l's kitchen as it was on the privileged nights, when I was a child, and I can see the white and black children grouped on the hearth, with the firelight playing on their faces and the shadows flickering upon the walls, clear back toward the cavernous gloom of the rear, and I can hear Uncle Dan'l telling the immortal tales which Uncle Remus Harris was to gather into his book and charm the world with, by and by; and I can feel again the creepy joy which quivered through me when the time for the ghost story was reached—and the sense of regret, too, which came over me, for it was always the last story of the evening and there was nothing between it and the unwelcome bed.

I can remember the bare wooden stairway in my uncle's house, and the turn to the left above the landing, and the rafters and the slanting roof over my bed, and the squares of moonlight on the floor, and the white cold world of snow outside, seen through the curtainless window. I can remember the howling of the wind and the quaking of the house on stormy nights, and how snug and cozy one felt, under the blankets, listening; and how the powdery snow used to sift in, around the sashes, and lie in little ridges on the floor and make the place look chilly in the morning and curb the wild desire to get up—in case there was any. I can remember how very dark that room was, in the dark of the moon, and how packed it was with ghostly stillness when one woke up by accident away in the night, and forgotten sins came flocking out of the secret chambers of the memory and wanted a hearing; and how ill chosen the time seemed for this kind of business; and how dismal was the hoohooing of the owl and the wailing of the wolf, sent mourning by on the night wind.

I remember the raging of the rain on that roof, summer nights, and how pleasant it was to lie and listen to it, and enjoy the white splendor of the lightning and the majestic booming and crashing of the thunder. It was a very satisfactory room, and there was a lightning rod which was reachable from the window, an adorable and skittish thing to climb up and down, summer nights, when there were duties on hand of a sort to make privacy desirable.

I remember the 'coon and 'possum hunts, nights, with the negroes, and the long marches through the black gloom of the woods, and the excitement which fired everybody when the distant bay of an experienced dog announced that the game was treed; then the wild scramblings and stumblings through briers and bushes and over roots to get to the spot; then the lighting of a fire and the felling of the tree, the joyful frenzy of the dogs and the negroes, and the weird picture it all made in the red glare —I remember it all well, and the delight that everyone got out of it, except the 'coon.

I remember the pigeon seasons, when the birds would come in millions and cover the trees and by their weight break down the branches. They were clubbed to death with sticks; guns were not necessary and were not used. I remember the squirrel hunts, and prairie-chicken hunts, and wild-turkey hunts, and all that; and how we turned out, mornings, while it was still dark, to go on these expeditions, and how chilly and dismal it was, and how often I regretted that I was well enough to go. A toot on a tin horn brought twice as many dogs as were needed, and in their happiness they raced and scampered about, and knocked small people down, and made no end of unnecessary noise. At the word, they vanished away toward the woods, and we drifted silently after them in the melancholy gloom. But presently the gray dawn stole over the world, the birds piped up, then the sun rose and poured light and comfort all around, everything was fresh and dewy and fragrant, and life was a boon again. After three hours of tramping we arrived back wholesomely tired, overladen with game, very hungry, and just in time for breakfast.

Father Teaches Me to be Prompt

CLARENCE DAY

FATHER MADE a great point of our getting down to breakfast on time. I meant to be prompt, but it never occurred to me that I had better try to be early. My idea was to slide into the room at the last moment. Consequently, I often was late.

My brothers were often late, too, with the exception of George. He was the only thoroughly reliable son Father had. George got down so early, Father pointed out to me, that he even had time to practice a few minutes on the piano.

The reason George was so prompt was that he was in a hurry to see the sporting page before Father got hold of the newspaper, and the reason he then played the piano was to signal to the rest of us, as we dressed, which team had won yesterday's ball game. He had made up a code for this purpose, and we leaned over the banisters, pulling on our stockings and shoes, to hear him announce the results. I don't remember now what the titles were of the airs he selected, but the general idea was that if he played a gay, lively air it meant that the Giants had won, and when the strains of a dirge or lament floated up to us, it meant that Pop Anson had beaten them.

As Father didn't approve of professional baseball, we said nothing to him about this arrangement. He led his life and we led ours, under his nose. He took the newspaper away from George the moment he entered the room, and George said good morning to him and stepped innocently into the parlor. Then, while Father watched him through the broad doorway and looked over the political headlines, George banged out the baseball news for us on the piano. Father used to admonish him with a chuckle not to thump it so hard, but George felt that he had to. We were at the top of the house, and he wanted to be sure that we'd hear him even if we were brushing our teeth. George always was thorough about things. He not only thumped the piano as hard as he could but he hammered out the tune over and over besides, while Father impatiently muttered to himself, "*Trop de zèle.*"

Upstairs, there was usually some discussion as to what kind of news George was sending. He had not been allowed to learn popular tunes, which it would have been easy for us to recognize, and the few classic selections which were available in his little music book sounded pretty much alike at a distance. George rendered these with plenty of good will and muscle but not a great deal of sympathy. He regarded some of the rules of piano-playing as needlessly complicated.

The fact remained that he was the one boy who was always on time, and Father was so pleased by this that he bought a watch for him with "George Parmly Day, Always on Time" engraved on the back. He told me that as I was the eldest he had meant to give me a watch first, and he showed me the one he had bought for me. It was just like George's except that nothing had been engraved on it yet. Father explained that to his regret he would have to put it away for a while, until I had earned it by getting down early to breakfast.

Time went on, without much improvement on my part. Dawdling had got to be a habit with me. Sometimes my lateness was serious. One morning, when breakfast was half over and I had nothing on but a pair of long woolen drawers, Father called up from the front hall, napkin in hand, that he wouldn't stand it and that I was to come down that instant. When I shouted indignantly that I wasn't dressed yet, he said he didn't care. "Come down just as you are, confound it!" he roared. I was tempted to take him at his word, but thought there might be some catch in it and wouldn't, though I hurried, of course, all I could. Father ate his usual hearty breakfast in a stormy mood, and I ate my usual hearty breakfast in a guilty and nervous one. Come what might, we always ate heartily. I sometimes wished afterward that I hadn't, but it never seemed to hurt Father.

Mother told Father that if he would give me the watch, she was sure I'd do better. He said that he didn't believe it, and that that was a poor way to bring a boy up. To prove to him that he was wrong, Mother at last unlocked her jewel box and gave me a watch which had belonged to one of her elderly cousins. It was really too valuable a watch for a boy to wear, she said, and I must be very careful of it. I promised I would.

This watch, however, turned out to be painfully delicate. It was old, I was young. We were not exactly made for each other. It had a back and front of thin gold, and as Mother had had the former owner's monogram shaved off the front cover, that cover used to sink in the middle when pressed. Also, the lid fitted so closely that there was barely room for the glass crystal over the face. Such a very thin crystal had to be used that any pressure on the lid broke it.

I didn't press on the lid, naturally, after the first time this happened. I was careful, and everything would have gone well enough if other boys had been careful, too. It was not practicable, however, for me to make them be careful enough. When I had a fight, friendly or otherwise, I used to ask my opponent if he would be so kind as not to punch me on the left side of my stomach. He might or might not listen. If he and I were too excited and kept on long enough, the watch crystal broke anyway. There was never time to take off my watch first, and anyhow there was no place to put it. A watch that goes around the streets in a boy's pocket has to take life as it comes. This watch had never been designed for any such fate.

The first two crystals I broke Mother paid for, as Father disapproved of the whole business and would have nothing to do with it. Mother was always short of small change, however, and I hated to trouble her—and she hated to be troubled, too. "Oh, Clarence, dear! You haven't broken your watch again?" she cried when I opened the cover the second time, to show her the shattered fragments. She was so upset that I felt too guilty to tell her the next time it happened, and from then on I was reduced to the necessity of paying for the damage myself.

My pocket money never exceeded a dollar a month. Every new crystal cost twenty-five cents. It was a serious drain.

Wrestling and rolling around on the floor with Sam Willets, my watch quite forgotten, I would suddenly hear a faint tinkle and know that I was once more insolvent. I would pick out the broken glass and leave the watch with no crystal till I had twenty-five cents on hand, but these delays made me nervous. I knew that Mother wanted to feel sure I was taking good care of the watch, and that she might look at it any evening. As soon as I had the money, I hurried over to Sixth Avenue, where two old Germans kept a tiny watch shop, and left it there to be fixed. One of my most dismal memories is of that stuffy little shop's smell of sauerkraut, and how tall the glass counter then seemed, and the slowness of those two old Germans. When I got there late and they made me leave the watch overnight, I didn't have one easy moment until I got it back the next day. Again and again I argued with them that twenty-five cents was too much, especially for a regular customer, but they said it didn't pay them to do the work even for that, because those thin old-fashioned crystals were hard to get.

I gave up at last. I told Mother I didn't want to wear the watch any more.

Then I found, to my amazement, that this way out of my troubles was barred. The watch was an heirloom. And an heirloom was a thing that its recipient must value and cherish. No good Chinese, I read later on in life, fails to honor his ancestors; and no good boy, I was told in my youth, fails to appreciate heirlooms.

I left Mother's room in low spirits. That night, as I wound up my watch with its slender key, I envied George. Father had selected the right kind for George; he knew what a boy needed. It had a thick nickel case, it had an almost unbreakable crystal, and it endured daily life imperturbably, even when dropped in the bathtub.

It seemed to me that I was facing a pretty dark future. The curse of great possessions became a living thought to me, instead of a mere phrase. The demands that such possessions made on their owners for upkeep were merciless. For months I had had no money for marbles. I couldn't even afford a new top. In some way that I didn't fully understand I was yoked to a watch I now hated—a delicate thing that would always make trouble unless I learned to live gingerly.

Then I saw a way out. All this time I had kept on being late for breakfast at least once a week, out of habit, but it now occurred to me that if I could reform, perhaps Father might relent and give me that reliable nickel watch he had bought. I reformed. I occasionally weakened in my new resolution at first, but every time that crystal got broken I was spurred on to fresh efforts. When I had at length established a record for promptness that satisfied Father, he had my name engraved on the watch he had bought, and presented it to me. He was a little surprised at the intense pleasure I showed on this occasion, and as he watched me hopping around the room in delight he said "There, there" several times. "Don't be so excited, confound it," he added. "You'll knock over that vase."

Mother said she couldn't see why Father should give me a nickel watch when I had a gold one already, but he laughed and told her that "that old thing" was no kind of a watch for a boy. She reluctantly laid it away again to rest in her jewel box.

Her parting shot at Father was that anyhow she had been right; she had said all along that a watch was what I needed to teach me how to be prompt.

Twelve

BOOTH TARKINGTON

THIS BUSY globe which spawns us is as incapable of flattery and as intent upon its own affair, whatever that is, as a gyroscope; it keeps steadily whirling along its lawful track, and, thus far seeming to hold a right of way, spins doggedly on, with no perceptible diminution of speed to mark the most gigantic human events—it did not pause to pant and recuperate even when what seemed to Penrod its principal purpose was accomplished, and an enormous shadow, vanishing westward over its surface, marked the dawn of his twelfth birthday.

To be twelve is an attainment worth the struggle. A boy, just twelve, is like a Frenchman just elected to the Academy.

Distinction and honour wait upon him. Younger boys show deference to a person of twelve: his experience is guaranteed, his judgment, therefore, mellow; consequently, his influence is profound. Eleven is not quite satisfactory: it is only an approach. Eleven has the disadvantage of six, of nineteen, of forty-four, and of sixty-nine. But, like twelve, seven is an honourable age, and the ambition to attain it is laudable. People look forward to being seven. Similarly, twenty is worthy, and so, arbitrarily, is twenty-one; forty-five has great solidity; seventy is most commendable and each year thereafter an increasing honour. Thirteen is embarrassed by the beginnings of a new colthood; the child becomes a youth. But twelve is the very top of boyhood.

Dressing, that morning, Penrod felt that the world was changed from the world of yesterday. For one thing, he seemed to own more of it; this day was *his* day. And it was a day worth owning; the midsummer sunshine, pouring gold through his window, came from a cool sky, and a breeze moved pleasantly in his hair as he leaned from the sill to watch the tribe of clattering blackbirds take wing, following their leader from the trees in the yard to the day's work in the open country. The blackbirds were his, as the sunshine and the breeze were his, for they all belonged to the day which was his birthday and therefore most surely his. Pride suffused him: he was twelve!

His father and his mother and Margaret seemed to understand the difference between to-day and yesterday. They were at the table when he descended, and they gave him a greeting which of itself marked the milestone. Habitually, his entrance into a room where his elders sat brought a cloud of apprehension: they were prone to look up in pathetic expectancy, as if their thought was, "What new awfulness is he going to start *now*?" But this morning they laughed; his mother rose and kissed him twelve times, so did Margaret; and his father shouted, "Well, well! How's the *man*?"

Then his mother gave him a Bible and "The Vicar of Wakefield"; Margaret gave him a pair of silver-mounted hair brushes; and his father gave him a "Pocket Atlas" and a small compass.

"And now, Penrod," said his mother, after breakfast, "I'm going to take you out in the country to pay your birthday respects to Aunt Sarah Crim."

Aunt Sarah Crim, Penrod's great-aunt, was his oldest living relative. She was ninety, and when Mrs. Schofield and Penrod alighted from a carriage at her gate they found her digging with a spade in the garden.

"I'm glad you brought him," she said, desisting from labour. "Jinny's baking a cake I'm going to send for his birthday party. Bring him in the house. I've got something for him."

She led the way to her "sitting-room," which had a pleasant smell, unlike any other smell, and, opening the drawer of a shining old what-not, took therefrom a boy's "sling-shot," made of a forked stick, two strips of rubber and a bit of leather.

"This isn't for you," she said, placing it in Penrod's eager hand. "No. It would break all to pieces the first time you tried to shoot it, because it is thirty-five years old. I want to send it back to your father. I think it's time. You give it to him from me, and tell him I say I believe I can trust him with it now. I took it away from him thirty-five years ago, one day after he'd killed my best hen with it, accidentally, and broken a glass pitcher on the back porch with it—accidentally. He doesn't look like a person who's ever done things of that sort, and I suppose he's forgotten it so well that he believes he never *did*, but if you give it to him from me I think he'll remember. You look like him, Penrod. He was anything but a handsome boy."

After this final bit of reminiscence—probably designed to be repeated to Mr. Schofield—she disappeared in the direction of the kitchen, and returned with a pitcher of lemonade and a blue china dish sweetly freighted with flat ginger cookies of a composition that was her own secret. Then, having set this collation before her guests, she presented Penrod with a superb, intricate, and very modern machine of destructive capacities almost limitless. She called it a pocket-knife.

"I suppose you'll do something horrible with it," she said, composedly. "I hear you do that with everything, anyhow, so you might as well do it with this, and have more fun out of it. They tell me you're the Worst Boy in Town."

"Oh, Aunt Sarah!" Mrs. Schofield lifted a protesting hand.

"Nonsense!" said Mrs. Crim.

"But on his birthday!"

"That's the time to say it. Penrod, aren't you the Worst Boy in Town?"

Penrod, gazing fondly upon his knife and eating cookies rapidly, answered as a matter of course, and absently, "Yes'm."

"Certainly!" said Mrs. Crim. "Once you accept a thing about yourself as established and settled, it's all right. Nobody minds. Boys are just like people, really."

"No, no!" Mrs. Schofield cried, involuntarily.

"Yes, they are," returned Aunt Sarah. "Only they're not quite so awful, because they haven't learned to cover themselves all over with little pretences. When Penrod grows up he'll be just the same as he is now, except that whenever he does what he wants to do he'll tell himself and other people a little story about it to make his reason for doing it seem nice and pretty and noble."

"No, I won't!" said Penrod suddenly.

"There's one cookie left," observed Aunt Sarah. "Are you going to eat it?"

"Well," said her great-nephew, thoughtfully, "I guess I better."

"Why?" asked the old lady. "Why do you guess you'd 'better'?"

"Well," said Penrod, with a full mouth, "it might get all dried up if nobody took it, and get thrown out and wasted."

"You're beginning finely," Mrs. Crim remarked. "A year ago you'd have taken the cookie without the same sense of thrift."

"Ma'am?"

"Nothing. I see that you're twelve years old, that's all. There are more cookies, Penrod." She went away, returning with a fresh supply and the observation, "Of course, you'll be sick before the day's over; you might as well get a good start."

Mrs. Schofield looked thoughtful. "Aunt Sarah," she ventured, "don't you really think we improve as we get older?"

"Meaning," said the old lady, "that Penrod hasn't much chance to escape the penitentiary if he doesn't? Well, we do learn to restrain ourselves in some things; and there are people who really want someone else to take the last cookie, though they aren't very common. But it's all right, the world seems to be getting on." She gazed whimsically upon her great-nephew and added, "Of course, when you watch a boy and think about him, it doesn't seem to be getting on very fast."

Penrod moved uneasily in his chair; he was conscious that he was her topic but unable to make out whether or not her observations were complimentary; he inclined to think they were not. Mrs. Crim settled the question for him.

"I suppose Penrod is regarded as the neighbourhood curse?"

"Oh, no," cried Mrs. Schofield. "He——"

"I dare say the neighbours are right," continued the old lady placidly. "He's had to repeat the history of the race and go through all the stages from the primordial to barbarism. You don't expect boys to be civilized, do you?"

"Well, I——"

"You might as well expect eggs to crow. No; you've got to take boys as they are, and learn to know them as they are."

"Naturally, Aunt Sarah," said Mrs. Schofield, "I *know* Penrod."

Aunt Sarah laughed heartily. "Do you think his father knows him, too?"

"Of course, men are different," Mrs. Schofield returned, apologetically. "But a mother knows——"

"Penrod," said Aunt Sarah, solemnly, "does your father understand you?"

"Ma'am?"

"About as much as he'd understand Sitting Bull!" she laughed. "And I'll tell you what your mother thinks you are, Penrod. Her real belief is that you're a novice in a convent."

"Ma'am?"

"Aunt Sarah!"

"I know she thinks that, because whenever you don't behave like a novice she's disappointed in you. And your father really believes that you're a decorous, well-trained young business man, and whenever you don't live up to that standard you get on his nerves and he thinks you need a walloping. I'm sure a day very seldom passes without their both saying they don't know what on earth to do with you. Does whipping do you any good, Penrod?"

"Ma'am?"

"Go on and finish the lemonade; there's about a glassful left. Oh, take it, take it; and don't say why! Of *course* you're a little pig."

Penrod laughed gratefully, his eyes fixed upon her over the rim of his up-tilted glass.

"Fill yourself up uncomfortably," said the old lady. "You're twelve years old, and you ought to be happy—if you aren't anything else. It's taken over nineteen hundred years of Christianity and some hundreds of thousands of years of other things to produce you, and there you sit!"

"Ma'am?"

"It'll be your turn to struggle and muss things up for the betterment of posterity, soon enough," said Aunt Sarah Crim. "Drink your lemonade!"

The Great Mountains

JOHN STEINBECK

IN THE humming heat of a midsummer afternoon the little boy Jody listlessly looked about the ranch for something to do. He had been to the barn, had thrown rocks at the swallows' nests under the eaves until every one of the little mud houses broke open and dropped its lining of straw and dirty feathers. Then at the ranch house he baited a rat trap with stale cheese and set it where Doubletree Mutt, that good big dog, would get his nose snapped. Jody was not moved by an impulse of cruelty; he was bored with the long hot afternoon. Doubletree Mutt put his stupid nose in the trap and got it smacked, and shrieked with agony and limped away with blood on his nostrils. No matter where he was hurt, Mutt limped. It was just a way he had. Once when he was young, Mutt got caught in a coyote trap, and always after that he limped, even when he was scolded.

When Mutt yelped, Jody's mother called from inside the house, "Jody! Stop torturing that dog and find something to do."

Jody felt mean then, so he threw a rock at Mutt. Then he took his sling-shot from the porch and walked up toward the brush line to try to kill a bird. It was a good slingshot, with store-bought rubbers, but while Jody had often shot at birds, he had never hit one. He walked up through the vegetable patch, kicking his bare toes into the dust. And on the way he found the perfect slingshot stone, round and slightly flattened and heavy enough to carry through the air. He fitted it into the leather pouch of his weapon and proceeded to the brush line. His eyes narrowed, his mouth worked strenuously; for the first time that afternoon he was intent. In the shade of the sagebrush the little birds were working, scratching in the leaves, flying restlessly a few feet and scratching again. Jody pulled back the rubbers of the sling and advanced cautiously. One little thrush paused and looked at him and crouched, ready to fly. Jody sidled nearer, moving one foot slowly after the other. When he was twenty feet away, he carefully raised the sling and aimed. The stone whizzed; the thrush started up and flew right into it. And down the little bird went with a broken head. Jody ran to it and picked it up.

"Well, I got you," he said.

The bird looked much smaller dead than it had alive. Jody felt a little mean pain in his stomach, so he took out his pocket-knife and cut off the bird's head. Then he disemboweled it, and took off its wings; and finally he threw all the pieces into the brush. He didn't care about the bird, or its life, but he knew what older people would say if they had seen him kill it; he was ashamed because of their potential opinion. He decided to forget the whole thing as quickly as he could, and never to mention it.

The hills were dry at this season, and the wild grass was golden, but where the spring-pipe filled the round tub and the tub spilled over, there lay a stretch of fine green grass, deep and sweet and moist. Jody drank from the mossy tub and washed the bird's blood from his hands in cold water. Then he lay on his back in the grass and looked up at the dumpling summer clouds. By closing one eye and destroying perspective he brought them down within reach so that he could put up his fingers and stroke them. He helped the gentle wind push them down the sky; it seemed to him that they went faster for his help. One fat white cloud he helped clear to the mountain rims and pressed it firmly over, out of sight. Jody wondered what it was seeing, then. He sat up the better to look at the great mountains where they went piling back, growing darker and more savage until they finished with one jagged ridge, high up against the west. Curious secret mountains; he thought of the little he knew about them.

"What's on the other side?" he asked his father once.

"More mountains, I guess. Why?"

"And on the other side of them?"

"More mountains. Why?"

"More mountains on and on?"

"Well, no. At last you come to the ocean."

"But what's in the mountains?"

"Just cliffs and brush and rocks and dryness."

"Were you ever there?"

"No."

"Has anybody ever been there?"

"A few people, I guess. It's dangerous, with cliffs and things. Why, I've read there's more unexplored country in the mountains of Monterey County than any place in the United States." His father seemed proud that this should be so.

"And at last the ocean?"

"At last the ocean."

"But," the boy insisted, "but in between? No one knows?"

"Oh, a few people do, I guess. But there's nothing there to get. And not much water. Just rocks and cliffs and greasewood. Why?"

"It would be good to go."

"What for? There's nothing there."

Jody knew something was there, something very wonderful because it wasn't known, something secret and mysterious. He could feel within himself that this was so. He said to his mother, "Do you know what's in the big mountains?"

She looked at him and then back at the ferocious range, and she said, "Only the bear, I guess."

"What bear?"

"Why the one that went over the mountain to see what he could see."

Jody questioned Billy Buck, the ranch hand, about the possibility of ancient cities lost in the mountains, but Billy agreed with Jody's father.

"It ain't likely," Billy said. "There'd be nothing to eat unless a kind of people that can eat rocks live there."

That was all the information Jody ever got, and it made the mountains dear to him, and terrible. He thought often of the miles of ridge after ridge until at last there was the sea. When the peaks were pink in the morning they invited him among them: and when the sun had gone over the edge in the evening and the mountains were a purple-like despair, then Jody was afraid of them; then they were so impersonal and aloof that their very imperturbability was a threat.

Now he turned his head toward the mountains of the east, the Gabilans, and they were jolly mountains, with hill ranches in their creases, and with pine trees growing on the crests. People lived there, and battles had been fought against the Mexicans on the slopes. He looked back for an instant at the Great Ones and shivered a little at the contrast. The foothill cup of the home ranch below him was sunny and safe. The house gleamed with white light and the barn was brown and warm. The red cows on the farther hill ate their way slowly toward the north. Even the dark cypress tree by the bunkhouse was usual and safe. The chickens scratched about in the dust of the farmyard with quick waltzing steps.

Then a moving figure caught Jody's eye. A man walked slowly over the brow of the hill, on the road from Salinas, and he was headed toward the house. Jody stood up and moved down toward the house too, for if someone was coming, he wanted to be there to see. By the time the boy had got to the house the walking man was only halfway down the road, a lean man, very straight in the shoulders. Jody could tell he was old only because his heels struck the ground with hard jerks. As he approached nearer, Jody saw that he was dressed in blue jeans and in a coat of the same material. He wore clodhopper shoes and an old flat-brimmed Stetson hat. Over his shoulder he carried a gunny sack, lumpy and full. In a few moments he had trudged close enough so that his face could be seen. And his face was as dark as dried beef. A mustache, blue-white against the dark skin, hovered over his mouth, and his hair was white, too, where it showed at his neck. The skin of his face had shrunk back against the skull until it defined bone, not flesh, and made the nose and chin seem sharp and fragile. The eyes were large and deep and dark, with eyelids stretched tightly over them. Irises and pupils were one, and very black, but the eyeballs were brown. There were no wrinkles in the face at all. This old man wore a blue denim coat buttoned to the throat with brass buttons, as all men do who wear no shirts. Out of the sleeves came strong bony wrists and hands gnarled and knotted and hard as peach branches. The nails were flat and blunt and shiny.

The old man drew close to the gate and swung down his sack when he confronted Jody. His lips fluttered a little and a soft impersonal voice came from between them.

"Do you live here?"

Jody was embarrassed. He turned and looked at the house, and he turned back and looked toward the barn where his father and Billy Buck were. "Yes," he said, when no help came from either direction.

"I have come back," the old man said. "I am Gitano, and I have come back."

Jody could not take all this responsibility. He turned abruptly, and ran into the house for help, and the screen door banged after him. His mother was in the kitchen poking out the clogged holes of a colander with a hairpin, and biting her lower lip with concentration.

"It's an old man," Jody cried excitedly. "It's an old *paisano* man, and he says he's come back."

His mother put down the colander and stuck the hairpin behind the sink board. "What's the matter now?" she asked patiently.

"It's an old man outside. Come on out."

"Well, what does he want?" She untied the strings of her apron and smoothed her hair with her fingers.

"I don't know. He came walking."

His mother smoothed down her dress and went out, and Jody followed her. Gitano had not moved.

"Yes?" Mrs. Tiflin asked.

Gitano took off his old black hat and held it with both hands in front of him. He repeated, "I am Gitano, and I have come back."

"Come back? Back where?"

Gitano's whole straight body leaned forward a little. His right hand described the circle of the hills, the sloping fields and the mountains, and ended at his hat again. "Back to the rancho. I was born here, and my father, too."

"Here?" she demanded. "This isn't an old place."

"No, there," he said, pointing to the western ridge. "On the other side there, in a house that is gone."

At last she understood. "The old 'dobe that's washed almost away, you mean?"

"Yes, *señora*. When the rancho broke up they put no more lime on the 'dobe, and the rains washed it down."

Jody's mother was silent for a little, and curious homesick thoughts ran through her mind, but quickly she cleared them out. "And what do you want here now, Gitano?"

"I will stay here," he said quietly, "until I die."

"But we don't need an extra man here."

"I can not work hard any more, *señora*. I can milk a cow, feed chickens, cut a little wood; no more. I will stay here." He indicated the sack on the ground beside him. "Here are my things."

She turned to Jody. "Run down to the barn and call your father."

Jody dashed away, and he returned with Carl Tiflin and Billy Buck behind him. The old man was standing as he had been, but he was resting now. His whole body had sagged into a timeless repose.

"What is it?" Carl Tiflin asked. "What's Jody so excited about?"

Mrs. Tiflin motioned to the old man. "He wants to stay here. He wants to do a little work and stay here."

"Well, we can't have him. We don't need any more men. He's too old. Billy does everything we need."

They had been talking over him as though he did not exist, and now, suddenly, they both hesitated and looked at Gitano and were embarrassed.

He cleared his throat. "I am too old to work. I come back where I was born."

"You weren't born here," Carl said sharply.

"No. In the 'dobe house over the hill. It was all one rancho before you came."

"In the mud house that's all melted down?"

"Yes. I and my father. I will stay here now on the rancho."

"I tell you you won't stay," Carl said angrily. "I don't need an old man. This isn't a big ranch. I can't afford food and doctor bills for an old man. You must have relatives and friends. Go to them. It is like begging to come to strangers."

"I was born here," Gitano said patiently and inflexibly.

Carl Tiflin didn't like to be cruel, but he felt he must. "You can eat here tonight," he said. "You can sleep in the little room of the old bunkhouse. We'll give you your breakfast in the morning, and then you'll have to go along. Go to your friends. Don't come to die with strangers."

Gitano put on his black hat and stooped for the sack. "Here are my things," he said.

Carl turned away. "Come on, Billy, we'll finish down at the barn. Jody, show him the little room in the bunkhouse."

He and Billy turned back toward the barn. Mrs. Tiflin went into the house, saying over her shoulder, "I'll send some blankets down."

Gitano looked questioningly at Jody. "I'll show you where it is," Jody said.

There was a cot with a shuck mattress, an apple box holding a tin lantern, and a backless rocking-chair in the little room of the bunkhouse. Gitano laid his sack carefully on the floor and sat down on the bed. Jody stood shyly in the room, hesitating to go. At last he said,

"Did you come out of the big mountains?"

Gitano shook his head slowly. "No, I worked down the Salinas Valley."

The afternoon thought would not let Jody go. "Did you ever go into the big mountains back there?"

The old dark eyes grew fixed, and their light turned inward on the years that were living in Gitano's head. "Once—when I was a little boy. I went with my father."

"Way back, clear into the mountains?"

"Yes."

"What was there?" Jody cried. "Did you see any people or any houses?"

"No."

"Well, what was there?"

Gitano's eyes remained inward. A little wrinkled strain came between his brows.

"What did you see in there?" Jody repeated.

"I don't know," Gitano said. "I don't remember."

"Was it terrible and dry?"

"I don't remember."

In his excitement, Jody had lost his shyness. "Don't you remember anything about it?"

Gitano's mouth opened for a word, and remained open while his brain sought the word. "I think it was quiet—I think it was nice."

Gitano's eyes seemed to have found something back in the years, for they grew soft and a little smile seemed to come and go in them.

"Didn't you ever go back in the mountains again?" Jody insisted.

"No."

"Didn't you ever want to?"

But now Gitano's face became impatient. "No," he said in a tone that told Jody he didn't want to talk about it any more. The boy was held by a curious fascination. He didn't want to go away from Gitano. His shyness returned.

"Would you like to come down to the barn and see the stock?" he asked.

Gitano stood up and put on his hat and prepared to follow.

It was almost evening now. They stood near the watering trough while the horses sauntered in from the hillsides for an evening drink. Gitano rested his big twisted hands on the top rail of the fence. Five horses came down and drank, and then stood about, nibbling at the dirt or rubbing their sides against the polished wood of the fence. Long after they had finished drinking an old horse appeared over the brow of the hill and came painfully down. It had long yellow teeth; its hooves were flat and sharp as spades, and its ribs and hip-bones jutted out under its skin. It hobbled up to the trough and drank water with a loud sucking noise.

"That's old Easter," Jody explained. "That's the first horse my father ever had. He's thirty years old." He looked up into Gitano's old eyes for some response.

"No good any more," Gitano said.

Jody's father and Billy Buck came out of the barn and walked over.

"Too old to work," Gitano repeated. "Just eats and pretty soon dies."

Carl Tiflin caught the last words. He hated his brutality toward old Gitano, and so he became brutal again.

"It's a shame not to shoot Easter," he said. "It'd save him a lot of pains and rheumatism." He looked secretly at Gitano, to see whether he noticed the parallel, but the big bony hands did not move, nor did the dark eyes turn from the horse. "Old things ought to be put out of their misery," Jody's father went on. "One shot, a big noise, one big pain in the head maybe, and that's all. That's better than stiffness and sore teeth."

Billy Buck broke in. "They got a right to rest after they worked all of their life. Maybe they like to just walk around."

Carl had been looking steadily at the skinny horse. "You can't imagine now what Easter used to look like," he said softly. "High neck, deep chest, fine barrel. He could jump a five-bar gate in stride. I won a flat race on him when I was fifteen years old. I could of got two hundred dollars for him any time. You wouldn't think how pretty he was." He checked himself, for he hated softness. "But he ought to be shot now," he said.

"He's got a right to rest," Billy Buck insisted.

Jody's father had a humorous thought. He turned to Gitano. "If ham and eggs grew on a side-hill I'd turn you out to pasture too," he said. "But I can't afford to pasture you in my kitchen."

He laughed to Billy Buck about it as they went on toward the house. "Be a good thing for all of us if ham and eggs grew on the side-hills."

Jody knew how his father was probing for a place to hurt in Gitano. He had been probed often. His father knew every place in the boy where a word would fester.

"He's only talking," Jody said. "He didn't mean it about shooting Easter. He likes Easter. That was the first horse he ever owned."

The sun sank behind the high mountains as they stood there, and the ranch was hushed. Gitano seemed to be more at home in the evening. He made a curious sharp sound with his lips and stretched one of his hands over the fence. Old Easter moved stiffly to him, and Gitano rubbed the lean neck under the mane.

"You like him?" Jody asked softly.

"Yes—but he's no damn good."

The triangle sounded at the ranch house. "That's supper," Jody cried. "Come on up to supper."

As they walked up toward the house Jody noticed again that Gitano's body was as straight as that of a young man. Only by a jerkiness in his movements and by the scuffling of his heels could it be seen that he was old.

The turkeys were flying heavily into the lower branches of the cypress tree by the bunkhouse. A fat sleek ranch cat walked across the road carrying a rat so large that its tail dragged on the ground. The quail on the side-hills were still sounding the clear water call.

Jody and Gitano came to the back steps and Mrs. Tiflin looked out through the screen door at them.

"Come running, Jody. Come in to supper, Gitano."

Carl and Billy Buck had started to eat at the long oilcloth-covered table. Jody slipped into his chair without moving it, but Gitano stood holding his hat until Carl looked up and said, "Sit down, sit down. You might as well get your belly full before you go on." Carl was afraid he might relent and let the old man stay, and so he continued to remind himself that this couldn't be.

Gitano laid his hat on the floor and diffidently sat down. He wouldn't reach for food. Carl had to pass it to him. "Here, fill yourself up." Gitano ate very slowly, cutting tiny pieces of meat and arranging little pats of mashed potato on his plate.

The situation would not stop worrying Carl Tiflin. "Haven't you got any relatives in this part of the country?" he asked.

Gitano answered with some pride. "My brother-in-law is in Monterey. I have cousins there, too."

"Well, you can go and live there, then."

"I was born here," Gitano said in gentle rebuke.

Jody's mother came in from the kitchen, carrying a large bowl of tapioca pudding.

Carl chuckled to her, "Did I tell you what I said to him? I said if ham and eggs grew on the side-hills I'd put him out to pasture, like old Easter."

Gitano stared unmoved at his plate.

"It's too bad he can't stay," said Mrs. Tiflin.

"Now don't you start anything," Carl said crossly.

When they had finished eating, Carl and Billy Buck and Jody went into the living-room to sit for a while, but Gitano, without a word of farewell or thanks, walked through the kitchen and out the back door. Jody sat and secretly watched his father. He knew how mean his father felt.

"This country's full of these old *paisanos*," Carl said to Billy Buck.

"They're damn good men," Billy defended them. "They can work older than white men. I saw one of them a hundred and five years old, and he could still ride a horse. You don't see any white men as old as Gitano walking twenty or thirty miles."

"Oh, they're tough, all right," Carl agreed. "Say, are you standing up for him too? Listen, Billy," he explained, "I'm having a hard enough time keeping this ranch out of the Bank of Italy without taking on anybody else to feed. You know that, Billy."

"Sure, I know," said Billy. "If you was rich, it'd be different."

"That's right, and it isn't like he didn't have relatives to go to. A brother-in-law and cousins right in Monterey. Why should I worry about him?"

Jody sat quietly listening, and he seemed to hear Gitano's gentle voice and its unanswerable, "But I was born here." Gitano was mysterious like the mountains. There were ranges back as far as you could see, but behind the last range piled up against the sky there was a great unknown country. And Gitano was an old man, until you got to the dull dark eyes. And in behind them was some unknown thing. He didn't ever say enough to let you guess what was inside, under the eyes. Jody felt himself irresistibly drawn toward the bunkhouse. He slipped from his chair while his father was talking and he went out the door without making a sound.

The night was very dark and far-off noises carried in clearly. The hamebells of a wood team sounded from way over the hill on the county road. Jody picked his way across the dark yard. He could see a light through the window of the little room of the bunkhouse. Because the night was secret he walked quietly up to the window and peered in. Gitano sat in the rocking-chair and his back was toward the window. His right arm moved slowly back and forth in front of him. Jody pushed the door open and walked in. Gitano jerked upright and, seizing a piece of deerskin, he tried to throw it over the thing in his lap, but the skin slipped away. Jody stood overwhelmed by the thing in Gitano's hand, a lean and lovely rapier with a golden basket hilt. The blade was like a thin ray of dark light. The hilt was pierced and intricately carved.

"What is it?" Jody demanded.

Gitano only looked at him with resentful eyes, and he picked up the fallen deerskin and firmly wrapped the beautiful blade in it.

Jody put out his hand. "Can't I see it?"

Gitano's eyes smoldered angrily and he shook his head.

"Where'd you get it? Where'd it come from?"

Now Gitano regarded him profoundly, as though he pondered. "I got it from my father."

"Well, where'd he get it?"

Gitano looked down at the long deerskin parcel in his hand. "I don' know?"

"Didn't he ever tell you?"

"No."

"What do you do with it?"

Gitano looked slightly surprised. "Nothing. I just keep it."

"Can't I see it again?"

The old man slowly unwrapped the shining blade and let the lamplight slip along it for a moment. Then he wrapped it up again. "You go now. I want to go to bed." He blew out the lamp almost before Jody had closed the door.

As he went back toward the house, Jody knew one thing more sharply than he had ever known anything. He must never tell anyone about the rapier. It would be a dreadful thing to tell anyone about it, for it would destroy some fragile structure of truth. It was a truth that might be shattered by division.

On the way across the dark yard Jody passed Billy Buck. "They're wondering where you are," Billy said.

Jody slipped into the living-room, and his father turned to him. "Where have you been?"

"I just went out to see if I caught any rats in my new trap."

"It's time you went to bed," his father said.

Jody was first at the breakfast table in the morning. Then his father came in, and last, Billy Buck. Mrs. Tiflin looked in from the kitchen.

"Where's the old man, Billy?" she asked.

"I guess he's out walking," Billy said. "I looked in his room and he wasn't there."

"Maybe he started early to Monterey," said Carl. "It's a long walk."

"No," Billy explained. "His sack is in the little room."

After breakfast Jody walked down to the bunkhouse. Flies were flashing about in the sunshine. The ranch seemed especially quiet this morning. When he was sure no one was watching him, Jody went into the little room, and looked into Gitano's sack. An extra pair of long cotton underwear was there, an extra pair of jeans and three pairs of worn socks. Nothing else was in the sack. A sharp loneliness fell on Jody. He walked slowly back toward the house. His father stood on the porch talking to Mrs. Tiflin.

"I guess old Easter's dead at last," he said. "I didn't see him come down to water with the other horses."

In the middle of the morning Jess Taylor from the ridge ranch rode down.

"You didn't sell that old gray crowbait of yours, did you, Carl?"

"No, of course not. Why?"

"Well," Jess said, "I was out this morning early, and I saw a funny thing. I saw an old man on an old horse, no saddle, only a piece of rope for a bridle. He wasn't on the road at all. He was cutting right up straight through the brush. I think he had a gun. At least I saw something shine in his hand."

"That's old Gitano," Carl Tiflin said. "I'll see if any of my guns are missing." He stepped into the house for a second. "Nope, all here. Which way was he heading, Jess?"

"Well, that's the funny thing. He was heading straight back into the mountains."

Carl laughed. "They never get too old to steal," he said. "I guess he just stole old Easter."

"Want to go after him, Carl?"

"Hell no, just save me burying that horse. I wonder where he got the gun. I wonder what he wants back there."

Jody walked up through the vegetable patch, toward the brush line. He looked searchingly at the towering mountains—ridge after ridge after ridge until at last there was the ocean. For a moment he thought he could see a black speck crawling up the farthest ridge. Jody thought of the rapier and of Gitano. And he thought of the great mountains. A longing caressed him, and it was so sharp that he wanted to cry to get it out of his breast. He lay down in the green grass near the round tub at the brush line. He covered his eyes with his crossed arms and lay there a long time, and he was full of a nameless sorrow.

A Vast Aerial World

THOMAS WOLFE

PENT IN his dark soul, Eugene sat brooding on a fire-lit book, a stranger in a noisy inn. The gates of his life were closing him in from their knowledge, a vast aerial world of phantasy was erecting its fuming and insubstantial fabric. He steeped his soul in streaming imagery, rifling the book-shelves for pictures and finding there such treasures as *With Stanley in Africa,* rich in the mystery of the jungle, alive with combat, black battle, the hurled spear, vast snake-rooted forests, thatched villages, gold and ivory; or Stoddard's *Lectures,* on whose slick heavy pages were stamped the most-visited scenes of Europe and Asia; a Book of Wonder, with enchanting drawings of all the marvels of the age—Santos Dumont in his balloon, liquid air poured from a kettle, all the navies of the earth lifted two feet from the water by an ounce of radium (Sir William Crookes), the building of the Eiffel Tower, the Flatiron Building, the stick-steered automobile, the submarine. After the earthquake in San Francisco there was a book describing it, its cheap green cover lurid with crumbling towers, shaken spires, toppling many-storied houses plunging into the splitting flame-jawed earth. And there was another called *Palaces of Sin,* or *The Devil in Society,* purporting to be the work of a pious millionaire, who had drained his vast fortune in exposing the painted sores that blemish the spotless-seeming hide of great position, and there were enticing pictures showing the author walking in a silk hat down a street full of magnificent palaces of sin.

Out of this strange jumbled gallery of pictures the pieced-out world was expanding under the brooding power of his imagination: the lost dark angels of the Doré "Milton" swooped into cavernous Hell beyond this upper earth of soaring or toppling spires, machine wonder, maced and mailed romance. And, as he thought of his future liberation into this epic world, where all the color of life blazed brightest far away from home, his heart flooded his face with lakes of blood.

He had heard already the ringing of remote church bells over a country-side on Sunday night; had listened to the earth steeped in the brooding symphony of dark, and the million-noted little night things; and he had heard thus the far retreating wail of a whistle in a distant valley, and faint thunder on the rails; and he felt the infinite depth and width of the golden world in the brief seductions of a thousand multiplex and mixed mysterious odors and sensations, weaving, with a blinding interplay and aural explosions, one into the other.

He remembered yet the East India Tea House at the Fair, the sandalwood, the turbans, and the robes, the cool interior and the smell of India tea; and he had felt now the nostalgic thrill of dew-wet mornings in Spring, the cherry scent, the cool clarion earth, the wet loaminess of the garden, the pungent breakfast smells and the floating snow of blossoms. He knew the inchoate sharp excitement of hot dandelions in young Spring grass at noon; the smell of cellars, cobwebs, and built-on secret earth; in July, of watermelons bedded in sweet hay, inside a farmer's covered wagon; of cantaloupe and crated peaches; and the scent of orange rind, bitter-sweet, before a fire of coals. He knew the good male smell of his father's sitting room; of the smooth worn leather sofa, with the gaping horse-hair rent; of the blistered varnished wood upon the hearth; of the heated calf-skin bindings; of the flat moist plug of apple tobacco, stuck with a red flag; of wood-smoke and burnt leaves in October; of the brown tired Autumn earth; of honey-suckle at night; of warm nasturtiums; of a clean ruddy farmer who comes weekly with printed butter, eggs and milk; of fat limp underdone bacon and of coffee; of a bakery-oven in the wind; of large deep-hued stringbeans smoking-hot and seasoned well with salt and butter; of a room of old pine boards in which books and carpets have been stored, long closed; of Concord grapes in their long white baskets.

Yes, and the exciting smell of chalk and varnished desks; the smell of heavy bread-sandwiches of cold fried meat and butter; the smell of new leather in a saddler's shop, or of a warm leather chair; of honey and of unground coffee; of barrelled sweet pickles and cheese and all the fragrant compost of the grocer's; the smell of stored apples in the cellar, and of orchard-apple smells, of pressed-cider pulp; of pears ripening on a sunny shelf, and of ripe cherries stewing with sugar on hot stoves before preserving; the smell of whittled wood, of all young lumber, of sawdust and shavings; of peaches stuck with cloves and pickled in brandy; of pinesap, and green pine-needles; of a horse's pared hoof; of chestnuts roasting, of bowls of nuts and raisins; of hot cracklin, and of young roast pork; of butter and cinnamon melting on hot candied yams.

Yes, and of the rank slow river, and of tomatoes rotten on the vine; the smell of rain-wet plums and boiling quinces; of rotten lily-pads; and of foul weeds rotting in green marsh scum; and the exquisite smell of the South, clean but funky, like a big woman; of soaking trees and the earth after heavy rain.

Yes, and the smell of hot daisy-fields in the morning; of melted puddling-iron in a foundry; the winter smell of horse-warm stables and smoking dung; of old oak and walnut; and the butcher's smell of meat, of strong slaughtered lamb, plump gouty liver, ground pasty sausages, and red beef; and of brown sugar melted with slivered bitter chocolate; and of crushed mint leaves, and of a wet lilac bush; of magnolia beneath the heavy moon, of dogwood and laurel; of an old caked pipe and Bourbon rye, aged in kegs of charred oak; the sharp smell of tobacco; of carbolic and nitric acids; the coarse true smell of a dog; of old imprisoned books; and the cool fern-smell near springs; of vanilla in cake-dough; and of cloven ponderous cheeses.

Yes, and of a hardware store, but mostly the good smell of nails; of the developing chemicals in a photographer's dark-room; and the young-life smell of paint and turpentine; of buckwheat batter and black sorghum; and of a negro and his horse, together; of boiling fudge; the brine smell of pickling vats; and the lush undergrowth smell of southern hills; of a slimy oyster-can, of chilled gutted fish; of a hot kitchen negress; of kerosene and linoleum; of sarsaparilla and guavas; and of ripe autumn persimmons; and the smell of the wind and the rain; and of the acrid thunder; of cold starlight, and the brittle-bladed frozen grass; of fog and the misted winter sun; of seed-time, bloom, and mellow dropping harvest.

And now, whetted intemperately by what he had felt, he began, at school, in that fecund romance, the geography, to breathe the mixed odors of the earth, sensing in every squat keg piled on a pier-head a treasure of golden rum, rich port, fat Burgundy; smelling the jungle growth of the tropics, the heavy odor of plantations, the salt-fish smell of harbors, voyaging in the vast, enchanting, but unperplexing world.

Now the innumerable archipelago had been threaded, and he stood, firm-planted, upon the unknown but waiting continent.

He learned to read almost at once, printing the shapes of words immediately with his strong visual memory; but it was weeks later before he learned to write, or even to copy, words. The ragged spume and wrack of fantasy and the lost world still floated from time to time through his clear schoolday morning brain, and although he followed accurately all the other instruction of his teacher, he was walled in his ancient unknowing world when they made letters. The children made their sprawling alphabets below a line of models, but all he accomplished was a line of jagged wavering spear-points on his sheet, which he repeated endlessly and rapturously, unable to see or understand the difference.

"I have learned to write," he thought.

Then, one day, Max Isaacs looked suddenly, from his exercise, on Eugene's sheet, and saw the jagged line.

"That ain't writin'," said he.

And clubbing his pencil in his warted grimy hand, he scrawled a copy of the exercise across the page.

The line of life, that beautiful developing structure of language that he saw flowing from his comrade's pencil, cut the knot in him that all instruction failed to do, and instantly he seized the pencil, and wrote the words in letters fairer and finer than his friend's. And he turned, with a cry in his throat, to the next page, and copied it without hesitation, and the next, the next. They looked at each other a moment with that clear wonder by which children accept miracles, and they never spoke of it again.

"That's writin' now," said Max. But they kept the mystery caged between them.

Eugene thought of this event later; always he could feel the opening gates in him, the plunge of the tide, the escape; but it happened like this one day at once. Still midget-near the live pelt of the earth, he saw many things that he kept in fearful secret, knowing that revelation would be punished with ridicule. One Saturday in Spring, he stopped with Max Isaacs above a deep pit in Central Avenue where city workmen were patching a broken water-main. The clay walls of their pit were much higher than their heads; behind their huddled backs there was a wide fissure, a window in the earth which opened on some dark subterranean passage. And as the boys looked, they gripped each other suddenly, for past the fissure slid the flat head of an enormous serpent; passed, and was followed by a scaled body as thick as a man's: the monster slid endlessly on into the deep earth and vanished behind the working and unwitting men. Shaken with fear they went away, they talked about it then and later in hushed voices, but they never revealed it.

He fell now easily into the School-Ritual; he choked his breakfast with his brothers every morning, gulped scalding coffee, and rushed off at the ominous warning of the final bell, clutching a hot paper-bag of food, already spattered hungrily with grease blots. He pounded along after his brothers, his heart hammering in his throat with excitement and, as he raced into the hollow at the foot of the Central Avenue hill, grew weak with nervousness, as he heard the bell ringing itself to sleep, jerking the slatting rope about in its dying echoes.

Ben, grinning evilly and scowling, would thrust his hand against the small of his back and rush him screaming, but unable to resist the plunging force behind, up the hill.

In a gasping voice he would sing the morning song, coming in pantingly on the last round of a song the quartered class took up at intervals:

"—Merrily, merrily, merrily, merrily,
Life is but a dream."

Or, in the frosty Autumn mornings:

"Waken, lords and ladies gay,
On the mountain dawns the day."

Or the Contest of the West Wind and the South Wind. Or the Miller's Song:

"I envy no man, no, not I,
And no one envies me."

He read quickly and easily; he spelled accurately. He did well with figures. But he hated the drawing lesson, although the boxes of crayons and paints delighted him. Sometimes the class would go into the woods, returning with specimens of flowers and leaves—the bitten flaming red of the maple, the brown pine comb, the brown oak leaf. These they would paint; or in Spring a spray of cherry-blossom, a tulip. He sat reverently before the authority of the plump woman who first taught him: he was terrified lest he do anything common or mean in her eyes.

The class squirmed: the little boys invented tortures or scrawled obscenities to the little girls. And the wilder and more indolent seized every chance of leaving the room, thus: "Teacher, may I be excused?" And they would go out into the lavatory, sniggering and dawdling about restlessly.

He could never say it, because it would reveal to her the shame of nature.

Once, deathly sick, but locked in silence and dumb nausea, he had vomited finally upon his cupped hands.

He feared and hated the recess periods, trembled before the brawling confusion of the mob and the playground, but his pride forbade that he skulk within, or secrete himself away from them. Eliza had allowed his hair to grow long; she wound it around her finger every morning into fat Fauntleroy curls: the agony and humiliation it caused him was horrible, but she was unable or unwilling to understand it, and mouth-pursingly thoughtful and stubborn to all solicitation to cut it. She had the garnered curls of Ben, Grover, and Luke stored in tiny boxes: she wept sometimes when she saw Eugene's, they were the symbol of his babyhood to her, and her sad heart, so keen in marking departures, refused to surrender them. Even when his thick locks had become the luxuriant colony of Harry Tarkinton's lice, she would not cut them: she held his squirming body between her knees twice a day and ploughed his scalp with a fine-toothed comb.

As he made to her his trembling passionate entreaties, she would smile with an affectation of patronizing humor, make a bantering humming noise in her throat, and say: "Why, say—you can't grow up yet. You're my baby." Suddenly baffled before the yielding inflexibility of her nature, which could be driven to action only after incessant and maddening prods, Eugene, screaming-mad with helpless fury, would understand the cause of Gant's frenzy.

At school, he was a desperate and hunted little animal. The herd, infallible in its banded instinct, knew at once that a stranger had been thrust into it, and it was merciless at the hunt. As the lunch-time recess came, Eugene, clutching his big grease-stained bag, would rush for the playground pursued by the yelping pack. The leaders, two or three big louts of advanced age and deficient mentality, pressed closely about him, calling out suppliantly, "You know me, 'Gene. You know me"; and still racing for the far end, he would open his bag and hurl to them one of his big sandwiches, which stayed them for a moment, as they fell upon its possessor and clawed it to fragments, but they were upon him in a moment more with the same yelping insistence, hunting him down into a corner of the fence, and pressing in with outstretched paws and wild entreaty. He would give them what he had, sometimes with a momentary gust of fury, tearing away from a greedy hand half of a sandwich and devouring it. When they saw he had no more to give, they went away.

The great fantasy of Christmas still kept him devout. Gant was his unwearied comrade; night after night in the late Autumn and early Winter, he would scrawl petitions to Santa Claus, listing interminably the gifts he wanted most, and transmitting each, with perfect trust, to the roaring chimney. As the flame took the paper from his hand and blew its charred ghost away with a howl, Gant would rush with him to the window, point to the stormy northern sky, and say: "There it goes! Do you see it?"

He saw it. He saw his prayer, winged with the stanch convoying winds, borne northward to the rimed quaint gables of Toyland, into frozen merry Elf land: heard the tiny silver anvil-tones, the deep-lunged laughter of the little men, the stabled cries of aerial reindeer. Gant saw and heard them, too.

He was liberally dowered with bright-painted gimcracks upon Christmas Day; and in his heart he hated those who advocated "useful" gifts. Gant bought him wagons, sleds, drums, horns—best of all, a small fireman's ladder wagon: it was the wonder, and finally the curse, of the neighborhood. During his unoccupied hours, he lived for months in the cellar with Harry Tarkinton and Max Isaacs: they strung the ladders on wires above the wagon, so that, at a touch, they would fall in accurate stacks. They would pretend to doze in their quarters, as firemen do, would leap to action suddenly, as one of them imitated the warning bell: "Clang-a-lang-a-lang." Then, quite beyond reason, Harry and Max yoked in a plunging team, Eugene in the driver's seat, they would leap out through the narrow door, gallop perilously to a neighbor's house, throw up ladders, open windows, effect entries, extinguish imaginary flames, and return oblivious to the shrieking indictment of the housewife.

For months they lived completely in this fantasy, modelling their actions on those of the town's firemen, and on Jannadeau, who was the assistant chief, child-proud over it: they had seen him, at the sound of the alarm, rush like a madman from his window in Gant's shop, leaving the spattered fragments of a watch upon his desk, and arriving at his duty just as the great wagon hurtled at full speed into the Square. The firemen loved to stage the most daring exhibitions before the gaping citizenry; helmeted magnificently, they hung from the wagons in gymnastic postures, one man holding another over rushing space, while number two caught in mid-air the diving heavy body of the Swiss, who deliberately risked his neck as he leaped for the rail. Thus, for one rapturous moment they stood poised triangularly over rocking speed: the spine of the town was chilled ecstatically.

And when the bells broke through the drowning winds at night, his demon rushed into his heart, bursting all cords that held him to the earth, promising him isolation and dominance over sea and land, inhabitation of the dark: he looked down on the whirling disk of dark forest and field, sloped over singing pines upon a huddled town, and carried its grated guarded fires against its own roofs, swerving and pouncing with his haltered storm upon their doomed and flaming walls, howling with thin laughter above their stricken heads and, fiend-voiced, calling down the bullet wind.

Or, holding in fief the storm and the dark and all the black powers of wizardry, to gaze, ghoul-visaged, through a storm-lashed window-pane, briefly planting unutterable horror in grouped and sheltered life; or, no more than a man, but holding, in your more than mortal heart, demoniac ecstasy, to crouch against a lonely storm-swept house, to gaze obliquely through the streaming glass upon a woman, or your enemy, and while still exulting in your victorious dark all-seeing isolation, to feel a touch upon your shoulder, and to look, haunter-haunted, pursuer-pursued, into the green corrupted hell-face of malignant death.

Death in the Fifth Grade

MARJORIE MARKS

As soon as the first bell rang and the children took their places, Miss Steineck knew that they knew. Hardly any of the twenty-six looked at her as they said good morning.

The grade mother had called her up the evening before. "I've telephoned all the Fifth Grade mothers," she said. "They promised to keep it from the children tonight. We all agreed it would be better if you told them. You've had so much experience and besides, they're so fond of you. You'll do it, won't you?"

Miss Steineck had said she would. Although she dreaded the ordeal, she recognized its assignment as a tribute. It was true, the children were fond of her, even though sometimes they succumbed to the temptation of drawing caricatures of her with exaggerated pince-nez and a very long neck, which they labeled "Miss Stiffneck." Still, she nearly always got results with children, because she respected them and was honest with them. That's what she told the mothers when they asked her. But of course in every class there were some she defied anyone to reach. "The doltish dregs," she called them in her thoughts. But even these, she felt, were not unkindly disposed toward her.

She had lain awake most of the night trying to think of a way to tell them. "You know, Norma has been very ill," she planned to begin and would go on to say that if she had lived she probably would never have been able to move about or have fun again. They would understand that it was better for her to die than to be an invalid all her life. They must have felt, as she did herself, that Norma was someone apart, especially marked by joy and grace.

All—even the doltish dregs—sat still as stones while, with exaggerated deliberateness, she checked the roll book. She was conscious, meanwhile, of Rosanne, synthetic sorrow on her fat face, dabbing at her eyes. Undoubtedly it was she who had told the others.

Quietly Miss Steineck shut the roll book and squared her shoulders. "You know, Norma has been very, very ill," she said. That was the way she had planned. So far, so good. The bell rang. There was a little flutter through the class. Evie and Carolyn exchanged nervous glances over Norma's empty desk. Miss Steineck wished now that she'd had the janitor take it away before school. She had debated during the night the wisdom of this and decided it would be less of a shock this way. But now, her sensibilities heightened by this situation, its emptiness accused her.

Jane, the youngest in the class, who hadn't much sense, piped up from the front row, "We all know she's dead, Miss Steineck, you don't need to tell us."

A snicker which was half a shudder passed through the group.

Rosanne mouthed sanctimoniously, lifting her eyes for approval from the teacher, "You mustn't say she's dead. She's gone to heaven to be an angel. That's what my mother says. It's true, isn't it, Miss Steineck?"

The eyes of all twenty-six implored her for an answer. But how could she answer? She had left heaven behind with high button boots for Sunday and a dime inside her glove for the collection. How could she tell them what she really believed—that Norma, the vivid, the golden-haired, the pink-cheeked, the winner of races, the gayest, the fairest in games, was not an angel fluttering about the Throne but simply had ceased to exist?

She couldn't say that, but she had to say something. Without knowing she was beginning, she said, "When I was a little girl, we lived on a farm and I had a pet crow. He was my special friend. Whenever I whistled outside the house he would come and I would feed him. He'd sit on my hand or my shoulder and when I took a walk he'd flutter along beside me. His name was Timmie and I loved him very much."

She looked at the class. No one had moved except Rosanne, hitching about in her seat. Apparently she thought an animal story too babyish for the fifth grade. Miss Steineck looked at the others. They were waiting quietly, their eyes still unwaveringly upon her. She went on. "I used to talk to Timmie and he would answer me. He was my friend for a whole summer. When winter came I put crumbs out for him and left a window open in the tool-shed for him to fly in when it got too cold outside. But one morning, the coldest I could remember, when I whistled for Timmie he didn't come. I whistled and whistled till my lips were sore. Finally at the end of the day, my father found him. He was lying at the edge of the woods, frozen stiff. His wings were spread out as though he'd tried to come when I called him. How I cried. For days and days. I felt I'd never be happy again. I knew I'd never forget the way poor Timmie looked with his body all stiff and his eyes not seeing. I asked the minister on Sunday if there was a heaven for crows and he laughed and said he'd never heard of one. Then I felt worse than ever."

She paused and cleared her throat. Nobody said anything. For an instant she felt panicky, seeing how scornful Rosanne was looking, but she went on. "Well, for weeks and weeks I cried myself to sleep. My parents tried their best to comfort me. My father promised me a parrot, but I wouldn't let him buy one. Nothing could take Timmie's place. I kept seeing him in my dreams, all stiff and dead in the snow.

"But one night," said Miss Steineck slowly, because she was seeing it as she spoke, "a wonderful thing happened. I dreamed that it was spring and all the leaves and flowers were budding. I stood in the freshly planted garden and called Timmie. He came right away. How his feathers glistened! I'd never seen him look so handsome. He perched on my hand and cocked his head and spoke to me in his hoarse voice. 'Why don't you remember me this way?' he asked and began to fly, around and around, up and up, in wonderful patterns and circles that got bigger and bigger until finally he flew so high that I couldn't see him any more. Then I woke up. But I wasn't sad now, because even though Timmie was dead, I was happy remembering him and the way he flapped his wings and how beautiful he was."

She surveyed the class. Nobody was looking at her. Nobody registered any reaction at all except Rosanne, who muttered sullenly, "I don't see what a silly crow has to do with Norma." There was a sort of assenting growl from a few of the doltish dregs, and then silence.

"I've made a fool of myself," Miss Steineck thought desperately. "I've failed them when they needed me most. Whatever possessed me to make such an exhibition of myself?" She felt the tight clamp of her pince-nez on her nose, as she always did when she was upset, and she knew that a red spot had appeared at the base of her neck. Rosanne was staring at it. She felt old and ugly and futile—Miss Stiffneck to the life.

The bell rang. "First period, Art," said Miss Steineck in her crispest voice. There was the rattle and bang of desk lids going up, the clatter of pencils and crayons being set out. The children were making as much noise as they could, to annoy her. Well, she deserved it. She had been an idiot.

Like a drill sergeant, she snapped out her orders. "Quiet, please. We'll have free work." (She felt capable of nothing else.) "Draw anything you like, using crayons. Plan to finish by the end of the period and sign your name in full in the lower right hand corner with the date." They set to work, while she made ferocious corrections with red pencil on the arithmetic homework papers.

As she marked automatically her C's and X's, she imagined the evening ahead of her, punctuated by indignant telephone calls from the mothers. Tomorrow, she knew, she would be summoned to the principal's office and be raked over the coals as she had been once before at the time of the great mumblety-peg war. "I can't imagine what you thought you were accomplishing by such unorthodox procedure," he would say sadly. "If it should happen again—" This was the threat of dismissal. Well, she certainly wouldn't blame him for wanting to replace her with a younger person, one with sensible ideas.

The bell rang. "Quietly, less noise, *please*," she sang out with a knife edge in her voice. Noisily they piled their drawings on her desk, noisily collected their equipment for history with Mr. MacVey in Room 103. Like hoodlums they scrambled for first place in line, brushing ruthlessly against a crayon landscape by Norma, which fluttered to the floor and was trampled on.

Carolyn said admiringly to Evie, who'd made first place, "Now that Norma isn't here, I guess you'll have a chance to win some races."

"I guess so," Evie giggled and Rosanne cried out in shocked tones, "It's awful to say such a thing." For once Miss Steineck agreed with her.

"The class may go now," she said, quietly icy. "Less noise, *please*." Regardless, they trampled up the corridor, William as usual making a noise like a muted saxophone.

Miss Steineck, smoothing Norma's crumpled drawing against her breast, gazed after them. "Cold-blooded little brats," she raged to herself. "I should know by this time it never pays to open your heart to them. I'll never be fooled into it again, never." She laughed aloud in self-derision as she picked up the drawings to transfer them to the side table.

Then her eyes were arrested by the topmost. It was a picture of a child with bright yellow hair, skipping rope in a field of brilliant flowers. Norma had loved to skip rope. Breathing hard, she turned to the next. This was Evie's. Evie did not draw well, but it was easy to see what she meant to convey—a group of children racing and far in advance of the others one girl with bright pink cheeks and yellow hair streaming behind her.

Miss Steineck sat down and went over the pictures one by one, skipping quickly over the products of the doltish dregs (the usual pretty-ladies by the girls and airplanes and boats by the boys). Her heart hammered at her thin ribs. For all the other pictures were about Norma; each was different; each about Norma doing one of the things she liked best—climbing, swimming, throwing a ball. There were two exceptions. One was William's—he was the best in drawing. He had done a large crow with wings spread wide against a vivid sunset sky. The other was Rosanne's—a minutely elaborate wreath of purple flowers, with Sinserest Simpathy printed beneath in neat black letters. Miss Steineck took pleasure in marking it with a large red X. Sp.

She laid the papers on the table. And then, to her own amazement, she found herself with her head on her desk, crying as she had not cried since Timmie died.

Ring Out, Wild Bells

WOLCOTT GIBBS

WHEN I finally got around to seeing Max Reinhardt's cinema version of "A Midsummer-Night's Dream," and saw a child called Mickey Rooney playing Puck, I remembered suddenly that long ago I had taken the same part.

Our production was given on the open-air stage at the Riverdale Country School, shortly before the war. The scenery was only the natural scenery of that suburban dell, and the cast was exclusively male, ranging in age from eleven to perhaps seventeen. While we had thus preserved the pure, Elizabethan note of the original, it must be admitted that our version had its drawbacks. The costumes were probably the worst things we had to bear, and even Penrod, tragically arrayed as Launcelot in his sister's stockings and his father's drawers, might have been embarrassed for us. Like Penrod, we were costumed by our parents, and like the Schofields, they seemed on the whole a little weak historically. Half of the ladies were inclined to favor the Elizabethan, and they had constructed rather bunchy ruffs and farthingales for their offspring; others, who had read as far as the stage directions and learned that the action took place in an Athenian wood, had produced something vaguely Athenian, usually beginning with a sheet. Only the fairies had a certain uniformity. For some reason their parents had all decided on cheesecloth, with here and there a little ill-advised trimming with tinsel.

My own costume was mysterious, but spectacular. As nearly as I have ever been able to figure things out, my mother found her inspiration for it in a Maxfield Parrish picture of a court jester. Beginning at the top, there was a cap with three stuffed horns; then, for the main part, a pair of tights that covered me to my wrists and ankles; and finally slippers with stuffed toes that curled up at the ends. The whole thing was made out of silk in alternate green and red stripes, and (unquestionably my poor mother's most demented stroke) it was covered from head to foot with a thousand tiny bells. Because all our costumes were obviously perishable, we never wore them in rehearsal, and naturally nobody knew that I was invested with these peculiar sound effects until I made my entrance at the beginning of the second act.

Our director was a man who had strong opinions about how Shakespeare should be played, and Puck was one of his favorite characters. It was his theory that Puck, being "the incarnation of mischief," never ought to be still a minute, so I had been coached to bound onto the stage, and once there to dance up and down, cocking my head and waving my arms.

"I want you to be a little whirlwind," this man said.

Even as I prepared to bound onto the stage, I had my own misgivings about those dangerously abundant gestures, and their probable effect on my bells. It was too late, however, to invent another technique for playing Puck, even if there had been room for anything but horror in my mind. I bounded onto the stage.

The effect, in its way, must have been superb. With every leap I rang like a thousand children's sleighs, my melodies foretelling God knows what worlds of merriment to the enchanted spectators. It was even worse when I came to the middle of the stage and went into my gestures. The other ringing had been loud but sporadic. This was persistent, varying only slightly in volume and pitch with the vehemence of my gestures. To a blind man, it must have sounded as though I had recklessly decided to accompany myself on a xylophone. A maturer actor would probably have made up his mind that an emergency existed, and abandoned his gestures as impracticable under the circumstances. I was thirteen, and incapable of innovations. I had been told by responsible authorities that gestures went with this part, and I continued to make them. I also continued to ring—a silvery music, festive and horrible.

If the bells were hard on my nerves, they were even worse for the rest of the cast, who were totally unprepared for my new interpretation. Puck's first remark is addressed to one of the fairies, and it is mercifully brief.

I said, "How now, spirit! Whither wander you?"

This unhappy child, already embarrassed by a public appearance in cheesecloth and tinsel, was also burdened with an opening speech of sixteen lines in verse. He began bravely:

> "*Over hill, over dale,*
> *Through brush, through brier,*
> *Over park, over pale,*
> *Through flood, through fire . . .*"

At the word "fire," my instructions were to bring my hands up from the ground in a long, wavery sweep, intended to represent fire. The bells pealed. To my startled ears, it sounded more as if they exploded. The fairy stopped in his lines and looked at me sharply. The jingling, however, had diminished; it was no more than as if a faint wind stirred my bells, and he went on:

"I do wander everywhere,
Swifter than the moone's sphere . . ."

Here again I had another cue, for a sort of swoop and dip indicating the swiftness of the moone's sphere. Again the bells rang out, and again the performance stopped in its tracks. The fairy was clearly troubled by these interruptions. He had, however, a child's strange acceptance of the inscrutable, and was even able to regard my bells as a last-minute adult addition to the program, nerve-racking but not to be questioned. I'm sure it was only this that got him through that first speech.

My turn, when it came, was even worse. By this time the audience had succumbed to a helpless gaiety. Every time my bells rang, laughter swept the spectators, and this mounted and mingled with the bells until everything else was practically inaudible. I began my speech, another long one, and full of incomprehensible references to Titania's changeling.

"Louder!" said somebody in the wings. "You'll have to talk louder."

It was the director, and he seemed to be in a dangerous state.

"And for heaven's sake, stop that jingling!" he said.

I talked louder, and I tried to stop the jingling, but it was no use. By the time I got to the end of my speech, I was shouting and so was the audience. It appeared that I had very little control over the bells, which continued to jingle in spite of my passionate efforts to keep them quiet.

All this had a very bad effect on the fairy, who by this time had many symptoms of a complete nervous collapse. However, he began his next speech:

"Either I mistake your shape and making quite,
Or else you are that shrewd and knavish sprite
Called Robin Goodfellow: are you not he
That . . ."

At this point I forgot that the rules had been changed and I was supposed to leave out the gestures. There was a furious jingling, and the fairy gulped.

"Are you not he that, that . . ."

He looked miserably at the wings, and the director supplied the next line, but the tumult was too much for him. The unhappy child simply shook his head.

"Say anything!" shouted the director desperately. "Anything at all!"

The fairy only shut his eyes and shuddered.

"All right!" shouted the director. "All right, Puck. *You* begin *your* next speech."

By some miracle, I actually did remember my next lines, and had opened my mouth to begin on them when suddenly the fairy spoke. His voice was a high, thin monotone, and there seemed to be madness in it, but it was perfectly clear.

"Four score and seven years ago," he began, "our fathers brought forth on this continent a new nation, conceived . . ."

He said it right through to the end, and it was certainly the most successful speech ever made on that stage, and probably one of most successful speeches ever made on any stage. I don't remember, if I ever knew, how the rest of us ever picked up the dull, normal thread of the play after that extraordinary performance, but we must have, because I know it went on. I only remember that in the next intermission the director cut off my bells with his penknife, and after that things quieted down and got dull.

A Mother in Mannville

MARJORIE KINNAN RAWLINGS

THE ORPHANAGE is high in the Carolina mountains. Sometimes in winter the snowdrifts are so deep that the institution is cut off from the village below, from all the world. Fog hides the mountain peaks, the snow swirls down the valleys, and a wind blows so bitterly that the orphanage boys who take the milk twice daily to the baby cottage reach the door with fingers stiff in an agony of numbness.

"Or when we carry trays from the cookhouse for the ones that are sick," Jerry said, "we get our faces frostbit, because we can't put our hands over them. I have gloves," he added. "Some of the boys don't have any."

He liked the late spring, he said. The rhododendron was in bloom, a carpet of color, across the mountainsides, soft as the May winds that stirred the hemlocks. He called it laurel.

"It's pretty when the laurel blooms," he said. "Some of it's pink and some of it's white."

I was there in the autumn. I wanted quiet, isolation, to do some troublesome writing. I wanted mountain air to blow out the malaria from too long a time in the subtropics. I was homesick, too, for the flaming of maples in October, and for corn shocks and pumpkins and black-walnut trees and the lift of hills. I found them all, living in a cabin that belonged to the orphanage, half a mile beyond the orphanage farm. When I took the cabin, I asked for a boy or man to come and chop wood for the fireplace. The first few days were warm, I found what wood I needed about the cabin, no one came, and I forgot the order.

I looked up from my typewriter one late afternoon, a little startled. A boy stood at the door, and my pointer dog, my companion, was at his side and had not barked to warn me. The boy was probably twelve years old, but undersized. He wore overalls and a torn shirt, and was barefooted.

He said, "I can chop some wood today."

I said, "But I have a boy coming from the orphanage."

"I'm the boy."

"You? But you're small."

"Size don't matter, chopping wood," he said. "Some of the big boys don't chop good. I've been chopping wood at the orphanage a long time."

I visualized mangled and inadequate branches for my fires. I was well into my work and not inclined to conversation. I was a little blunt.

"Very well. There's the ax. Go ahead and see what you can do."

I went back to work, closing the door. At first the sound of the boy dragging brush annoyed me. Then he began to chop. The blows were rhythmic and steady, and shortly I had forgotten him, the sound no more of an interruption than a consistent rain. I suppose an hour and a half passed, for when I stopped and stretched, and heard the boy's steps on the cabin stoop, the sun was dropping behind the farthest mountain, and the valleys were purple with something deeper than the asters.

The boy said, "I have to go to supper now. I can come again tomorrow evening."

I said, "I'll pay you now for what you've done," thinking I should probably have to insist on an older boy. "Ten cents an hour?"

"Anything is all right."

We went together back of the cabin. An astonishing amount of solid wood had been cut. There were cherry logs and heavy roots of rhododendron, and blocks from the waste pine and oak left from the building of the cabin.

"But you've done as much as a man," I said. "This is a splendid pile."

I looked at him, actually, for the first time. His hair was the color of the corn shocks and his eyes, very direct, were like the mountain sky when rain is pending—gray, with a shadowing of that miraculous blue. As I spoke, a light came over him, as though the setting sun had touched him with the same suffused glory with which it touched the mountains. I gave him a quarter.

"You may come tomorrow," I said, "and thank you very much."

He looked at me, and at the coin, and seemed to want to speak, but could not, and turned away.

"I'll split kindling tomorrow," he said over his thin ragged shoulder. "You'll need kindling and medium wood and logs and backlogs."

At daylight I was half wakened by the sound of chopping. Again it was so even in texture that I went back to sleep. When I left my bed in the cool morning, the boy had come and gone, and a stack of kindling was neat against the cabin wall. He came again after school in the afternoon and worked until time to return to the orphanage. His name was Jerry; he was twelve years old, and he had been at the orphanage since he was four. I could picture him at four, with the same grave gray-blue eyes and the same—independence? No, the word that comes to me is "integrity."

The word means something very special to me, and the quality for which I use it is a rare one. My father had it—there is another of whom I am almost sure—but almost no man of my acquaintance possesses it with the clarity, the purity, the simplicity of a mountain stream. But the boy Jerry had it. It is bedded on courage, but it is more than brave. It is honest, but it is more than honesty. The ax handle broke one day. Jerry said the woodshop at the orphanage would repair it. I brought money to pay for the job and he refused it.

"I'll pay for it," he said. "I broke it. I brought the ax down careless."

"But no one hits accurately every time," I told him. "The fault was in the wood of the handle. I'll see the man from whom I bought it."

It was only then that he would take the money. He was standing back of his own carelessness. He was a free-will agent and he chose to do careful work, and if he failed, he took the responsibility without subterfuge.

And he did for me the unnecessary thing, the gracious thing, that we find done only by the great of heart. Things no training can teach, for they are done on the instant, with no predicated experience. He found a cubby-hole beside the fireplace that I had not noticed. There, of his own accord, he put kindling and "medium" wood, so that I might always have dry fire material ready in case of sudden wet weather. A stone was loose in the rough walk to the cabin. He dug a deeper hole and steadied it, although he came, himself, by a short cut over the bank. I found that when I tried to return his thoughtfulness with such things as candy and apples, he was wordless. "Thank you" was, perhaps, an expression for which he had had no use, for his courtesy was instinctive. He only looked at the gift and at me, and a curtain lifted, so that I saw deep into the clear well of his eyes, and gratitude was there, and affection, soft over the firm granite of his character.

He made simple excuses to come and sit with me. I could no more have turned him away than if he had been physically hungry. I suggested once that the best time for us to visit was just before supper, when I left off my writing. After that, he waited always until my typewriter had been some time quiet. One day I worked until nearly dark. I went outside the cabin, having forgotten him. I saw him going up over the hill in the twilight toward the orphanage. When I sat down on my stoop, a place was warm from his body where he had been sitting.

He became intimate, of course, with my pointer, Pat. There is a strange communion between a boy and a dog. Perhaps they possess the same singleness of spirit, the same kind of wisdom. It is difficult to explain, but it exists. When I went across the state for a week end, I left the dog in Jerry's charge. I gave him the dog whistle and the key to the cabin, and left sufficient food. He was to come two or three times a day and let out the dog, and feed and exercise him. I should return Sunday night, and Jerry would take out the dog for the last time Sunday afternoon and then leave the key under an agreed hiding place.

My return was belated and fog filled the mountain passes so treacherously that I dared not drive at night. The fog held the next morning, and it was Monday noon before I reached the cabin. The dog had been fed and cared for that morning. Jerry came early in the afternoon, anxious.

"The superintendent said nobody would drive in the fog," he said. "I came just before bedtime last night and you hadn't come. So I brought Pat some of my breakfast this morning. I wouldn't have let anything happen to him."

"I was sure of that. I didn't worry."

"When I heard about the fog, I thought you'd know."

He was needed for work at the orphanage and he had to return at once. I gave him a dollar in payment, and he looked at it and went away. But that night he came in the darkness and knocked at the door.

"Come in, Jerry," I said, "if you're allowed to be away this late."

"I told maybe a story," he said. "I told them I thought you would want to see me."

"That's true," I assured him, and I saw his relief. "I want to hear about how you managed with the dog."

He sat by the fire with me, with no other light, and told me of their two days together. The dog lay close to him, and found a comfort there that I did not have for him. And it seemed to me that being with my dog, and caring for him, had brought the boy and me, too, together, so that he felt that he belonged to me as well as to the animal.

"He stayed right with me," he told me, "except when he ran in the laurel. He likes the laurel. I took him up over the hill and we both ran fast. There was a place where the grass was high and I lay down in it and hid. I could hear Pat hunting for me. He found my trail and he barked. When he found me, he acted crazy, and he ran around and around me, in circles."

We watched the flames.

"That's an apple log," he said. "It burns the prettiest of any wood."

We were very close.

He was suddenly impelled to speak of things he had not spoken of before, nor had I cared to ask him.

"You look a little bit like my mother," he said. "Especially in the dark, by the fire."

"But you were only four, Jerry, when you came here. You have remembered how she looked, all these years?"

"My mother lives in Mannville," he said.

For a moment, finding that he had a mother shocked me as greatly as anything in my life has ever done, and I did not know why it disturbed me. Then I understood my distress. I was filled with a passionate resentment that any woman should go away and leave her son. A fresh anger added itself. A son like this one—The orphanage was a wholesome place, the executives were kind, good people, the food was more than adequate, the boys were healthy, a ragged shirt was no hardship, nor the doing of clean labor. Granted, perhaps, that the boy felt no lack, what blood fed the bowels of a woman who did not yearn over this child's lean body that had come in parturition out of her own? At four he would have looked the same as now. Nothing, I thought, nothing in life could change those eyes. His quality must be apparent to an idiot, a fool. I burned with questions I could not ask. In any, I was afraid, there would be pain.

"Have you seen her, Jerry—lately?"

"I see her every summer. She sends for me."

I wanted to cry out, "Why are you not with her? How can she let you go away again?"

He said, "She comes up here from Mannville whenever she can. She doesn't have a job now."

His face shone in the firelight.

"She wanted to give me a puppy, but they can't let any one boy keep a puppy. You remember the suit I had on last Sunday?" He was plainly proud. "She sent me that for Christmas. The Christmas before that"—he drew a long breath, savoring the memory—"she sent me a pair of skates."

"Roller skates?"

My mind was busy, making pictures of her, trying to understand her. She had not, then, entirely deserted or forgotten him. But why, then—I thought, "I must not condemn her without knowing."

"Roller skates. I let the other boys use them. They're always borrowing them. But they're careful of them."

What circumstance other than poverty—

"I'm going to take the dollar you gave me for taking care of Pat," he said, "and buy her a pair of gloves."

I could only say, "That will be nice. Do you know her size?"

"I think it's 8½," he said.

He looked at my hands.

"Do you wear 8½?" he asked.

"No. I wear a smaller size, a 6."

"Oh! Then I guess her hands are bigger than yours."

I hated her. Poverty or no, there was other food than bread, and the soul could starve as quickly as the body. He was taking his dollar to buy gloves for her big stupid hands, and she lived away from him, in Mannville, and contented herself with sending him skates.

"She likes white gloves," he said. "Do you think I can get them for a dollar?"

"I think so," I said.

I decided that I should not leave the mountains without seeing her and knowing for myself why she had done this thing.

The human mind scatters its interests as though made of thistledown, and every wind stirs and moves it. I finished my work. It did not please me, and I gave my thoughts to another field. I should need some Mexican material.

I made arrangements to close my Florida place. Mexico immediately, and doing the writing there, if conditions were favorable. Then, Alaska with my brother. After that, heaven knew what or where.

I did not take time to go to Mannville to see Jerry's mother, nor even to talk with the orphanage officials about her. I was a trifle abstracted about the boy, because of my work and plans. And after my first fury at her—we did not speak of her again—his having a mother, any sort at all, not far away, in Mannville, relieved me of the ache I had had about him. He did not question the anomalous relation. He was not lonely. It was none of my concern.

He came every day and cut my wood and did small helpful favors and stayed to talk. The days had become cold, and often I let him come inside the cabin. He would lie on the floor in front of the fire, with one arm across the pointer, and they would both doze and wait quietly for me. Other days they ran with a common ecstasy through the laurel, and since the asters were now gone, he brought me back vermilion maple leaves, and chestnut boughs dripping with imperial yellow. I was ready to go.

I said to him, "You have been my good friend, Jerry. I shall often think of you and miss you. Pat will miss you too. I am leaving tomorrow."

He did not answer. When he went away, I remember that a new moon hung over the mountains, and I watched him go in silence up the hill. I expected him the next day, but he did not come. The details of packing my personal belongings, loading my car, arranging the bed over the seat, where the dog would ride, occupied me until late in the day. I closed the cabin and started the car, noticing that the sun was in the west and I should do well to be out of the mountains by nightfall. I stopped by the orphanage and left the cabin key and money for my light bill with Miss Clark.

"And will you call Jerry for me to say good-by to him?"

"I don't know where he is," she said. "I'm afraid he's not well. He didn't eat his dinner this noon. One of the other boys saw him going over the hill into the laurel. He was supposed to fire the boiler this afternoon. It's not like him; he's unusually reliable."

I was almost relieved, for I knew I should never see him again, and it would be easier not to say good-by to him.

I said, "I wanted to talk with you about his mother—why he's here—but I'm in more of a hurry than I expected to be. It's out of the question for me to see her now too. But here's some money I'd like to leave with you to buy things for him at Christmas and on his birthday. It will be better than for me to try to send him things. I could so easily duplicate—skates, for instance."

She blinked her honest spinster's eyes.

"There's not much use for skates here," she said.

Her stupidity annoyed me.

"What I mean," I said, "is that I don't want to duplicate things his mother sends him. I might have chosen skates if I didn't know she had already given them to him."

She stared at me.

"I don't understand," she said. "He has no mother. He has no skates."

Love Among the Ruins

BERTHA DAMON

CHILDREN FEEL what their elders forget, our touching kinship with animals. To me a chipmunk was a far more real personality than Great-Uncle Aaron, and the mousehole gnawed in the lower left corner of the door to down cellar a more delightful habitation for the mind to contemplate than the parsonage. In a kind of ecstasy I regarded a yellow wake of chickens streaming miraculously astern of everyday henhood; hung over nests of baby birds, though not much was to be seen but mouths; and scratched with adoring straw the warty backs of hoptoads, who seemed to me to have found out some secret of life I didn't know and to be bearing it with sad eyes and bitter grin.

The stories I wanted Grandma endlessly to tell me were all about animals—some squirrel who lived in a hollow tree, sat on a cushion of green velvet moss, washed his paws in an acorn washbowl of dewdrops. If moral content was afforded by the development that one day he disobeyed his grandma, got caught in a trap, made his escape, and resolved to be henceforth a perfect squirrel child—I liked that too. It seemed so like human life, as it ought to be anyhow.

But all this, though enthralling, was too outside me. I wanted not to look on, but to participate. I wanted not merely to behold through a windowpane of separateness, but to have something in my arms and in my heart, cared for by me, for me caring. More and more I came to feel that something was lacking. I was lonely. The inside curves of my arms ached because there was nothing to hold. I asked Grandma to please let me have a little pet. But Grandma did not approve.

She gave numerous reasons. A kitten, of course, would catch birds; chickens would get out and injure the flowers (though I wondered if a regiment of chickens could do in a year what Juno the cow could do and often did in half a day); a lamb would be noisy; and so on, one set of reasons against one sort of pet, another against another. If you had got yourself a zoology book and read off to Grandma the list of all possible animals from amoeba to zebra, there wouldn't have been an animal that would have stumped her for a reason against it as a possession even, let alone a pet.

So then I tried to think a doll might do. But Grandma didn't think even a doll was necessary. I pondered the advertisements in the magazines lent us sometimes by neighbors. Each glowing word I knew by heart, and for a long time words had to suffice. Then quite casually a visitor gave me a doll—an excessive doll. She was almost as big as I, with a pink-and-white wax face that cracked when cold and smudged when warm, blue glass eyes with "real" lashes, "real" hair, and when squeezed she would squawk. I named her Pansy, which in those days seemed to me the name fullest of velvet and lovely associations.

I found out right away she was no good. She looked so real, she thwarted my imagination. She wasn't real, so she thwarted my love. The imaginative need I satisfied by throwing Pansy under the sofa and adopting a smooth forked stick of white birch from the woodbox, which I could animate. And I tried to fill the need for affection by looking around for something alive—that would get by Grandma.

There didn't seem to be anything alive to be had. Then one happy day I found a little green snake. He tried his best to disappear into the grass he so much resembled, but I managed to catch him and hold him tight. He was slender, lustrous, and had a small bright eye with a remarkably unloving expression. I sought to win his gratitude and affection. I took my "jewel box"—which held two strings of beads, a silver ring, and a dried bronze beetle—emptied it gladly of these soulless treasures, and lined it with cotton and tiny ferns for the snake's home. I offered him bits of lump sugar, which he refused. Suspecting that he might be carnivorous, I offered him flies; the live ones got away, the dead ones spoiled. And always the green snake remained abstemious, and the cold ungrateful expression in his eye did not soften. Presently he became quite sluggish. I touched him anxiously to see if he had a fever or anything, and found to my distress that he felt quite cool. I held him a good long while over a candle flame to warm him; even that seemed to do no good. The next morning he was stiff. He was, indeed, dead. "The little port had seldom seen a costlier funeral" than the one I gave him. I buried him, jewel box and all, smothered with bridal wreath and forget-me-nots, in a shallow grave dug with a tablespoon. On the mounded grave I set up a headstone made from a tin box cover and inscribed in blue pencil, with an epitaph influenced by "the best that had been thought and said" in our North Stonefield cemetery:

Requiescat in pace
Mr. Emerald Coyle lies here
greatly lamented for his untimely
Demise
Memento mori

After this sorrow an itinerant tomcat lingered for a few days around the place. Again I thought love had come. To me he did not seem tough-looking. His dull molasses-colored coat was rather charming. His white cravat and stockings might have been better laundered, it is true, but I excused their condition on the ground that he probably had no mother to look out for him. His round head, thick neck, and heavy shoulders seemed to me indicative of heroic strength, futher attested by ancient scars —doubtless received in some earlier Sir Galahadlike encounters, some high competition in romance and "battles long ago." His tail had somehow got broken.

I called this old cat many lovely names—Kitty-bird was one. He liked that name best, I thought; there seemed to be an extra glitter in his eye as he listened and rolled the name purringly under his tongue. He was somewhat of a philosopher, Tom was; a cat has to be, as have all animals who deal with people. This Kitty-bird business may have suggested to Tom the unity of all experience, the One and the Many—he being the One and tasty little birds the Many. But even before Kitty-bird had attracted the unfavorable attention of Grandma he went away. He was yowling like everything one day, and Alice said: "O poor Kitty-bird, have you tried *everything*?" He turned back one chewed ear and lashed his tail, meditating the question: shortly after, he went away for good, as tomcats will.

Then I came to know an affection more reciprocal. Uncle William, taking pity on the extremities of my desire, gave me a beautiful noble old hen. She had, to be sure, reached her ovopause, but to me seemed unimpaired for petting purposes. I named her Lady Speckle. I taught her to flap up to my lifted hand for corn and even to perch, uncertainly in more ways than one, on my shoulder while I stalked proudly about. For weeks the mere thought of Lady Speckle made my heart warm and my life rich.

But one day when I came home from District School no Lady Speckle ran across her pen, clucking welcome. I looked through all the yard and the mowing lot and the spring lot, fearful that she might for the first time have broken the law of God and Grandma and left her pen. Silence through all the grass. I went into the house. Grandma spoke of certain matters, but not of hens. Aunt Martha spoke of nothing. I dared not ask the question. But oh, oh, when I went into the pantry for my bread and milk—there on a stoneware platter cold in death and browned in the oven lay the unmistakable remains (the term is more accurate than usual, for she was partly eaten) of what had been Lady Speckle.

Some critic with cool dispassionate logic may challenge the argument of my youthful despair. "An undistributed middle," he will say. But I knew better. The middle, and more than that, was unquestionably distributed. And I knew too that it was not the "fallacy of accident." It was all intentional.

The snake's death, the cat's infidelity, while grievous, were reasonably simple losses. This loss involved cannibalism on Grandma's part—no, it couldn't have been cannibalism, for Grandma was a vegetarian in whom was no variableness neither shadow of turning; it must have been thrift: guests had come . . . thrift one and the same with discipline had proved irresistible to Grandma, and the funeral baked meats had coldly furnished forth the festal table. This loss was more complicated: I had lost not only my congenial henly companion; I had lost a certain trustfulness toward Grandma. For some time I endured my lonely grief.

Finally a desperate plan occurred to me: perhaps if I hatched a chicken myself Grandma would let it stay. It would be so little to begin with, so harmless-looking. It would grow up slowly and perhaps Grandma would never realize when it reached reprehensible henhood. Secretly I selected a nice brown egg from those Uncle Aaron's hens supplied us, and brooded over the problem of my approaching maternity.

Night work would be easy. I could sleep on the egg, carefully, keeping awake pretty much. But daytimes? Although it was late May I privately returned to wearing my long flannel drawers. Inside one leg of these just above the stocking a nice warm pouch could be contrived, and there the egg would lie in steady body warmth. So each morning I carefully transferred the warm egg—my nights had not seemed lonely—from the bed to this peripatetic nest. All day I had to guard against jumping or any sudden movement; my style was cramped, but in my heart already I was cheered by faint imaginary peepings and the surety that after the appointed term I should forget all my sufferings for joy that a wee chick was born into the world.

Came a day, and it was the sixth of incubation, when I was sent to bring in from the woodpile some wood for the fireplace. With the measured step and slow of expectant maternity, I stalked into the sitting room with my four good sticks of maple, but as I stood on the very hearth one stick slipped. I sprang—and oh, what a miscarriage of all my happy hopes! As the—what shall I say?—eggnog dripped fatally down on the braided rug, Grandma was amazed; she even murmured some wild words of sending for Dr. Hale. "No, no, Grandma, it's too late—I mean—" And sobbing in the manner of many a luckless maiden before me, I was obliged to Tell All.

Grandma was quite overcome. For all Grandma was a grandma, the expression on her face turned unmistakably spinsterish. She perhaps felt that I had laid my hand on the sacred and taboo Art of Reproduction. Anyhow, the way Grandma took on, you would have thought my unborn egg was illegitimate and not a planned-for chicken. I was sent to bed, not at all for my health, but for punishment. "Nice girls do not do so," Grandma said.

Alice was mean to me, too. She never came upstairs that day till bedtime; then she opened my door and I thought she was going to give me some sympathy. But instead she just grinned and pointed out the west window in the direction of Uncle Aaron's henhouse and quoted "The rude forefathers of the omelette sleep"—from Gray's *Elegy* Grandma had made us learn.

A long, long time after this the puppy drama was enacted. Let me say right here that Uncles are of two sorts: those who are born Uncles, which is common; and those who become Uncles for the Kingdom of Heaven's sake, not so common. Uncle William wasn't our born Uncle; he was a friend, a grownup who did not seem on so alien a plane as other grownups. He imagined what feelings little girls might have, so we conferred on him the title of Uncle, having nothing else in our power to bestow.

Uncle William heard about that hen's end, maybe he suspected about that egg, and he next tried a Divine Experiment. He gave me, after a suitable period, a puppy—an actual living puppy! I suppose Uncle William hoped—all sorts of things. Puppies have many desirable qualities; they have been known to make their way in the most unexpected quarters; and it is neither Christian nor customary to eat them.

He was only a puppy, not a collie, not a spaniel. His mother, it seemed, must have had some off day. And here, at length, in a world of sin and no less sorrow was a puppy—soft and with a merry eye—to make amends. To me even his smell was engaging: his breath, an inexplicable whiff of garlic; the rest of him a delightful blend of leather, musk, and something charmingly like a mousetrap. There was no guile in him, nor any guilt; clearly he had had no part in the Original Fall. I named him Happy because he was and I was.

I can't talk much about this idyl of Happy and me. We had five months together in which he was the rapturous receiver of all the love I had to give; in which I was no longer an orphan, a leftover, but one with an important place in the cosmos: I was a worshiped divinity. My lyings-down were not lonely any more when he too lay down to guard; the circle that had always felt broken since Mama died seemed so much less so. My little walks were not solitary any more, but perfect with companionship—for that word may be applied to the scurrying whisk of a buoyant behind and the departing flaps of delighted fringed hind paws. Let's not talk long about his perfections and his ways. You have had a puppy and you know, or you haven't had a puppy and no one could ever make you know.

I said Happy had neither guile nor guilt. He had not. In all his character there was no least flaw: there was, however, a—well, a tendency. In pure innocence, carefree ebullience, canine *joie de vivre* Happy would sometimes, sometimes, chase birds, even the songbirds that Grandma was accustomed to attract around the back entry door by putting out crumbs and popcorn. There was not murder in Happy's heart, only glee, and the impulse of a thoroughgoing extravert to meet and, in spite of clumsy paws, to mingle gleefully. The birds, who must have been selfish introverts, didn't feel about Happy as he did about them. They whirred up and away with jittery twitters. Around Grandma's back entry door they got scarcer and scarcer. And one day in late March, there lay, on the faintly greening sodden grass beyond the flagstones a bluebird, dead.

The next afternoon—as usual on the way home from school I hurried for the last half mile. As usual I tiptoed up to the house, stole to the west window of the sitting room to look in and see Happy, ever aware of my stealthiest tread, nose pressed to the crack of the door, ridiculous illegitimate tail wagging. It was always the high moment of the day. That afternoon I could see no Happy there—only a sort of emptiness, or rather dog-lessness, which was far worse. Where could he be? Happy let nothing on earth interfere with his share in my homecoming. Sometimes, as is the touching lot of dogs, he was long kept waiting by me, never I for a moment by him. Caught in a stone wall after a woodchuck? Smashed in a skunk trap?—surmises not horrid enough. I tore in.

"Grandma, where is Happy? He—O Grandma?"

She looked up from the cotton lace she was knitting, a gift for a friend. Her hand shook a little as she laid it down.

"Bertha," she said, "I must tell you something and you must hear. You have been for a long while now a disobedient little girl. You have known very well it is the Rule you shall not have pets. Yet for a long time you have kept"—Grandma avoided his name—"this puppy. Because he had been given to you in good faith by your Uncle William, out of deference to his feelings I had to let you keep—the puppy, for a while anyway. It was not a good thing for you but I permitted it, weakly. But now he'd got to be nearly a grown dog, and it turned out he was a bad dog, vicious." (I squirmed in agony. This defamation of Happy was a sharp knife in my mind.) "He has taken life; he is—he was a murderer. And so" (Grandma's eyes were clear and direct, but her mouth trembled) "justice is justice," said Grandma, "and has to be done."

"Justice, Grandma? What do you mean! Not . . . ?"

"Happy has been taken away," said Grandma. "I got John Tuttle to take him away. You know well that whoever does wrong gets punished according to the wrong he has done. That is the Rule."

(O God of my fathers! Are you so cruel, imposing punishments, delighting in vengeance? The Old Testament says so over and over again, and Grandma and most of North Stonefield are full of the Old Testament from birth. Is there no New, no merciful Testament?)

"Where is he now? Where did you—did you—bury him, I mean?"

"It is not best you should know," said Grandma, resuming her knitting.

(That old cry, "Tell me where you have laid him!" To me not answered.)

"Anyway I shall find him in Heaven!" I screamed.

This was clearly a moment for establishing my orthodoxy.

"No," Grandma said, "no indeed. Do not add the sin of blasphemy. You forget the Book of Revelation says, 'Without are dogs and all uncleanness.' "

Maybe Grandma thought that text justified her a little more. It did me no good.

"Then me too," I said, purposely sinning in syntax as well as in Christian hope. "Me too—and so much for the New Testament! I hate the whole Bible, now, if you want to know. Sometimes I think the real God didn't have much to do with writing it—so there!"

I went out as fast as I could, stumbling a good deal, though the floor seemed way down below my feet, and I felt faint because it did not seem to be solid, but kept letting me sink. And then by some not realized means I was in the old orchard. I crumpled down at the foot of the Peck's Pleasant tree. My throat was stretched with a great ache that nearly split it. A hand seemed squeezing my heart. I could not cry. I spread myself face down on the earth, hard, desperately trying for some sense of support and comfort. But this pain that was filling me was not to be reached by comfort. It was unbearable, yet it must be borne.

But not by lying still. I got up; I walked round. All my refuges seemed to be dim, nonexistent. Even the brook was just nothing. "Happy! Happy!" No pad, pad of furry feet. "Happy!" Never again. He would have comforted me. Somewhere his cold loving nose was pressing to get to me. But this awful new wall of immateriality was in the way. He could never get through to me again, not so long as I lived and he did not.

I knew desperately that all my life I was going to be lonely. There seemed in the world no warm love that depended on me, upon which I could depend; only grownups who did not believe in touchings and foolish sweet words. Could love be given to any of these or love be had from them?

I sat down under the big maple that stood farthest from the gate. A little wind went through its branches and it made a sound of breathing; I looked at its widespread arms. It was the tree Grandpa had planted for my mother the day she was born. I looked at it a long while. It stood whispering and yet seemed deeply quiet. I went up to it and timidly touched it. Suddenly I put my arms hard around its big trunk and stood for a long time, my cheek pressed to its corrugated bark that hurt a little, but not so much as it felt good.

"I do love you, Tree," I said. "Oh, if it is possible, love me a little."

It was perhaps a week or so later that Grandma, seeing my preoccupation and wishing to fortify me, looked up from the book she was reading.

"Bertha," she said, "listen to these fine lines by Matthew Arnold in a poem called *Self-Dependence*." (It was just like Grandma and her sort to go offering you an intellectual solace when what you were perishing for was an emotional one.) Grandma read earnestly, emphasizing the words she thought taught the best lesson:

> *These demand not that the things without them*
> *Yield them love, amusement, sympathy.*
>
> . . . . .
>
> *For self-poised they live,*
>
> . . . . .
>
> *Bounded by themselves, and unregardful*
> *In what state God's other works may be.*

But I let the words pour over me—not meaning anything, not sinking in. My mind had seen Grandma coming with her alien ideas and had hastily made a shelter of words for itself wherein it could hide. Over this, like rain over a tent, Grandma's words poured, pattering and beating, but they could not reach me, could not drench me and make me cold. This was the secret word-shelter where I was hiding: "Tree, Tree, darling Tree, we love each other."

An Underground Episode

EDMUND WARE

THREE FIGURES leaned against the slanting rain—Alamo Laska, Nick Christopher, and the boy who had run away from home. They rested on their long-handled shovels and, as they gazed into the crater which by their brawn they had hollowed in the earth, the blue clay oozed back again, slowly devouring the fruits of their toil.

Laska, the nomad, thought of the wild geese winging southward to warm bayous. Nick's heart, under the bone and muscle of his great chest, swelled with sweet thoughts of his wife and child who lived in a foreign city across an ocean. The boy felt the sting of rain against his cheeks and dreamed of his mother who seemed lovely and far away.

It was Sunday. The regular deep-trench gang lounged in their warm boarding house and drank dago red, while out on the job the three men toiled alone. They breathed heavily, and the gray steam crawled upon their backs, for it was cold.

"Look at 'er filling in," growled Laska, "faster than a man could dig."

"Mud's get inna pipe," said Nick. "The Inspector make us tear him out if she fill any more."

Backed close to the edge of the crater stood a giant trench-digging machine. In the dusk it appeared as a crouched and shadowy animal—silent, gloomy, capable. But a broken piston had crippled its engines and they were swathed in tarpaulin.

A long gray mound stretched away from the crater opposite the machine. Buried thirty feet below the mound was the new-laid sewer pipe. From the bottom of the pit at the machine, the pipe ran a hundred yards horizontally under the surface, opening in a manhole. This hundred yards of new-laid pipe was the reason for the three men digging in the rain. They had dug eleven hours trying to uncover the open end of the pipe in order to seal it against the mud. But rain and ooze and storm had bested them. The bank had caved, and the mud had crawled into the mouth of the pipe, obstructing it.

"It's getting dark fast," said Laska, "an' we're licked."

"We can't do nothing more," said the boy.

Nick Christopher scraped the mud from his shovel. He looked up into the whirlpools of the sky. "In a year I go old country. I see my wife. I see my kid."

"Nick," said Laska, "go over to the shanty and get a couple of lanterns and telephone Stender. Tell him if he don't want the Inspector on our tail to get out here quick with a gang."

Nick stuck his shovel in the mud and moved away across the plain toward the shanty.

The cold had crept into the boy. It frightened him, and in the darkness his eyes sought Laska's face. "How could we clean out the pipe, even when the gang got down to it?"

"Maybe we could flush her out with a fire hose," said Laska.

"There's no water plug within a mile."

Laska said nothing. The boy waited for him to reply, but he didn't. Picking up his damp shirt, the boy pulled it on over his head. He did not tuck in the tails, and they flapped in the wind, slapping against him. He looked like a gaunt, serious bird, striving to leave the ground. He was bare-headed, and his yellow hair was matted and stringy with dampness. His face was thin, a little sunken, and fine drops of moisture clung to the fuzz on his cheeks. His lips were blue with cold. He was seventeen.

Laska stared into the pit. It was too dark to see bottom, but something in the black hole fascinated him. "If we could get a rope through the pipe we could drag sandbags through into the manhole. That would clean her out in good shape."

"How could we get a rope through?"

"I dunno. Stender'll know." Laska walked over to the digging machine and leaned against its towering side. The rain had turned to sleet. "It's cold," he said.

The boy followed Laska, and went close to him for warmth and friendship. "How *could* we get a rope through?"

Laska's shoulders lifted slowly. "You'll see. You'll see when Stender gets here. Say, it's freezing."

After a long time of waiting, a yellow light flamed into being in the shanty, and they heard the muffled scraping of boots on the board floor. The shanty door opened. A rectangle of light stood out sharply.

Swart figures crossed and re-crossed the lighted area, pouring out into the storm.

"Ho!" called Laska.

"Ho!" came the answer, galloping to them in the wind.

They heard the rasping of caked mud on dungarees, the clank of shovels, the voice of Stender, the foreman. Lanterns swung like yellow pendulums. Long-legged shadows reached and receded.

The diggers gathered about the rim of the pit, staring. Stender's face showed in the lantern light. His lips were wrinkled, as if constantly prepared for blasphemy. He was a tall, cursing conqueror. Orders shot from his throat, and noisily the men descended into the pit and began to dig. They drew huge, gasping breaths like mired beasts fighting for life.

The boy watched, his eyes bulging in the dark. Hitherto he had thought very briefly of sewers, regarding them as unlovely things. But Laska and Nick and Stender gave them splendor and importance. The deep-trench men were admirable monsters. They knew the clay, the feel and pattern of it, for it had long been heavy in their minds and muscles. They were big in three dimensions and their eyes were black and barbarous. When they ate it was with rough and tumble relish, and as their bellies fattened, they spoke tolerantly of enemies. They played lustily with a view to satiation. They worked stupendously. They were diggers in clay, transformed by lantern light into a race of giants.

Through the rain came Stender, his black slicker crackling. "They're down," he said. "Angelo just struck the pipe."

Laska grunted.

Stender blew his nose with his fingers, walked away and climbed down into the hole. They lost sight of him as he dropped over the rim. The sound of digging had ceased and two or three men on the surface rested on their shovels, the light from below gleaming in their flat faces. Laska and the boy knew that Stender was examining the pipe. They heard him swearing at what he had found.

After a moment he clambered up over the rim and held up a lantern. His cuddy, gripped firmly between his teeth, was upside down to keep out the wet.

"Someone's got to go through the pipe," he said, raising his voice. "There's fifty bucks for the man that'll go through the pipe into the manhole with a line tied to his foot. Fifty bucks!"

There was a moment of quiet. The men thought of the fifty dollars, and furtively measured themselves against the deed at hand. It seemed to the boy that he was the only one who feared the task. He did not think of the fifty dollars, but thought only of the fear. Three hundred feet through a rathole, eighteen inches in diameter. Three hundred feet of muck, of wet black dark, and no turning back. But, if he did not volunteer, they would know that he was afraid. The boy stepped from behind Laska and said uncertainly: "I'll go, Stender," and he wished he might snatch back the words; for, looking about him, he saw that not a man among those present could have wedged his shoulders into the mouth of an eighteen-inch pipe. He was the only volunteer. They had known he would be the only one.

Stender came striding over holding the lantern above his head. He peered into the boy's face. "Take off your clothes," he said.

"Take off my clothes?"

"That's what I said."

"You might get a buckle caught in a joint," said Laska. "See?"

The boy saw only that he had been trapped very cunningly. At home he could have been openly fearful, for at home everything about him was known. There, quite simply, he could have said: "I won't do it. I'm frightened. I'll be killed." But here the diggers in clay were lancing him with looks. And Laska was bringing a ball of line, one end of which would be fastened to his ankle.

"Just go in a sweater," said Laska. "A sweater an' boots over your woolens. We'll be waiting for you at the manhole."

He wanted so desperately to dive off into the night that he felt his legs bracing for a spring, and a tight feeling in his throat. Then, mechanically, he began to take off his clothes. Nick had gone clumping off to the shanty and shortly he returned with a pair of hip boots. "Here, kid. I get 'em warm for you inna shanty."

He thrust his feet into the boots, and Laska knelt and tied the heavy line to his ankle. "Too tight?"

"No. It's all right, I guess."

"Well—come on."

They walked past Stender who was pacing up and down among the men. They slid down into the crater, deepened now by the diggers. They stood by the partly covered mouth of the pipe. They were thirty feet below the surface of the ground.

Laska reached down and tugged at the knot he had tied in the line, then he peered into the mouth of the tube. He peered cautiously, as if he thought it might be inhabited. The boy's glance wandered up the wet sides of the pit. Over the rim a circle of bland yellow faces peered at him. Sleet tinkled against lanterns, spattered down and stung his flesh.

"Go ahead in," said Laska.

The boy blanched.

"Just keep thinking of the manhole, where you'll come out," said Laska.

The boy's throat constricted. He seemed to be bursting with a pressure from inside. He got down on his belly in the slush-ice and mud. It penetrated slowly to his skin, and spread over him. He put his head inside the mouth of the pipe, drew back in horror. Some gibbering words flew from his lips. His voice sounded preposterously loud. Laska's voice was already shopworn with distance. "You can make it! Go ahead."

He lay on his left side, and, reaching out with his left arm, caught a joint and drew himself in. The mud oozed up around him, finding its way upon him, welling up against the left side of his face. He pressed his right cheek against the ceiling of the pipe to keep the muck from covering his mouth and nose. Laska's voice was far and muffled. Laska was in another world—a sane world of night, of storm, and the mellow glow of lanterns.

"Are you makin' it all right, kid?"

The boy cried out, his ears ringing with his cry. It re-echoed from the sides of the pipe. The sides hemmed him, pinned him, closed him in on every side with their paralyzing circumference.

There is no darkness like the darkness underground that miners know. It borrows something from night, from tombs, from places used by bats. Such fluid black can terrify a flame, and suffocate, and drench a mind with madness. There is a fierce desire to struggle, to beat one's hands against the prison. The boy longed to lift his pitiful human strength against the walls. He longed to claw at his eyes in the mad certainty that more than darkness curtained them.

He had moved but a few feet on his journey when panic swept him. Ahead of him the mud had built into a stolid wave. Putting forth his left hand, he felt a scant two inches between the wave's crest and the ceiling of the pipe. There was nothing to do but go back. If he moved ahead, it meant death by suffocation. He tried to back away, but caught his toe in a joint of the pipe. He was entombed! In an hour he would be a body. The cold and dampness would kill him before they could dig down to him. Nick and Laska would pull him from the muck, and Laska would say: "Huh, his clock's stopped."

He thrashed with delirious strength against his prison. He felt the skin tearing from the backs of his hands as he flailed the rough walls. And some gods must have snickered, for above the walls of the pipe were thirty feet of unyielding clay, eight thousand miles of earth below. A strength, a weight, a night, each a thousand times his most revolting dream, leaned upon the boy, depressing, crushing, stamping him out. The ground gave no cry of battle. It did no bleeding, suffered no pain, uttered no groans. It flattened him silently. It swallowed him in its foul despotism. It dropped its merciless weight upon his mind. It was so inhuman, so horribly incognizant of the God men swore had made it.

In the midst of his frenzy, when he had beaten his face against the walls until it bled, he heard a ringing voice he knew was real, springing from human sympathy. It was Laska, calling: "Are you all right, kid?"

In that instant the boy loved Laska as he loved his life. Laska's voice sheered the weight from him, scattered the darkness, brought him new balance and a hope to live.

"Fine!" he answered in a cracking yell. He yelled again, loving the sound of his voice, and thinking how foolish yelling was in such a place.

With his left hand he groped ahead and found that the wave of mud had settled, levelled off by its own weight. He drew his body together, pressing it against the pipe. He straightened, moved ahead six inches. His fingers found a loop of oakum dangling from a joint, and he pulled himself on, his left arm forward, his right arm behind over his hip, like a swimmer's.

He had vanquished panic, and he looked ahead to victory. Each joint brought him twenty inches nearer his goal. Each twenty inches was a plateau which enabled him to vision a new plateau—the next joint. The joints were like small deceitful rests upon a march.

He had been more than an hour on the way. He did not know how far he had gone, a third, perhaps even a half of the distance. He forgot the present, forgot fear, wet, cold, blackness; he lost himself in dreaming of the world of men outside the prison. It was as if he were a small superb island in hell.

He did not know how long he had been counting the joints, but he found himself whispering good numbers: "Fifty-one, fifty-two, fifty-three. . . ." Each joint, when he thought of it, appeared to take up a vast time of squirming in the muck, and the line dragged heavily behind his foot.

Suddenly, staring into the darkness so that it seemed to bring a pain to his eyes, he saw a pallid ray. He closed his eyes, opened them, and looked again. The ray was real, and he uttered a whimper of relief. He knew that the ray must come from Stender's lantern. He pictured Stender and a group of the diggers huddled in the manhole, waiting for him. The men and the manhole grew magnificent in his mind, and he thought of them worshipfully.

"Seventy-six, seventy-seven, seventy-eight. . . ."

The ray grew slowly, like a worth-while thing. It took an oval shape, and the oval grew fat, like an egg, then round. It was a straight line to the manhole, and the mud had thinned.

Through the pipe, into the boy's ears, a voice rumbled like half-hearted thunder. It was Stender's voice: "How you makin' it?"

"Oh, just fine!" His cry came pricking back into his ears like a shower of needles.

There followed a long span of numbness. The cold and wet had dulled his senses, so that whenever the rough ceiling of the pipe ripped his face, he did not feel it; so that struggling in the muck became an almost pleasant and normal thing, since all elements of fear and pain and imagination had been removed. Warmth and dryness became alien to him. He was a creature native to darkness, foreign to light.

The round yellow disk before him gave him his only sense of living. It was a sunlit landfall, luring him on. He would close his eyes and count five joints, then open them quickly, cheering himself at the perceptible stages of progress.

Then, abruptly, it seemed, he was close to the manhole. He could hear men moving. He could see the outline of Stender's head as Stender peered into the mouth of the pipe. Men kneeled, pushing each other's heads to one side, in order to watch him squirm toward them. They began to talk excitedly. He could hear them breathing, see details—and Stender and Laska reached in. They got their hands upon him. They hauled him to them, as if he were something they wanted to inspect scientifically. He felt as if they thought he was a rarity, a thing of great oddness. The light dazzled him. It began to move around and around, and to dissolve into many lights, some of which danced locally on a bottle. He heard Stender's voice: "Well, he made it all right. What do you know?"

"Here, kid," said Laska, holding the bottle to his mouth. "Drink all of this that you can hold."

He could not stand up. He believed calmly that his flesh and bones were constructed of putty. He could hear no vestige of the song of victory he had dreamed of hearing. He looked stupidly at his hands, which bled painlessly. He could not feel his arms and legs at all. He was a vast sensation of lantern light and the steam of human beings breathing in a damp place.

Faces peered at him. The faces were curious, and surprised. He felt a clouded, uncomprehending resentment against them. Stender held him up on one side, Laska on the other. They looked at each other across him. Suddenly Laska stooped and gathered him effortlessly into his arms.

"You'll get covered with mud," mumbled the boy.

"Damn if he didn't make it all right," said Stender. "Save us tearing out the pipe."

"Hell with the pipe," said Laska.

The boy's wet head fell against Laska's chest. He felt the rise and fall of Laska's muscles, and knew that Laska was climbing with him up the iron steps inside the manhole. Night wind smote him. He buried his head deeper against Laska. Laska's body became a mountain of warmth. He felt a heavy sighing peace, like a soldier who has been comfortably wounded and knows that war for him is over.

Black Boy

KAY BOYLE

AT THAT time, it was the forsaken part, it was the other end of the city, and on early spring mornings there was no one about. By soft words, you could woo the horse into the foam, and ride her with the sea knee-deep around her. The waves came in and out there, as indolent as ladies, gathered up their skirts in their hands and, with a murmur, came tiptoeing across the velvet sand.

The wooden promenade was high there, and when the wind was up the water came running under it like wild. On such days, you had to content yourself with riding the horse over the deep white drifts of dry sand on the other side of the walk; the horse's hoofs here made no sound and the sparks of sand stung your face in fury. It had no body to it, like the mile or two of sand packed hard that you could open out on once the tide was down.

My little grandfather, Puss, was alive then, with his delicate gait and ankles, and his belly pouting in his dove-gray clothes. When he saw from the window that the tide was sidling out, he put on his pearl fedora and came stepping down the street. For a minute, he put one foot on the sand, but he was not at ease there. On the boardwalk, over our heads, was some other wind of life in progress. If you looked up, you could see it in motion through the cracks in the timber: rolling-chairs, and women in high heels proceeding, if the weather were fair.

"You know," my grandfather said, "I think I might like to have a look at a shop or two along the boardwalk." Or, "I suppose you don't feel like leaving the beach for a minute," or, "If you would go with me, we might take a chair together, and look at the hats and the dresses and roll along in the sun."

He was alive then, taking his pick of the broad easy chairs and the black boys.

"There's a nice skinny boy," he'd say. "He looks as though he might put some action into it. Here you are, Sonny. Push me and the little girl down to the Million Dollar Pier and back."

The cushions were red with a sheen of dew over them. And Puss settled back on them and took my hand in his. In his mind there was no hesitation about whether he would look at the shops on one side, or out on the vacant side where there was nothing shining but the sea.

"What's your name, Charlie?" Puss would say without turning his head to the black boy pushing the chair behind our shoulders.

"Charlie's my name, sir," he'd answer with his face dripping down like tar in the sun.

"What's your name, Sonny?" Puss would say another time, and the black boy answered, "Sonny's my name, sir."

"What's your name, Big Boy?"

"Big Boy's my name."

He never wore a smile on his face, the black boy. He was thin as a shadow but darker, and he was pushing and sweating, getting the chair down to the Million Dollar Pier and back again, in and out through the people. If you turned towards the sea for a minute, you could see his face out of the corner of your eye, hanging black as a bat's wing, nodding and nodding like a dark heavy flower.

But in the early morning, he was the only one who came down onto the sand and sat under the beams of the boardwalk, sitting idle there, with a languor fallen on every limb. He had long bones. He sat idle there, with his clothes shrunk up from his wrists and his ankles, with his legs drawn up, looking out at the sea.

"I might be a king if I wanted to be" was what he said to me.

Maybe I was twelve years old, or maybe I was ten when we used to sit eating dog biscuits together. Sometimes, when you broke them in two, a worm fell out and the black boy lifted his sharp finger and flecked it carelessly from off his knee.

"I seen kings," he said, "with a kind of cloth over they heads, and kind of jewels-like around here and here. They weren't any blacker than me, if as black," he said. "I could be almost anything I made up my mind to be."

"King Nebuchadnezzar," I said. "He wasn't a white man."

The wind was off the ocean and was filled with alien smells. It was early in the day, and no human sign was given. Overhead were the green beams of the boardwalk and no wheel or step to sound it.

"If I was king," said the black boy with his biscuit in his fingers, "I wouldn't put much stock in hanging around here."

Great crystal jelly-beasts were quivering in a hundred different colors on the wastes of sand around us. The dogs came, jumping them, and when they saw me still sitting still, they wheeled like gulls and sped back to the sea.

"I'd be travelling around," he said, "here and there. Now here, now there. I'd change most of my habits."

His hair grew all over the top of his head in tight dry rosettes. His neck was longer and more shapely than a white man's neck, and his fingers ran in and out of the sand like the blue feet of a bird.

"I wouldn't have much to do with pushing chairs around under them circumstances," he said. "I might even give up sleeping out here on the sand."

Or if you came out when it was starlight, you could see him sitting there in the clear white darkness. I could go and come as I liked, for whenever I went out the door, I had the dogs shouldering behind me. At night, they shook the taste of the house out of their coats and came down across the sand. There he was, with his knees up, sitting idle.

"They used to be all kinds of animals come down here to drink in the dark," he said. "They was a kind of a mirage came along and gave that impression. I seen tigers, lions, lambs, deer; I seen ostriches drinking down there side by side with each other. They's the Northern Lights gets crossed some way and switches the wrong picture down."

It may be that the coast has changed there, for even then it was changing. The lighthouse that had once stood far out on the wild rocks near the outlet was standing then like a lighted torch in the heart of the town. And the deep currents of the sea may have altered so that the clearest water runs in another direction, and houses may have been built down as far as where the brink used to be. But the brink was so perilous then that every word the black boy spoke seemed to fall into a cavern of beauty.

"I seen camels; I seen zebras," he said. "I might have caught any one of them if I'd felt inclined."

And the street was so still and wide then that when Puss stepped out of the house, I could hear him clearing his throat of the sharp salty air. He had no intention of soiling the soles of his boots, but he came down the street to find me.

"If you feel like going with me," he said, "we'll take a chair and see the fifty-seven varieties changing on the electric sign."

And then he saw the black boy sitting quiet. His voice drew up short on his tongue and he touched his white mustache.

"I shouldn't think it a good idea," he said, and he put his arm through my arm. "I saw another little oak not three inches high in the Jap's window yesterday. We might roll down the boardwalk and have a look at it. You know," said Puss, and he put his kid gloves carefully on his fingers, "that black boy might do you some kind of harm."

"What kind of harm could he do with me?" I said.

"Well," said Puss with the garlands of lights hanging around him, "he might steal some money from you. He might knock you down and take your money away."

"How could he do that?" I said. "We just sit and talk there."

Puss looked at me sharply.

"What do you find to sit and talk about?" he said.

"I don't know," I said. "I don't remember. It doesn't sound like much to tell it."

The burden of his words was lying there on my heart when I woke up in the morning. I went out by myself to the stable and led the horse to the door and put the saddle on her. If Puss were ill at ease for a day or two, he could look out the window in peace and see me riding high and mighty away. The day after tomorrow, I thought, or the next day, I'll sit down on the beach again and talk to the black boy. But when I rode out, I saw him seated idle there, under the boardwalk, heedless, looking away to the cool wide sea. He had been eating peanuts and the shells lay all around him. The dogs came running at the horse's heels, nipping the foam that lay along the tide.

The horse was as shy as a bird that morning, and when I drew her up beside the black boy, she tossed her head on high. Her mane went back and forth, from one side to the other, and a flight of joy in her limbs sent her forelegs like rockets into the air. The black boy stood up from the cold smooth sand, unsmiling, but a spark of wonder shone in his marble eyes. He put out his arm in the short tight sleeve of his coat and stroked her shivering shoulder.

"I was going to be a jockey once," he said, "but I changed my mind."

I slid down on one side while he climbed up the other.

"I don't know as I can guide him right," he said as I held her head. "The kind of saddle you have, it gives you nothing to grip your knees around. I ride them with their bare skin."

The black boy settled himself on the leather and put his feet in the stirrups. He was quiet and quick with delight, but he had no thought of smiling as he took the reins in his hand.

I stood on the beach with the dogs beside me, looking after the horse as she ambled down to the water. The black boy rode easily and straight, letting the horse stretch out and sneeze and canter. When they reached the jetty, he turned her casually and brought her loping back.

"Some folks licks hell out of their horses," he said. "I'd never raise a hand to one, unless he was to bite me or do something I didn't care for."

He sat in the saddle at ease, as though in a rocker, stroking her shoulder with his hand spread open, and turning in the stirrups to smooth her shining flank.

"Jockeys make a pile of money," I said.

"I wouldn't care for the life they have," said the black boy. "They have to watch their diet so careful."

His fingers ran delicately through her hair and laid her soft mane back on her neck.

When I was up on the horse again, I turned her towards the boardwalk.

"I'm going to take her over the jetty," I said. "You'll see how she clears it. I'll take her up under the boardwalk to give her a good start."

I struck her shoulder with the end of my crop, and she started towards the tough black beams. She was under it, galloping, when the dogs came down the beach like mad. They had chased a cat out of cover and were after it, screaming as they ran, with a wing of sand blowing wide behind them, and when the horse saw them under her legs, she jumped sideways in sprightliness and terror and flung herself against an iron arch.

For a long time I heard nothing at all in my head except the melody of someone crying, whether it was my dead mother holding me in comfort, or the soft wind grieving over me where I had fallen. I lay on the sand asleep; I could feel it running with my tears through my fingers. I was rocked in a cradle of love, cradled and rocked in sorrow.

"Oh, my little lamb, my little lamb pie!" Oh, sorrow, sorrow, wailed the wind, or the tide, or my own kin about me. "Oh, lamb, oh, lamb!"

I could feel the long swift fingers of love untying the terrible knot of pain that bound my head. And I put my arms around him and lay close to his heart in comfort.

Puss was alive then, and when he met the black boy carrying me up to the house, he struck him square across the mouth.

The Stranger Within Our Gates

ROBERT BENCHLEY

ONE OF the problems of child education which is not generally included in books on the subject is the Visiting Schoolmate. By that is meant the little friend whom your child brings home for the holidays. What is to be done with him, the Law reading as it does?

He is usually brought home because his own home is in Nevada, and if he went 'way out there for Christmas he would no sooner get there than he would have to turn right around and come back—an ideal arrangement on the face of it. But there is something in the idea of a child away from home at Christmas-time that tears at the heart-strings, and little George is received into the bosom of your family with open arms and a slight catch in the throat. Poor little nipper! He must call up his parents by telephone on Christmas Day; they will miss him so. (It later turns out that even when George's parents lived in Philadelphia he spent his vacations with friends, his parents being no fools.)

For the first day George is a model of politeness. "George is a nice boy," you say to your son; "I wish you knew more like him." "George seems to be a very manly little chap for fourteen," your wife says after the boys have gone to bed. "I hope that Bill is impressed." Bill, as a matter of fact, does seem to have caught some of little George's gentility and reserve, and the hope for his future which had been practically abandoned is revived again under his schoolmate's influence.

The first indication that George's stay is not going to be a blessing comes at the table, when, with confidence born of one day's association, he announces flatly that he does not eat potatoes, lamb or peas, the main course of the meal consisting of potatoes, lamb and peas. "Perhaps you would like an egg, George?" you suggest. "I hate eggs," says George, looking out the window while he waits for you to hit on something that he does like.

"I'm afraid you aren't going to get much to eat tonight, then, George," you say. "What is there for dessert?"

"A nice bread pudding with raisins," says your wife.

George, at the mention of bread pudding, gives what is known as "the bird," a revolting sound made with the tongue and lower lip. "I can't eat raisins anyway," he adds, to be polite. "They make me come out in a rash."

"Ah-h! The old raisin-rash," you say. "Well, we'll keep you away from raisins, I guess. And just what is it that you can eat, George? You can tell me. I am your friend."

Under cross-examination it turns out that George can eat beets if they are cooked just right, a rare species of eggplant grown only in Nevada, and all the ice cream in the world. He will also cram down a bit of cake now and then for manners' sake.

All this would not be so bad if it were not for the fact that, coincidentally with refusing the lamb, George criticizes your carving of it. "My father carves lamb across the grain instead of the way you do," he says, a little crossly.

"Very interesting," is your comment.

"My father says that only old ladies carve straight down like that," he goes on.

"Well, well," you say pleasantly between your teeth. "That makes me out sort of an old lady, doesn't it?"

"Yes, sir," says George.

"Perhaps you have a different kind of lamb in Nevada," you suggest, hacking off a large chunk. (You have never carved so badly.) "A kind that feeds on your special kind of eggplant."

"We don't have lamb very often," says George. "Mostly squab and duck."

"You stick to squab and duck, George," you say, "and it will be just dandy for that rash of yours. Here take this and like it!" And you toss him a piece of lamb which, oddly enough, is later found to have disappeared from his plate.

It also turns out later that George's father can build sailboats, make a monoplane that will really fly, repair a broken buzzer and imitate birds, none of which you can do and none of which you have ever tried to do, having given it to be understood that they *couldn't* be done. You begin to hate George's father almost as much as you do George.

"I suppose your father writes articles for the magazines, too, doesn't he, George?" you ask sarcastically.

"Sure," says George with disdain. "He does that Sundays—Sunday afternoons."

This just about cleans up George so far as you are concerned, but there are still ten more days of vacation. And during these ten days your son Bill is induced by George to experiment with electricity to the extent of blowing out all the fuses in the house and burning the cigarette-lighter out of the sedan; he is also inspired to call the cook a German spy who broils babies, to insult several of the neighbors' little girls to the point of tears and reprisals, and to refuse spinach. You know that Bill didn't think of these things himself, as he never could have had the imagination.

On Christmas Day all the little presents that you got for George turn out to be things that he already has, only his are better. He incites Bill to revolt over the question of where the tracks to the electric train are to be placed (George maintaining that in his home they run through his father's bathroom, which is the only sensible place for tracks to run). He breaks several of little Barbara's more fragile presents and says that she broke them herself by not knowing how to work them. And the day ends with George running a high temperature and coming down with mumps, necessitating a quarantine and enforced residence in your house for a month.

This is just a brief summary of the Visiting Schoolmate problem. Granted that every child should have a home to go to at Christmas, could there not be some sort of state subsidy designed to bring their own homes on to such children as are unable to go home themselves? On such a day each home should be a sanctuary, where only members of the tribe can gather and overeat and quarrel. Outsiders just complicate matters, especially when outsiders cannot be spanked.

A Visit of Charity

EUDORA WELTY

IT WAS mid-morning—a very cold, bright day. Holding a potted plant before her, a girl of fourteen jumped off the bus in front of the Old Ladies' Home, on the outskirts of town. She wore a red coat, and her straight yellow hair was hanging down loose from the pointed white cap all the little girls were wearing that year. She stopped for a moment beside one of the prickly dark shrubs with which the city had beautified the Home, and then proceeded slowly toward the building, which was of whitewashed brick and reflected the winter sunlight like a block of ice. As she walked vaguely up the steps she shifted the small pot from hand to hand; then she had to set it down and remove her mittens before she could open the heavy door.

"I'm a Campfire Girl. . . . I have to pay a visit to some old lady," she told the nurse at the desk. This was a woman in a white uniform who looked as if she were cold; she had close-cut hair which stood up on the very top of her head exactly like a sea wave. Marian, the little girl, did not tell her that this visit would give her a minimum of only three points in her score.

"Acquainted with any of our residents?" asked the nurse. She lifted one eyebrow and spoke like a man.

"With any old ladies? No—but—that is, any of them will do," Marian stammered. With her free hand she pushed her hair behind her ears, as she did when it was time to study Science.

The nurse shrugged and rose. "You have a nice *multiflora cineraria* there," she remarked as she walked ahead down the hall of closed doors to pick out an old lady.

There was loose, bulging linoleum on the floor. Marian felt as if she were walking on the waves, but the nurse paid no attention to it. There was a smell in the hall like the interior of a clock. Everything was silent until, behind one of the doors, an old lady of some kind cleared her throat like a sheep bleating. This decided the nurse. Stopping in her tracks, she first extended her arm, bent her elbow, and leaned forward from the hips—all to examine the watch strapped to her wrist; then she gave a loud double-rap on the door.

"There are two in each room," the nurse remarked over her shoulder.

"Two what?" asked Marian without thinking. The sound like a sheep's bleating almost made her turn around and run back.

One old woman was pulling the door open in short, gradual jerks, and when she saw the nurse a strange smile forced her old face dangerously awry. Marian, suddenly propelled by the strong, impatient arm of the nurse, saw next the side-face of another old woman, even older, who was lying flat in bed with a cap on and a counterpane drawn up to her chin.

"Visitor," said the nurse, and after one more shove she was off up the hall.

Marian stood tongue-tied; both hands held the potted plant. The old woman, still with that terrible, square smile (which was a smile of welcome) stamped on her bony face, was waiting. . . . Perhaps she said something. The old woman in bed said nothing at all, and she did not look around.

Suddenly Marian saw a hand, quick as a bird claw, reach up in the air and pluck the white cap off her head. At the same time, another claw to match drew her all the way into the room, and the next moment the door closed behind her.

"My, my, my," said the old lady at her side.

Marian stood enclosed by a bed, a washstand, and a chair; the tiny room had altogether too much furniture. Everything smelled wet—even the bare floor. She held onto the back of the chair, which was wicker and felt soft and damp. Her heart beat more and more slowly, her hands got colder and colder, and she could not hear whether the old women were saying anything or not. She could not see them very clearly. How dark it was! The window shade was down, and the only door was shut. Marian looked at the ceiling. . . . It was like being caught in a robber's cave, just before one was murdered.

"Did you come to be our little girl for a while?" the first robber asked.

Then something was snatched from Marian's hand—the little potted plant.

"Flowers!" screamed the old woman. She stood holding the pot in an undecided way. "Pretty flowers," she added.

Then the old woman in bed cleared her throat and spoke. "They are not pretty," she said, still without looking around, but very distinctly.

Marian suddenly pitched against the chair and sat down in it.

"Pretty flowers," the first old woman insisted. "Pretty—pretty. . . ."

Marian wished she had the little pot back for just a moment—she had forgotten to look at the plant herself before giving it away. What did it look like?

"Stinkweeds," said the other old woman sharply. She had a bunchy white forehead and red eyes like a sheep. Now she turned them toward Marian. The fogginess seemed to rise in her throat again, and she bleated, "Who—are—you?"

To her surprise, Marian could not remember her name. "I'm a Campfire Girl," she said finally.

"Watch out for the germs," said the old woman like a sheep, not addressing anyone.

"One came out last month to see us," said the first old woman.

A sheep or a germ? wondered Marian dreamily, holding onto the chair.

"Did not!" cried the other old woman.

"Did so! Read to us out of the Bible, and we enjoyed it!" screamed the first.

"Who enjoyed it!" said the woman in bed. Her mouth was unexpectedly small and sorrowful, like a pet's.

"We enjoyed it," insisted the other. "You enjoyed it—I enjoyed it."

"We all enjoyed it," said Marian, without realizing that she had said a word.

The first old woman had just finished putting the potted plant high, high on the top of the wardrobe, where it could hardly be seen from below. Marian wondered how she had ever succeeded in placing it there, how she could ever have reached so high.

"You mustn't pay any attention to old Addie," she now said to the little girl. "She's ailing today."

"Will you shut your mouth?" said the woman in bed. "I am not."

"You're a story."

"I can't stay but a minute—really, I can't," said Marian suddenly. She looked down at the wet floor and thought that if she were sick in here they would have to let her go.

With much to-do the first old woman sat down in a rocking chair—still another piece of furniture!—and began to rock. With the fingers of one hand she touched a very dirty cameo pin on her chest. "What do you do at school?" she asked.

"I don't know . . ." said Marian. She tried to think but she could not.

"Oh, but the flowers are beautiful," the old woman whispered. She seemed to rock faster and faster; Marian did not see how anyone could rock so fast.

"Ugly," said the woman in bed.

"If we bring flowers—" Marian began, and then fell silent. She had almost said that if Campfire Girls brought flowers to the Old Ladies' Home, the visit would count one extra point, and if they took a Bible with them on the bus and read it to the old ladies, it counted double. But the old woman had not listened, anyway; she was rocking and watching the other one, who watched back from the bed.

"Poor Addie is ailing. She has to take medicine—see?" she said, pointing a horny finger at a row of bottles on the table and rocking so high that her black comfort shoes lifted off the floor like a little child's.

"I am no more sick than you are," said the woman in bed.

"Oh yes you are!"

"I just got more sense than you have, that's all," said the other old woman, nodding her head.

"That's only the contrary way she talks when *you all* come," said the first old lady with sudden intimacy. She stopped the rocker with a neat pat of her feet and leaned toward Marian. Her hand reached over—it felt like a petunia leaf, clinging and just a little sticky.

"Will you hush! Will you hush!" cried the other one.

Marian leaned back rigidly in her chair.

"When I was a little girl like you, I went to school and all," said the old woman in the same intimate, menacing voice. "Not here—another town. . . ."

"Hush!" said the sick woman. "You never went to school. You never came and you never went. You never were anywhere—only here. You never were born! You don't know anything. Your head is empty, your heart and hands and your old black purse are all empty, even that little old box that you brought with you you brought empty—you showed it to me. And yet you talk, talk, talk, talk, talk all the time until I think I'm losing my mind. Who are you? You're a stranger—a perfect stranger! Don't you know you're a stranger? Is it possible that they have actually done a thing like this to anyone—sent them in a stranger to talk, and rock, and tell away her whole long rigmarole? Do they seriously suppose that I'll be able to keep it up, day in, day out, night in, night out, living in the same room with a terrible old woman—forever?"

Marian saw the old woman's eyes grow bright and turn toward her. This old woman was looking at her with despair and calculation in her face. Her small lips suddenly dropped apart, and exposed a half circle of false teeth with tan gums.

"Come here, I want to tell you something," she whispered. "Come here!"

Marian was trembling, and her heart nearly stopped beating altogether for a moment.

"Now, now, Addie," said the first old woman. "That's not polite. Do you know what's really the matter with old Addie today?" She, too, looked at Marian; one of her eyelids drooped low.

"The matter?" the child repeated stupidly. "What's the matter with her?"

"Why, she's mad because it's her birthday!" said the first old woman, beginning to rock again and giving a little crow as though she had answered her own riddle.

"It is not, it is not!" screamed the old woman in bed. "It is not my birthday, no one knows when that is but myself, and will you please be quiet and say nothing more, or I'll go straight out of my mind!" She turned her eyes toward Marian again, and presently she said in the soft, foggy voice, "When the worst comes to the worst, I ring this bell, and the nurse comes." One of her hands was drawn out from under the patched counterpane—a thin little hand with enormous black freckles. With a finger which would not hold still she pointed to a little bell on the table among the bottles.

"How old are you?" Marian breathed. Now she could see the old woman in bed very closely and plainly, and very abruptly, from all sides, as in dreams. She wondered about her—she wondered for a moment as though there were nothing else in the world to wonder about. It was the first time such a thing had happened to Marian.

"I won't tell!"

The old face on the pillow, where Marian was bending over it, slowly gathered and collapsed. Soft whimpers came out of the small open mouth. It was a sheep that she sounded like—a little lamb. Marian's face drew very close, the yellow hair hung forward.

"She's crying!" She turned a bright, burning face up to the first old woman.

"That's Addie for you," the old woman said spitefully.

Marian jumped up and moved toward the door. For the second time, the claw almost touched her hair, but it was not quick enough. The little girl put her cap on.

"Well, it was a real visit," said the old woman, following Marian through the doorway and all the way out into the hall. Then from behind she suddenly clutched the child with her sharp little fingers. In an affected, high-pitched whine she cried, "Oh, little girl, have you a penny to spare for a poor old woman that's not got anything of her own? We don't have a thing in the world—not a penny for candy—not a thing! Little girl, just a nickel—a penny—"

Marian pulled violently against the old hands for a moment before she was free. Then she ran down the hall, without looking behind her and without looking at the nurse, who was reading *Field & Stream* at her desk. The nurse, after another triple motion to consult her wrist watch, asked automatically the question put to visitors in all institutions: "Won't you stay and have dinner with *us*?"

Marian never replied. She pushed the heavy door open into the cold air and ran down the steps.

Under the prickly shrub she stopped and quickly, without being seen, retrieved a red apple she had hidden there.

Her yellow hair under the white cap, her scarlet coat, her bare knees all flashed in the sunlight as she ran to meet the big bus rocketing through the street.

"Wait for me!" she shouted. As though at an imperial command, the bus ground to a stop.

She jumped on and took a big bite out of the apple.

Youth's Furnishings

CORNELIA OTIS SKINNER

THE DAY arrives in the life of every son's mother when, looking across the breakfast table at her offspring, she realizes that not only has he reached the stage when he needs new clothes, he has stretched out well beyond it. His coat looks as if it were intended for a bell-hop and the sleeves have become so short anyone might think he'd pushed them back for the purpose of washing his hands . . . anyone, that is, who doesn't know small boys. His shirt-tails can no longer be confined below his vest, his collar, if buttoned, would strangle him and his shorts live up to their name in a manner almost indecent. His ties have started growing whiskers and although she is at the moment spared the horrid sight, she knows that underneath this inadequate outer covering his underwear has shrunk to the ripping point and his socks are out at every toe, like mitts. Even his shoes are the sort one finds along beaches. With a little boy everything goes to pieces at once and he emerges from all his clothing with the inevitability, if not the beauty, of the moth from the chrysalis. To complicate things, this metamorphosis always takes place at an unseasonable time of year when it is too cool for summer garments to do anything but give him pneumonia and when winter clothes seem to induce symptoms of scarlet fever in the tiny wearer. The only sensible solution would be to put the child to bed for the interim. However, every mother drags her protesting son to the boys' department of the most convenient emporium and attempts in one fell shopping-trip to do what is known as "outfit" him for the approaching season. It's a bad day for all concerned and one that proves to be a severe test of mother-love and filial piety with both these tender emotions exhibiting alarming indications of snapping.

The mother starts in by announcing in tones of forced gladness, trying to make it sound like an invitation to a barbecue, that they're going to go shopping and won't it be fun. The little boy who knows darn well it won't be, meets the suggestion with a barrage of protest. He thinks of urgent things he has to do, he invents engagements with fictitious buddies in the park, he insists he has to get his homework done, he complains of a headache; he even goes so far as to say he feels like spending the morning practicing his scales on whatever instrument he happens to afflict his family with. The mother, steeling herself, remains adamant and sends the child off for his cap and coat. He obeys with the alacrity of a reluctant snail, all the while muttering baleful words to the effect that he hates those old stores anyway, he hates getting those old clothes, he hates all that old shopping, and pale but determined, she bundles him off before "old mothers" are added to the category of anathema.

In my household these crises arise about twice a year. I try my best to make it as painless as possible. I select a near-by department store and a time of day when the crowds will be few. I give solemn oaths that it won't take long; I even dangle the News Reel and a double-chocolate-frosted-peppermint-whatever as rewards for submissive behavior. It does little good. After muttering a violent "phooey" which is his equivalent for darkest blasphemy, he sets forth in a black mood which no subsequent occurrence is likely to dissipate. He regards all mankind as his enemy. Even the local taxi-driver, with whom he is usually on rotarian terms, is in league against him. The store, when finally we reach it, he considers an edifice planned and constructed solely for the purpose of annoying him and succeeding beyond the architect's most savage dreams. Everything is very awful to him . . . the display of merchandise on the ground floor, which in his contempt he is apt to brush off when passing counters, leaving me to pick up and face the saleswoman who clearly takes us for a light-fingered team; the elevators jammed with shoppers onto whose feet he has an unfortunate way of backing, the necessity for removing his cap and overcoat and then the inhuman cruelty of being made to carry them. Added to his exasperation is a profound shame for his mother who displays what he considers an embarrassing inability to locate the various departments. I try to divert him by switching from the lift to the escalator for which he has invented a little pastime of his own which consists in gaining the middle of the incline and sticking there, jumping rhythmically down one step at a time in the same technique as the Ben Hur chariot race and involving some pretty lively encounters with ascending passengers. Even this distraction palls. From the moment of the first shove of the revolving door he has begun saying, "When are we going to go?" and he keeps it up like a leitmotif in tones that range from those of fiery aggressiveness to heartbreaking pathos. Eventually we reach the boys' department and I assure him that with a little co-operation and fortitude on his part, it won't take long. For a moment he shows signs of becoming moderately resigned to the inevitable, then some misguided salesman approaches him with the best of intentions and a much too cheerful smile and calls him "Sonny," whereat he reverts to his mood of homeric wrath. I must admit I too am discomfited by these alert young men who behave as if they'd just received a citation from Dale Carnegie. Their high-pressure friendliness gets me down. I feel I should start things off by shaking hands with them and inquiring after their little sister. They seem to expect the average mother to act and talk as if she'd stepped off the front page of *Good Housekeeping*. And what's worse, I do. I find myself looking tenderly maternal and in a voice of treacle saying, "How do you do. I'm looking for a suit (as if I'd mislaid it somewhere). It's for my little boy." It wouldn't be much of a surprise to hear myself referring to him as "my bairn."

"And what age is the youngster?" the salesman asks in the bright manner of a Scout Master. To my child "youngster" is as much fighting language as "Sonny" and he retreats to a vantage position behind the folds of my coat, glowering like Achilles from his tent.

I am not by nature the chatty type, yet I find that for some reason I unburden myself to this repulsive young man at an alarming rate. I tell him the boy's age, adding with the happy pride of the mother of an Asbury Park prize baby that he wears two sizes larger. At which the salesman says, "Well, well, you'd never guess it, now, would you?" And I echo fatuously, "No you wouldn't, now, would you?" I explain how rapidly he's growing and how he takes after his father. I tell what grade he's in or about to be dropped from. If I had one of his English compositions with me I'd probably exhibit it. This flow of confidences continues during the selection of clothes. I describe what sort of things he'll need for the country and why, and in connection with things like corduroy pants I hear myself coming forth with such tender confessions as, "My little boy is very susceptible to poison ivy." My child listens to this just long enough to become more ashamed than ever of his mother, then disappears.

It is remarkable with what suddenness little boys in stores can vanish into thin air. They wander off to distant departments, one sees the tops of their heads setting behind far-off counters, then when one rushes over to get them, they're no longer there. They venture out through doors marked EXIT and stay so long one is about to put in a police alarm when they come strolling back from a completely opposite direction. They discover appalling things to do such as spinning revolving tie-racks or opening and shutting those deep hat-pins, into one of which they drop their gloves and promptly forget which one it was. At intervals they are retrieved and brought back to the scene of their tribulation where they express their boredom by flinging themselves across the nearest glass show-counter which, because God is good, fails to shatter under the impact.

Suits and a coat being the most important items and the only ones for which the presence of the child is essential, I try to procure them at the start and we each have decided and divergent views on what we want. I imagine all sons and mothers come to blows over the matter of choice of apparel. With her inherent instinct for "keeping him young as long as possible" the average parent is hard put to it not to select attire that the average child considers a gross insult to his years. Certainly, were I to follow my own inclinations, I'd dress my boy like Peter Pan until he were ready for Harvard. His taste, on the other hand, runs to garments not only far too old for him but absolutely mortician sobriety. Given his choice, he'd with rapture set forth to school every morning in a Prince Albert. Along with these soberly conventional tastes goes an alarming love of things like leather helmets that have goggles on them, western belts made in Japan and tasty wind-breakers adorned with the portraits of such celebrities as Dopey and Mickey Mouse. It would scarcely surprise me to see him some day appear for a children's party in his best dark-blue suit, patent pumps, a carnation in his button-hole and a white cloth cap that says "Purina Chows."

Finally we manage to compromise on something neither of us likes very much and I then drag him under protest to the fitting-room. Here we immure ourselves, the bright young salesman, the tailor, my child and myself in a diminutive cubicle which gives one the sensation of trying to fit something in an overcrowded elevator. If the keep-smiling salesman has succeeded in making me go folksy the tailor who is usually a taciturn individual with no lighter moments has an insidious way of shaming me. His professional pride is at stake, he always wants the suit to fit, whereas I hold out for its being an accurate size too large so the child can "grow into it." I try to make my tone convey the fact that though simple folk we still are proud but the man clearly considers us small-time custom. Then there is that awkward moment when, blushing prettily, I hear myself saying, "Are you sure it's big enough in the . . . has he enough room . . . er. Darling (this to the small boy), just lean over a moment, will you?"

During the fitting my son alternately groans, sighs, complains of overwhelming fatigue and repeats his "When are we going to go?" refrain. He swipes a piece of chalk from the tailor and for a last-resource pastime begins to mark up the walls. I remonstrate feebly and the salesman, still smiling, says, "There's nothing like a boy, is there?" And I answer, "No, thank God!"

Our next stop is the shoe department. Here my offspring lies in a state of collapse half on the chair, half over the stool. He can just bring himself to thrust his foot into the shoe clerk's discouraged face and with what little energy is left in him, he improves the time producing sort of castanet effects with a couple of wooden foot measurers. After shoes, we head for the underwear department although from the complaints of my appendage we ought by right to be heading for the Bellevue Emergency ward. During the course of this trek, in the manner of a hare in a paper chase, he manages to scatter behind him cap, scarf, gloves, the cap pistol he's brought along in case of attack and finally his coat which for most of the time he's been dragging after him, holding it by one of the cuffs. One by one I salvage them and turn myself into a beast of burden. By now his wrath has subsided into pitiful hopelessness. His is the resigned air of someone who knows he's not long for this world. As a matter of fact I begin to get alarmed about him myself. He appears to be growing very weak and is deathly pallid except for a hectic flush on either cheekbone. I place an anxious hand on his neck and it seems to me definitely feverish. I start imagining he's "coming down" with something in its most virulent form. The shopping list still shows any number of items not as yet crossed off . . . but in a panic I let them go. We board the first elevator with a DOWN sign and gain the street. I make for the curb to signal the nearest vacant taxi, although it crosses my mind that maybe what I'd better send for would be an ambulance. Then I glance with trepidation at my child. Escape from the store and fresh air have restored him to life. His pallor is fled, his fever abated, his weakness turned miraculously into buoyant energy.

"How do you feel?" I ask with concern.

"Swell," comes the outrageous answer. "Say, Mum, how about taking me to a shooting gallery?"

"No!" This is one time I am firm. "Very regrettable accidents have occurred sometimes at shooting galleries."

Weep No More, My Lady

JAMES STREET

THE MOONLIGHT symphony of swamp creatures hushed abruptly, and the dismal bog was as peaceful as unborn time and seemed to brood in its silence. The gaunt man glanced back at the boy and motioned for him to be quiet, but it was too late. Their presence was discovered. A jumbo frog rumbled a warning and the swamp squirmed into life as its denizens scuttled to safety.

Fox fire was glowing to the west and the bayou was slapping the cypress knees when suddenly a haunting laugh echoed through the wilderness, a strange chuckling yodel ending in a weird "gro-o-o."

The boy's eyes were wide and staring. "That's it, Uncle Jess. Come on! Let's catch it!"

"Uh, oh." The man gripped his shotgun. "That ain't no animal. That's a thing."

They hurried noiselessly in the direction of the sound that Skeeter had been hearing for several nights. Swamp born and reared, they feared nothing they could shoot or outwit, so they slipped out of the morass and to the side of a ridge. Suddenly, Jesse put out his hand and stopped the child, then pointed up the slope. The animal, clearly visible in the moonlight, was sitting on its haunches, its head cocked sideways as it chuckled. It was a merry and rather melodious little chuckle.

Skeeter grinned in spite of his surprise, then said, "Sh-h-h. It'll smell us."

Jesse said, "Can't nothing smell that far. Wonder what the durn thing is?" He peered up the ridge, studying the creature. He had no intention of shooting unless attacked, for Jesse Tolliver and his nephew never killed wantonly.

The animal, however, did smell them and whipped her nose into the wind, crouched and braced. She was about sixteen inches high and weighed twenty-two pounds. Her coat was red and silky and there was a blaze of white down her chest and a circle of white around her throat. Her face was wrinkled and sad, like a wise old man's.

Jesse shook his head. "Looks som'n like a mixture of bloodhound and terrier from here," he whispered. "It beats me——"

"It's a dog, all right," Skeeter said.

"Can't no dog laugh."

"That dog can." The boy began walking toward the animal, his right hand outstretched. "Heah. Heah. I ain't gonna hurt you."

The dog, for she was a dog, cocked her head from one side to the other and watched Skeeter. She was trembling, but she didn't run. And when Skeeter knelt by her, she stopped trembling, for the ways of a boy with a dog are mysterious. He stroked her, and the trim little creature looked up at him and blinked her big hazel eyes. Then she turned over and Skeeter scratched her. She closed her eyes, stretched and chuckled, a happy mixture of chortle and yodel. Jesse ambled up and the dog leaped to her feet and sprang between the boy and the man.

Skeeter calmed her. "That's just Uncle Jess."

Jesse, still bewildered, shook his head again. "I still say that ain't no dog. She don't smell and she don't bark. Ain't natural. And look at her! Licking herself like a cat."

"Well, I'll be a catty wampus," Skeeter said. "Never saw a dog do that before." However, he was quick to defend any mannerism of his friend and said, "She likes to keep herself clean. She's a lady and I'm gonna name her that, and she's mine 'cause I found her."

"Lady, huh?"

"No, sir. My Lady. If I name her just plain Lady, how folks gonna know she's mine?" He began stroking his dog again. "Gee m'netty, Uncle Jess, I ain't never had nothing like this before."

"It still don't make sense to me," Jesse said. But he didn't care, for he was happy because the child was happy.

Like most mysteries, there was no mystery at all about My Lady. She was a lady, all right, an aristocratic Basenji, one of those strange barkless dogs of Africa. Her ancestors were pets of the Pharaohs and her line was well established when the now proud races of men were wandering about Europe, begging handouts from Nature. A bundle of nerves and muscles, she would fight anything, and could scent game up to eighty yards. She had the gait of an antelope and was odorless, washing herself before and after meals. However, the only noises she could make were a piercing cry that sounded almost human and that chuckling little chortle. She could chuckle only when happy and she had been happy in the woods. Now she was happy again.

As most men judge values, she was worth more than all the possessions of Jesse and his nephew. Several of the dogs had been shipped to New Orleans to avoid the dangerous upper route, thence by motor to a northern kennel. While crossing Mississippi, My Lady had escaped from the station wagon. Her keeper had advertised in several papers, but Jesse and Skeeter never saw papers.

Skeeter said, "Come on, M'Lady. Let's go home."

The dog didn't hesitate, but walked proudly at the boy's side to a cabin on the bank of the bayou. Skeeter crumbled corn bread, wet it with pot likker and put it before her. She sniffed the food disdainfully at first, then ate it only when she saw the boy fix a bowl for his uncle. She licked herself clean and explored the cabin, sniffing the brush brooms, the piles of wild pecans and hickory nuts, and then the cots. Satisfied at last, she jumped on Skeeter's bed, tucked her nose under her paws and went to sleep.

"Acts like she owns the place," Jesse said.

"Where you reckon she came from?" The boy slipped his overall straps from his shoulders, flexed his stringy muscles and yawned.

"Lord knows. Circus maybe." He looked at M'Lady quickly. "Say, maybe she's a freak and run off from some show. Bet they'd give us two dollars for her."

Skeeter's face got long. "You don't aim to get rid of her?"

The old man put his shotgun over the mantel and lit his pipe. "Skeets, if you want that thing, I wouldn't get shed of her for a piece of bottom land a mile long. Already plowed and planted."

"I reckoned you wouldn't, 'cause you like me so much. And I know how you like dogs, 'cause I saw you cry when yours got killed. But you can have part of mine."

Jesse sat down and leaned back, blowing smoke into the air to drive away mosquitoes. The boy got a brick and hammer and began cracking nuts, pounding the meat to pulp so his uncle could chew it. Skeeter's yellow hair hadn't been cut for months and was tangled. He had freckles too. And his real name was Jonathan. His mother was Jesse's only sister and died when the child was born. No one thereabouts ever knew what happened to his father. Jesse, a leathery, toothless old man with faded blue eyes, took him to bring up and called him Skeeter because he was so little.

In the village, where Jesse seldom visited, folks wondered if he were fit'n to rear a little boy. They considered him shiftless and no-count. Jesse had lived all of his sixty years in the swamp and his way of life was a torment to folks who believed life must be lived by rules. He earned a few dollars selling jumbo frogs and pelts, but mostly he just paddled around the swamp, watching things and teaching Skeeter about life.

The villagers might have tried to send Skeeter to an orphanage, but for Joe (Cash) Watson, the storekeeper. Cash was a hard man, but fair. He often hunted with Jesse, and the old man had trained Cash's dogs. When there was talk of sending Skeeter away, Cash said, "You ain't agonna do it. You just don't take young'uns away from their folks." And that's all there was to it.

Jesse never coveted the "frills and furbelows of damn-fool folks" and yearned for only two things—a twenty-gauge shotgun for Skeeter and a set of Roebuckers for himself, as he called store-bought teeth. Cash had promised him the gun and the best false teeth in the catalogue for forty-six dollars. Jesse had saved $9.37.

"Someday I'm gonna get them Roebuckers," he often told Skeeter. "Then I'm gonna eat me enough roastin' ears to kill a goat. Maybe I can get a set with a couple of gold teeth in 'em. I seen a man once with six gold teeth."

Once Skeeter asked him, "Why don't you get a job with the W. P. and A. and make enough money to buy them Roebuckers?"

"I don't want 'em that bad," Jesse said.

So he was happy for Skeeter to have M'Lady, thinking the dog would sort of make up for the shotgun.

The boy cracked as many nuts as his uncle wanted, then put the hammer away. He was undressing when he glanced over at his dog. "Gosh, Uncle Jess. I'm scared somebody'll come get her."

"I ain't heard of nobody losing no things around here. If'n they had, they'd been to me 'fo' now, being's I know all about dogs and the swamp."

"That's so," Skeeter said. "But you don't reckon she belonged to another fellow like me, do you? I know how I'd feel if I had a dog like her and she got lost."

Jesse said, "She didn't belong to another fellow like you. If'n she had, she wouldn't be so happy here."

Skeeter fed M'Lady biscuits and molasses for breakfast, and although the Basenji ate it, she still was hungry when she went into the swamp with the boy. He was hoping he could find a bee tree or signs of wild hogs. They were at the edge of a clearing when M'Lady's chokebore nose suddenly tilted and she froze to a flash point, pausing only long enough to get set. Then she darted to the bayou, at least sixty yards away, dived into a clump of reeds and snatched a water rat. She was eating it when Skeeter ran up.

"Don't do that," he scolded. "Ain't you got no more sense than run into water after things? A snake or a gator might snatch you."

The Basenji dropped the rat and tucked her head. She knew the boy was displeased, and when she looked up at him her eyes were filled and a woebegone expression was on her face.

Skeeter tried to explain, "I didn't mean to hurt your feelings. Don't cry." He stepped back quickly and stared at her, at the tears in her eyes. "She is crying! Be John Brown!" Skeeter called her and ran toward the cabin, where Jesse was cutting splinters.

"Uncle Jess! Guess what else my dog can do!"

"Whistle?" the old man laughed.

"She can cry! I declare to goodness! Not out loud, but she can cry just the same."

Jesse knew that most dogs will get watery-eyed on occasion, but, not wanting to ridicule M'Lady's accomplishments, asked, "What made her cry?"

"Well, sir, we were walking along and all of a sudden she got a scent and flash pointed and then——" Skeeter remembered something.

"Then what?"

Skeeter sat on the steps. "Uncle Jess," he said slowly, "we must have been fifty or sixty yards from that rat when she smelled it."

"What rat? What's eating you?"

The child told him the story and Jesse couldn't believe it. For a dog to pick up the scent of a water rat at sixty yards simply isn't credible. Jesse reckoned Skeeter's love for M'Lady had led him to exaggerate.

Skeeter knew Jesse didn't believe the story, so he said, "Come on. I'll show you." He whistled for M'Lady.

The dog came up. "Hey," Jesse said. "That thing knows what a whistle means. Shows she's been around folks." He caught the dog's eye and commanded, "Heel!"

But M'Lady cocked her head quizzically. Then she turned to the boy and chuckled softly. She'd never heard the order before. That was obvious. Her nose came up into the breeze and she wheeled.

Her curved tail suddenly was still and her head was poised.

"Flash pointing," Jesse said. "Well, I'll be a monkey's uncle!"

M'Lady held the strange point only for a second, though, then dashed toward a corn patch about eighty yards from the cabin.

Halfway to the patch, she broke her gait and began creeping. A whir of feathered lightning sounded in the corn and a covey of quail exploded almost under her nose. She sprang and snatched a bird.

"Partridges!" Jesse's jaw dropped.

The child was as motionless as stone, his face white and his eyes wide in amazement. Finally he found his voice, "She was right here when she smelled them birds. A good eighty yards."

"I know she ain't no dog now," Jesse said. "Can't no dog do that."

"She's fast as greased lightning and ain't scared of nothing." Skeeter still was under the spell of the adventure. "She's a hunting dog from way back."

"She ain't no dog a-tall, I'm telling you. It ain't human." Jesse walked toward M'Lady and told her to fetch the bird, but the dog didn't understand. Instead, she pawed it. "Well," Jesse said. "One thing's certain. She ain't no bird hunter."

"She can do anything," Skeeter said. "Even hunt birds. Maybe I can make a bird dog out'n her. Wouldn't that be som'n?"

"You're batty. Maybe a coon dog, but not a bird dog. I know 'bout dogs."

"Me too," said Skeeter. And he did. He'd seen Jesse train many dogs, even pointers, and had helped him train Big Boy, Cash Watson's prize gun dog.

Jesse eyed Skeeter and read his mind.

"It can't be done, Skeets."

"Maybe not, but I aim to try. Any dog can run coons and rabbits, but it takes a pure D humdinger to hunt birds. Ain't no sin in trying, is it?"

"Naw," Jesse said slowly. "But she'll flush birds."

"I'll learn her not to."

"She won't hold no point. Any dog'll flash point. And she'll hunt rats."

"I'm gonna learn her just to hunt birds. And I'm starting right now," Skeeter said. He started walking away, then turned. "I seen a man once train a razorback hawg to point birds. You know as good as me that if a dog's got pure D hoss sense and a fellow's got bat brains, he can train the dog to hunt birds."

"Wanta bet?" Jesse issued the challenge in an effort to keep Skeeter's enthusiasm and determination at the high-water mark.

"Yes, sir. If I don't train my dog, then I'll cut all the splinters for a year. If I do, you cut 'em."

"It's a go," Jesse said.

Skeeter ran to the bayou and recovered the rat M'Lady had killed. He tied it around his dog's neck. The Basenji was indignant and tried to claw off the hateful burden. Failing, she ran into the house and under a bed, but Skeeter made her come out. M'Lady filled up then and her face assumed that don't-nobody-love-me look. The boy steeled himself, tapped M'Lady's nose with the rat, and left it around her neck.

"You done whittled out a job for yourself," Jesse said. "If'n you get her trained, you'll lose her in the brush. She's too fast and too little to keep up with."

"I'll bell her," Skeeter said. "I'm gonna learn her ever'thing. I got us a gun dog, Uncle Jess."

The old man sat on the porch and propped against the wall. "Bud, I don't know what that thing is. But you're a thoroughbred. John dog my hide!"

If Skeeter had loved M'Lady one bit less, his patience would have exploded during the ordeal of training the Basenji. It takes judgment and infinite patience to train a bird dog properly, but to train a Basenji, that'll hunt anything, to concentrate only on quail took something more than discipline and patience. It never could have been done except for that strange affinity between a boy and a dog, and the blind faith of a child.

M'Lady's devotion to Skeeter was so complete that she was anxious to do anything to earn a pat. It wasn't difficult to teach her to heel and follow at Skeeter's feet regardless of the urge to dash away and chase rabbits. The boy used a clothesline as a guide rope and made M'Lady follow him. The first time the dog tried to chase an animal, Skeeter pinched the rope around her neck just a bit and commanded, "Heel!" And when she obeyed, Skeeter released the noose. It took M'Lady only a few hours to associate disobedience with disfavor.

The dog learned that when she chased and killed a rat or rabbit, the thing would be tied around her neck. The only things she could hunt without being disciplined were quail. Of course, she often mistook the scent of game chickens for quail and hunted them, but Skeeter punished her by scolding. He never switched his dog, but to M'Lady a harsh word from the boy hurt more than a hickory limb.

Jesse watched the dog's progress and pretended not to be impressed. He never volunteered suggestions. M'Lady learned quickly, but the task of teaching her to point birds seemed hopeless. Skeeter knew she'd never point as pointers do, so he worked out his own system. He taught her to stand motionless when he shouted "Hup!" One day she got a scent of birds, paused or pointed for a moment as most animals will, and was ready to spring away when Skeeter said "Hup!"

M'Lady was confused. Every instinct urged her to chase the birds, but her master had said stand still. She broke, however, and Skeeter scolded her. She pouted at first, then filled up, but the boy ignored her until she obeyed the next command, then he patted her and she chuckled.

The lessons continued for days and weeks, and slowly and surely M'Lady learned her chores. She learned that the second she smelled birds she must stop and stand still until Skeeter flushed them. That she must not quiver when he shot.

Teaching her to fetch was easy, but teaching her to retrieve dead birds without damaging them was another matter. M'Lady had a hard mouth—that is, she sank her teeth into the birds. Skeeter used one of the oldest hunting tricks of the backwoods to break her.

He got a stick and wrapped it with wire and taught his dog to fetch it. Only once did M'Lady bite hard on the stick, and then the wire hurt her sensitive mouth. Soon she developed a habit of carrying the stick on her tongue and supporting it lightly with her teeth. Skeeter tied quail feathers on the stick, and soon M'Lady's education was complete.

Skeeter led Jesse into a field one day and turned his dog loose. She flashed to a point almost immediately. It was a funny point and Jesse almost laughed. The dog's curved tail poked up over her back, she spraddled her front legs and sort of squatted, her nose pointing the birds, more than forty yards away. She remained rigid until the boy flushed and shot, then she leaped away, seeking and fetching dead birds.

Jesse was mighty proud. "Well, Skeets, looks like you got yourself a bird hunter."

"Yes, sir," Skeeter said. "And you got yourself a job." He pointed toward the kindling pile.

The swamp was dressing for winter when Cash Watson drove down that day to give his Big Boy a workout in the wild brush.

He fetched Jesse a couple of cans of smoking tobacco and Skeeter a bag of peppermint jawbreakers. He locked his fine pointer in the corncrib for the night and was warming himself in the cabin when he noticed M'Lady for the first time. She was sleeping in front of the fire.

"What's that?" he asked.

"My dog," said Skeeter. "Ain't she a beaut?"

"She sure is," Cash grinned at Jesse. Skeeter went out to the well and Cash asked his old friend, "What the devil kind of mutt is that?"

"Search me," Jesse said. "Skeets found her in the swamp. I reckon she's got a trace of bloodhound in her and some terrier and a heap of just plain dog."

M'Lady cocked one ear and got up and stretched; then, apparently not liking the company, turned her tail toward Cash and strutted out, looking for Skeeter.

The men laughed. "Som'n wrong with her throat," Jesse said. "She can't bark. When she tries, she makes a funny sound, sort of a cackling, chuckling yodel. Sounds like she's laughing."

"Well," Cash said, "trust a young'un to love the orner'st dog he can find."

"Wait a minute," Jesse said. "She ain't no-count. She's a bird-hunting fool."

Just then Skeeter entered and Cash jestingly said, "Hear you got yourself a bird dog, son."

The boy clasped his hands behind him and rocked on the balls of his feet as he had seen the men do. "Well, now, I'll tell you, Mr. Cash. M'Lady does ever'thing except tote the gun."

"She must be fair to middling. Why not take her out with Big Boy tomorrow? Do my dog good to hunt in a brace."

"Me and my dog don't want to show Big Boy up. He's a pretty good ol' dog."

"Whoa!" Cash was every inch a bird-dog man and nobody could challenge him without a showdown. Besides, Skeeter was shooting up and should be learning a few things about life. "Any old boiler can pop off steam." Cash winked at Jesse.

"Well, now, sir, if you're itching for a run, I'll just double-dog dare you to run your dog against mine. And anybody who'll take a dare will pull up young cotton and push a widow woman's ducks in the water."

Cash admired the boy's confidence. "All right, son. It's a deal. What are the stakes?"

Skeeter started to mention the twenty-gauge gun he wanted, but changed his mind quickly. He reached down and patted M'Lady, then looked up. "If my dog beats yours, then you get them Roebuckers for Uncle Jess."

Jesse's chest suddenly was tight. Cash glanced from the boy to the man and he, too, was proud of Skeeter. "I wasn't aiming to go that high. But all right. What do I get if I win?"

"I'll cut you ten cords of stove-wood."

"And a stack of splinters?"

"Yes, sir."

Cash offered his hand and Skeeter took it. "It's a race," Cash said. "Jesse will be the judge."

The wind was rustling the sage and there was a nip in the early-morning air when they took the dogs to a clearing and set them down. Skeeter snapped a belt around M'Lady's neck and, at word from Jesse, the dogs were released.

Big Boy bounded away and began circling, ranging into the brush. M'Lady tilted her nose into the wind and ripped away toward the sage, her bell tinkling. Cash said, "She sure covers ground." Skeeter made no effort to keep up with her, but waited until he couldn't hear the bell, then ran for a clearing where he had last heard it. And there was M'Lady on a point.

Cash almost laughed out loud. "That ain't no point, son. That's a squat."

"She's got birds."

"Where?"

Jesse leaned against a tree and watched the fun.

Skeeter pointed toward a clump of sage. "She's pointing birds in that sage."

Cash couldn't restrain his mirth. "Boy, now that's what I call some pointing. Why, Skeeter, it's sixty or seventy yards to that sage."

Just then Big Boy flashed by M'Lady, his head high. He raced to the edge of the sage, caught the wind, then whipped around, freezing to a point. Cash called Jesse's attention to the point.

"That's M'Lady's point," Skeeter said. "She's got the same birds Big Boy has."

Jesse sauntered up. "The boy's right, Cash. I aimed to keep my mouth out'n this race, but M'Lady is pointing them birds. She can catch scents up to eighty yards."

Cash said, "Aw, go on. You're crazy." He walked over and flushed the birds.

Skeeter picked one off and ordered M'Lady to fetch. When she returned with the bird, the boy patted her and she began chuckling.

Cash really studied her then for the first time. "Hey!" he said suddenly. "A Basenji! That's a Basenji!"

"A what?" Jesse asked.

"I should have known." Cash was very excited. "That's the dog that was lost by them rich Yankees. I saw about it in the paper." He happened to look at Skeeter then and wished he had cut out his tongue.

The boy's lips were compressed and his face was drawn and white. Jesse had closed his eyes and was rubbing his forehead.

Cash, trying to dismiss the subject, said, "Just 'cause it was in the paper don't make it so. I don't believe that's the same dog, come to think of it."

"Do you aim to tell 'em where the dog is?" Skeeter asked.

Cash looked at Jesse, then at the ground. "It ain't none of my business."

"How 'bout you, Uncle Jess?"

"I ain't telling nobody nothin'."

"I know she's the same dog," Skeeter said. "On account of I just know it. But she's mine now." His voice rose and trembled. "And ain't nobody gonna take her away from me." He ran into the swamp. M'Lady was at his heels.

Cash said, "Durn my lip. I'm sorry, Jesse. If I'd kept my big mouth shut he'd never known the difference."

"It can't be helped now," Jesse said.

" 'Course she beat Big Boy. Them's the best hunting dogs in the world. And she's worth a mint of money."

They didn't feel up to hunting and returned to the cabin and sat on the porch. Neither had much to say, but kept glancing toward the swamp where Skeeter and M'Lady were walking along the bayou. "Don't you worry," he said tenderly. "Ain't nobody gonna bother you."

He sat on a stump and M'Lady put her head on his knee. She wasn't worrying. Nothing could have been more contented than she was.

"I don't care if the sheriff comes down." Skeeter pulled her onto his lap and held her. "I don't give a whoop if the governor comes down. Even the President of the United States! The whole shebang can come, but ain't nobody gonna mess with you."

His words gave him courage and he felt better, but for only a minute. Then the tug-of-war between him and his conscience started.

"Once I found a Barlow knife and kept it and it was all right," he mumbled.

But this is different.

"Finders, keepers; losers, weepers."

No, Skeeter.

"Well, I don't care. She's mine."

Remember what your Uncle Jess said.

"He said a heap of things."

Yes, but you remember one thing more than the rest. He said, "Certain things are right and certain things are wrong. And nothing ain't gonna ever change that. When you learn that, then you're fit'n to be a man." Remember, Skeeter?

A feeling of despair and loneliness almost overwhelmed him. He fought off the tears as long as he could, but finally he gave in, and his sobs caused M'Lady to peer into his face and wonder why he was acting that way when she was so happy. He put his arms around her neck and pulled her to him. "My li'l' old puppy dog. Poor li'l' old puppy dog. But I got to do it."

He sniffed back his tears and got up and walked to the cabin. M'Lady curled up by the fire and the boy sat down, watching the logs splutter for several minutes. Then he said, almost in a whisper, "Uncle Jess, if you keep som'n that ain't yours, it's the same as stealing, ain't it?"

Cash leaned against the mantel and stared into the fire.

Jesse puffed his pipe slowly. "Son, that's som'n you got to settle with yourself."

Skeeter stood and turned his back to the flames, warming his hands.

"Mr. Cash," he said slowly, "when you get back to your store, please let them folks know their dog is here."

"If that's how it is——"

"That's how it is," Skeeter said.

The firelight dancing on Jesse's face revealed the old man's dejection, and Skeeter, seeing it, said quickly, "It's best for M'Lady. She's too good for the swamp. They'll give her a good home."

Jesse flinched, and Cash, catching the hurt look in his friend's eyes, said, "Your dog outhunted mine, Skeets. You win them Roebuckers for your uncle."

"I don't want 'em," Jesse said, rather childishly. "I don't care if'n I never eat no roastin' ears." He got up quickly and hurried outside. Cash reckoned he'd better be going, and left Skeeter by the fire, rubbing his dog.

Jesse came back in directly and pulled up a chair. Skeeter started to speak, but Jesse spoke first. "I been doing a heap of thinking lately. You're sprouting up. The swamp ain't no place for you."

Skeeter forgot about his dog and faced his uncle, bewildered.

"I reckon you're too good for the swamp too," Jesse said. "I'm aiming to send you into town for a spell. I can make enough to keep you in fit'n clothes and all." He dared not look at the boy.

"Uncle Jess!" Skeeter said reproachfully. "You don't mean that. You're just saying that on account of what I said about M'Lady. I said it just to keep you from feeling so bad about our dog going away. Gee m'netty, Uncle Jess. I ain't ever gonna leave you." He buried his face in his uncle's shoulder. M'Lady put her head on Jesse's knee and he patted the boy and rubbed the dog.

"Reckon I'll take them Roebuckers," he said at last. "I been wanting some for a long, long time."

Several days later Cash drove down and told them the man from the kennels was at his store. Skeeter didn't say a word, but called M'Lady and they got in Cash's car. All the way to town, the boy was silent. He held his dog's head in his lap.

The keeper took just one look at M'Lady and said, "That's she, all right. Miss Congo III." He turned to speak to Skeeter, but the boy was walking away. He got a glance at Skeeter's face, however. "Hell," he muttered. "I wish you fellows hadn't told me. I hate to take a dog away from a kid."

"He wanted you to know," Cash said.

"Mister"—Jesse closed his left eye and struck his swapping nose—"I'd like to swap you out'n that hound. Now, course she ain't much 'count——"

The keeper smiled in spite of himself. "If she was mine, I'd give her to the kid. But she's not for sale. The owner wants to breed her and establish her line in this country. And if she was for sale, she'd cost more money than any of us will ever see." He called Skeeter and offered his hand. Skeeter shook it.

"You're a good kid. There's a reward for this dog."

"I don't want no reward." The boy's words tumbled out. "I don't want nothing, except to be left alone. You've got your dog, mister. Take her and go on. Please." He walked away again, fearing he would cry.

Cash said, "I'll take the reward and keep it for him. Someday he'll want it."

Jesse went out to the store porch to be with Skeeter. The keeper handed Cash the money. "It's tough, but the kid'll get over it. The dog never will."

"Is that a fact?"

"Yep. I know the breed. They never forget. That dog'll never laugh again. They never laugh unless they're happy."

He walked to the post where Skeeter had tied M'Lady. He untied the leash and started toward his station wagon. M'Lady braced her front feet and looked around for the boy. Seeing him on the porch, she jerked away from the keeper and ran to her master.

She rubbed against his legs. Skeeter tried to ignore her. The keeper reached for the leash again and M'Lady crouched, baring her fangs. The keeper shrugged, a helpless gesture.

"Wild elephants couldn't pull that dog away from that boy," he said.

"That's all right, mister." Skeeter unsnapped the leash and tossed it to the keeper. Then he walked to the station wagon, opened the door of a cage and called, "Heah, M'Lady!" she bounded to him. "Up!" he commanded. She didn't hesitate, but leaped into the cage. The keeper locked the door.

M'Lady, having obeyed a command, poked her nose between the bars, expecting a pat. The boy rubbed her head. She tried to move closer to him, but the bars held her. She looked quizzically at the bars, then tried to nudge them aside. Then she clawed them. A look of fear suddenly came to her eyes and she fastened them on Skeeter, wistfully at first, then pleadingly. She couldn't make a sound, for her unhappiness had sealed her throat. Slowly her eyes filled up.

"Don't cry no more, M'Lady. Ever'thing's gonna be all right." He reached out to pat her, but the station wagon moved off, leaving him standing there in the dust.

Back on the porch, Jesse lit his pipe and said to his friend, "Cash, the boy has lost his dog and I've lost a boy."

"Aw, Jesse, Skeeter wouldn't leave you."

"That ain't what I mean. He's growned up, Cash. He don't look no older, but he is. He growed up that day in the swamp."

Skeeter walked into the store and Cash followed him. "I've got that reward for you, Jonathan."

It was the first time anyone ever had called him that and it sounded like man talk.

"And that twenty-gauge is waiting for you," Cash said. "I'm gonna give it to you."

"Thank you, Mr. Cash." The boy bit his lower lip. "But I don't aim to do no more hunting. I don't never want no more dogs."

"Know how you feel. But if you change your mind, the gun's here for you."

Skeeter looked back toward the porch where Jesse was waiting, and said, "Tell you what, though. When you get them Roebuckers, get some with a couple of gold teeth in 'em. Take it out of the reward money."

"Sure, Jonathan."

Jesse joined them, and Skeeter said, "We better be getting back toward the house."

"I'll drive you down," Cash said. "But first I aim to treat you to some lemon pop and sardines."

"That's mighty nice of you," Jesse said, "but we better be gettin' on."

"What's the hurry?" Cash opened the pop.

"It's my time to cut splinters," Jesse said. "That's what I get for betting with a good man."

That's What Happened to Me

MICHAEL FESSIER

I HAVE done things and had things happen to me and nobody knows about it. So I am writing about it so that people will know. Although there are a lot of things I could tell about, I will just tell about the jumping because that is the most important. It gave me the biggest thrill. I mean high jumping, standing and running. You probably never heard of a standing high jumper but that's what I was. I was the greatest jumper ever was.

I was going to high school and I wasn't on any team. I couldn't be because I had to work for a drug store and wash bottles and deliver medicine and sweep the floor. So I couldn't go out for any of the teams because the job started soon's school was over. I used to crab to the fellows about how old man Patch made me wash so many bottles and so they got to calling me Bottles Barton and I didn't like it. They'd call me Bottles in front of the girls and the girls'd giggle.

Once I poked one of the fellows for calling me Bottles. He was a big fellow and he played on the football team and I wouldn't have hit him because I was little and couldn't fight very well. But he called me Bottles before Anna Louise Daniels and she laughed and I was so mad I didn't know whether I wanted to hit her or the football player but finally I hit him. He caught my arm and threw me down and sat on me and pulled my nose.

"Look, Anna Louise," he said, "it stretches."

He pulled my nose again and Anna Louise put her arms around herself and jumped up and down and laughed and then I knew that it was her I should have taken the first poke at. I was more mad at her than the football player although it was him pulling my nose and sitting on me.

The next day I met Anna Louise in the hall going to the ancient history class and she was with a couple of other girls and I tried to go past without them noticing me. I don't know why but I had a funny feeling like as if somebody was going to throw a rock at me or something. Anna Louise looked at me and giggled.

"Hello, old rubbernose," she said.

The girls giggled and I hurried down the hall and felt sick and mad and kind of like I was running away from a fight, although nobody'd expect me to fight a girl. And so they called me Bottles sometimes and Rubbernose other times and always whoever was near would laugh. They didn't think it was funny because Jimmy Wilkins was called Scrubby or Jack Harris was called Doodles. But they thought it was funny I was called Rubbernose and Bottles and they never got tired of laughing. It was a new joke every time.

Scrubby pitched for the baseball team and Doodles was quarterback of the football team.

I could have pitched for the baseball team or played quarterback on the football team. I could have pitched no hit games and I could have made touchdowns from my own ten yard line. I know I could. I had it all figured out. I went over how I'd throw the ball and how the batter'd miss and it was easy. I figured out how to run and dodge and straight-arm and that was easy too. But I didn't get the chance because I had to go right to Patch's Drug Store after school was out.

Old man Patch was a pretty good guy but his wife she was nothing but a crab. I'd wash bottles and old man Patch he would look at them and not say anything. But Mrs. Patch, old lady Patch, she would look at the bottles and wrinkle her nose and make me wash half of them over again. When I swept up at night she'd always find some corner I'd missed and she'd bawl me out. She was fat and her hair was all straggly and I wondered why in the deuce old man Patch ever married her, although I guess maybe she didn't look so awful when she was a girl. She couldn't have been very pretty though.

They lived in back of the drug store and when people came in at noon or at six o'clock either old man or old lady Patch'd come out still chewing their food and look at the customer and swallow and then ask him what he wanted.

I studied salesmanship at high school and I figured this wasn't very good for business and I wanted to tell them but I never did.

One of the fellows at school was in waiting for a prescription and he saw me working at some of the things I did at the drug store. So when another fellow asked me what I did this fellow he laughed and said, "Old Bottles! Why, he rates at that store. Yes he does! He rates like an Armenian's helper."

That's about the way I did rate but I was planning on how I'd someday own a real, modern drug store and run the Patches out of business so I didn't mind so much.

What I did mind was Anna Louise at school. She was the daughter of a doctor and she thought she was big people and maybe she was but she wasn't any better'n me. Maybe my clothes weren't so good but that was only temporary. I planned on having twenty suits some day.

I wanted to go up to her and say, "Look here, Anna Louise, you're not so much. Your father isn't a millionaire and some day I'm going to be one. I'm going to have a million dollars and twenty suits of clothes." But I never did.

After she laughed at me and started calling me Rubbernose, I began planning on doing things to make her realize I wasn't what she thought I was. That's how the jumping came about.

It was the day before the track meet and everybody was talking about whether or not our school could win. They figured we'd have to win the high jump and pole vault to do it.

"Lord, if we only had old Heck Hansen back," said Goobers MacMartin. "He'd outjump those Fairfield birds two inches in the high and a foot in the pole vault."

"Yeah," somebody else said, "but we haven't got Heck Hansen. What we got is pretty good but not good enough. Wish we had a jumper."

"We sure need one," I said.

There was a group of them all talking, boys and girls, and I was sort of on the outside listening.

"Who let you in?" Goobers asked me.

Frank Shay grabbed me by the arm and dragged me into the center of the circle.

"The very man we've been looking for," he said. "Yessir. Old Bottles Rubbernose Barton. He can win the jumping events for us."

"Come on, Bottles," they said. "Save the day for us. Be a good old Rubbernose."

Anna Louise was one who laughed the most and it was the third time I'd wanted to pop her on the nose.

I went away from there and didn't turn back when they laughed and called and whistled at me.

"She'd be surprised if I did," I said.

I kept thinking this over and pretty soon I said, "Well, maybe you could."

Then when I was sweeping the drug store floor I all of a sudden said, "I can."

"You can what?" Mrs. Patch asked me.

"Nothing," I said.

"You can hurry about sweeping the floor, that's what you can do," she said.

There was a big crowd out for the track meet and we were tied when I went up to our coach. It was just time for the jumping to start.

"What the hell you doing in a track suit?" he asked me.

"I'm going to save the day for Brinkley," I said. "I'm going to jump."

"No, you aren't," he said. "You run along and start a marble game with some other kid."

I looked him in the eye and I spoke in a cold, level tone of voice.

"Mr. Smith," I said, "the track meet depends on the high jump and the pole vault and unless I am entered we will lose those two events and the meet. I can win and I am willing to do it for Brinkley. Do you want to win the meet?"

He looked amazed.

"Where have you been all the time?" he asked. "You talk like you've got something on the ball."

I didn't say anything, I just smiled.

The crowd all rushed over to the jumping pits and I took my time going over. When everybody had jumped but me the coach turned and said, "Come on now, Barton, let's see what you can do."

"Not yet," I said.

"What do you mean?" he asked.

"I'll wait until the last man has been eliminated," I said. "Then I'll jump."

The crowd laughed but I just stared coldly at them. The coach tried to persuade me to jump but I wouldn't change my mind.

"I stake everything on one jump," I said. "Have faith in me."

He looked at me and shook his head and said, "Have it your own way."

They started the bar a little over four feet and pretty soon it was creeping up toward five feet and a half. That's always been a pretty good distance for high school jumpers. When the bar reached five feet seven inches all our men except one was eliminated. Two from Fairfield were still in the event. They put the bar at five feet nine inches and one man from Fairfield made it. Our man tried hard but he scraped the bar and knocked it off.

The crowd started yelling, thinking Fairfield had won the event.

"Wait a minute," I yelled. "I haven't jumped yet."

The judges looked at their lists and saw it was so. Maybe you think it was against the rules for them to allow me to skip my turn but anyway that's the way it was.

"You can't make that mark," one of the judges said. "Why try? You're not warmed up."

"Never mind," I said.

I walked up close to the jumping standard and stood there.

"Go ahead and jump," one of the judges said.

"I will," I said.

"Well, don't stand there," he said. "Come on back here so's you can get a run at it."

"I don't want any run at the bar," I said. "I'll jump from here."

The judge yelled at the coach and told him to take me out on account of I was crazy.

I swung my arms in back of me and sprung up and down a second and then I jumped over the bar with inches to spare. When I came down it was so silent I could hear my footsteps as I walked across the sawdust pit. The judge that'd crabbed at me just stood and looked. His eyes were bugged out and his mouth hung open.

"Good Lord!" he said. "Almighty most loving Lord!"

Our coach came up and he stood beside the judge and they both looked the same, bug-eyed.

"Did you see that?" the coach asked. "Tell me you didn't. Please do. I'd rather lose this track meet than my mind."

The judge turned slowly and looked at him.

"Good Lord!" he said, "there's two of us."

All of a sudden everybody started yelling and the fellows near me pounded me on the back and tried to shake my hand. I smiled and brushed them aside and walked over to the judge.

"What's the high school record for this state?" I asked.

"Five feet eleven inches," he said.

"Put her at six," I said.

They put the bar at six and I gathered myself together and gave a heave and went over the bar like I was floating. It was easy. Well, that just knocked the wind out of everybody. They'd thought I couldn't do anything and there I'd broken the state record for the high jump without a running start.

The crowd surrounded me and tried to shake my hand and the coach and judge got off to one side and reached out and pinched each other's cheek and looked at the bar and shook their heads. Frank Shay grabbed my hand and wrung it and said, "Gosh, Bottles, I was just kidding the other day. I didn't know you were such a ring-tailed wonder. Say, Bottles, we're having a frat dance tonight. Will you come?"

"You know what you can do with your frat," I said. "I don't approve of them. They're undemocratic."

A lot of the fellows that'd made fun of me before crowded around and acted as if I'd been their friend all along.

When Anna Louise crowded through the gang and said, "Oh, you're marvelous," I just smiled at her and said, "Do you think so?" and walked away. She tagged around after me but I talked mostly with two other girls.

They didn't usually have a public address system at our track meets but they started using one then.

"Ladies and gentlemen," the announcer said, "you have just witnessed a record-breaking performance by Bottles Barton——."

He went on like that telling them what an astonishing thing I'd done and it came to me I didn't mind being called Bottles any more. In fact, I kind of liked it.

Mr. and Mrs. Patch came up and Mrs. Patch tried to kiss me but I wouldn't let her. Old man Patch shook my hand.

"You've made our drug store famous," he said. "From now on you're a clerk. No more bottle washing."

"We'll make him a partner," old lady Patch said.

"No, you won't," I said. "I think I'll go over to the McManus Pharmacy."

Then they called the pole vault and I did like I'd done before. I wouldn't jump until our men'd been eliminated. The bar was at eleven feet.

"It's your turn," our coach told me. "Ever use a pole before?"

"Oh, sure," I told him.

He gave me a pole and the crowd cleared away and grew silent. Everyone was watching me.

I threw the pole down and smiled at the crowd. The coach yelled for me to pick up the pole and jump. I picked it up and threw it ten feet away from me. Everybody gasped. Then I took a short run and went over the bar at eleven feet. It was simple.

This time the coach and the judge took pins and poked them in one another's cheeks. The coach grabbed me and said, "When I wake up I'm going to be so mad at you I'm going to give you the beating of your life."

Anna Louise came up and held my arm and said, "Oh, Bottles, you're so wonderful. I've always thought so. Please forgive me for calling you Rubbernose. I want you to come to our party tonight."

"All right," I said. "I'll forgive you but don't you call me Rubbernose again."

They moved the bar up again and the fellow from Fairfield couldn't make it. I took a short run and went over. I did it so easy it came to me I could fly if I wanted to but I decided not to try it on account of people wouldn't think it so wonderful if a fellow that could fly jumped eleven feet without a pole. I'd won the track meet for Brinkley High and the students all came down out of the stand and put me on their shoulders and paraded me around and around the track. A lot of fellows were waving papers at me asking me to sign them and get $1000 a week as a professional jumper. I signed one which threw in an automobile.

That's what I did once and nobody knows about it, so I am writing about it so that people will know.

Two Soldiers

WILLIAM FAULKNER

Me and Pete would go down to Old Man Killegrew's and listen to his radio. We would wait until after supper, after dark, and we would stand outside Old Man Killegrew's parlor window, and we could hear it because Old Man Killegrew's wife was deaf, and so he run the radio as loud as it would run, and so me and Pete could hear it plain as Old Man Killegrew's wife could, I reckon, even standing outside with the window closed.

And that night I said, "What? Japanese? What's a pearl harbor?" and Pete said, "Hush."

And so we stood there, it was cold, listening to the fellow in the radio talking, only I couldn't make no heads nor tails neither out of it. Then the fellow said that would be all for a while, and me and Pete walked back up the road to home, and Pete told me what it was. Because he was nigh twenty and he had done finished the Consolidated last June and he knowed a heap: about them Japanese dropping bombs on Pearl Harbor and that Pearl Harbor was across the water.

"Across what water?" I said. "Across that Government reservoy up at Oxford?"

"Naw," Pete said. "Across the big water. The Pacific Ocean."

We went home. Maw and Pap was already asleep, and me and Pete laid in the bed, and I still couldn't understand where it was, and Pete told me again—the Pacific Ocean.

"What's the matter with you?" Pete said. "You're going on nine years old. You been in school now ever since September. Ain't you learned nothing yet?"

"I reckon we ain't got as fer as the Pacific Ocean yet," I said.

We was still sowing the vetch then that ought to been all finished by the fifteenth of November, because Pap was still behind, just like he had been ever since me and Pete had knowed him. And we had firewood to git in, too, but every night me and Pete would go down to Old Man Killegrew's and stand outside his parlor window in the cold and listen to his radio;

then we would come back home and lay in the bed and Pete would tell me what it was. That is, he would tell me for a while. Then he wouldn't tell me. It was like he didn't want to talk about it no more. He would tell me to shut up because he wanted to go to sleep, but he never wanted to go to sleep.

He would lay there, a heap stiller than if he was asleep, and it would be something, I could feel it coming out of him, like he was mad at me even, only I knowed he wasn't thinking about me, or like he was worried about something, and it wasn't that neither, because he never had nothing to worry about. He never got behind like Pap, let alone stayed behind. Pap give him ten acres when he graduated from the Consolidated, and me and Pete both reckoned Pap was durn glad to get shut of at least ten acres, less to have to worry with himself; and Pete had them ten acres all sowed to vetch and busted out and bedded for the winter, and so it wasn't that. But it was something. And still we would go down to Old Man Killegrew's every night and listen to his radio, and they was at it in the Philippines now, but General MacArthur was holding um. Then we would come back home and lay in the bed, and Pete wouldn't tell me nothing or talk a-tall. He would just lay there still as a ambush and when I would touch him, his side or his leg would feel hard and still as iron, until after a while I would go to sleep.

Then one night—it was the first time he had said nothing to me except to jump on me about not chopping enough wood at the wood tree where we was cutting—he said, "I got to go."

"Go where?" I said.

"To that war," Pete said.

"Before we even finish gittin' in the firewood?"

"Firewood, hell," Pete said.

"All right," I said. "When we going to start?"

But he wasn't even listening. He laid there, hard and still as iron in the dark. "I got to go," he said. "I jest ain't going to put up with no folks treating the Unity States that way."

"Yes," I said. "Firewood or no firewood, I reckon we got to go."

This time he heard me. He laid still again, but it was a different kind of still.

"You?" he said. "To a war?"

"You'll whup the big uns and I'll whup the little uns," I said.

Then he told me I couldn't go. At first I thought he just never wanted me tagging after him, like he wouldn't leave me go with him when he went sparking them girls of Tull's. Then he told me the Army wouldn't leave me go because I was too little, and then I knowed he really meant it and that I couldn't go nohow noways. And somehow I hadn't believed until then that he was going himself, but now I knowed he was and that he wasn't going to leave me go with him a-tall.

"I'll chop the wood and tote the water for you-all then!" I said. "You got to have wood and water!"

Anyway, he was listening to me now. He wasn't like iron now.

He turned onto his side and put his hand on my chest because it was me that was laying straight and hard on my back now.

"No," he said. "You got to stay here and help Pap."

"Help him what?" I said. "He ain't never caught up nohow. He can't get no further behind. He can sholy take care of this little shirttail of a farm while me and you are whupping them Japanese. I got to go too. If you got to go, then so have I."

"No," Pete said. "Hush now. Hush." And he meant it, and I knowed he did. Only I made sho from his own mouth. I quit.

"So I just can't go then," I said.

"No," Pete said. "You just can't go. You're too little, in the first place, and in the second place—".

"All right," I said. "Then shut up and leave me go to sleep."

So he hushed then and laid back. And I laid there like I was already asleep, and pretty soon he was asleep and I knowed it was the wanting to go to the war that had worried him and kept him awake, and now that he had decided to go, he wasn't worried any more.

The next morning he told Maw and Pap. Maw was all right. She cried.

"No," she said, crying, "I don't want him to go. I would rather go myself in his place, if I could. I don't want to save the country. Them Japanese could take it and keep it, so long as they left me and my family and my children alone. But I remember my brother Marsh in that other war. He had to go to that one when he wasn't but nineteen, and our mother couldn't understand it then any more than I can now. But she told Marsh if he had to go, he had to go. And so, if Pete's got to go to this one, he's got to go to it. Jest don't ask me to understand why."

But Pap was the one. He was the feller. "To the war?" he said. "Why, I just don't see a bit of use in that. You ain't old enough for the draft, and the country ain't being invaded. Our President in Washington, D. C., is watching the conditions and he will notify us. Besides, in that other war your ma just mentioned, I was drafted and sent clean to Texas and was held there nigh eight months until they finally quit fighting. It seems to me that that, along with your Uncle Marsh who received a actual wound on the battlefields of France, is enough for me and mine to have to do to protect the country, at least in my lifetime. Besides, what'll I do for help on the farm with you gone? It seems to me I'll get mighty far behind."

"You been behind as long as I can remember," Pete said. "Anyway, I'm going. I got to."

"Of course he's got to go," I said. "Them Japanese—"

"You hush your mouth!" Maw said, crying. "Nobody's talking to you! Go and get me a armful of wood! That's what you can do!"

So I got the wood. And all the next day, while me and Pete and Pap was getting in as much wood as we could in that time because Pete said how Pap's idea of plenty of wood was one more stick laying against the wall that Maw ain't put on the fire yet, Maw was getting Pete ready to go. She washed and mended his clothes and cooked him a shoe box of vittles. And that night me and Pete laid in the bed and listened to her packing his grip and crying, until after a while Pete got up in his nightshirt and went back there, and I could hear them talking, until at last Maw said, "You got to go, and so I want you to go. But I don't understand it, and I won't never, and so don't expect me to." And Pete come back and got into the bed again and laid again still and hard as iron on his back, and then he said, and he wasn't talking to me, he wasn't talking to nobody: "I got to go. I just got to."

"Sho you got to," I said. "Them Japanese—" He turned over hard, he kind of surged over onto his side, looking at me in the dark.

"Anyway, you're all right," he said. "I expected to have more trouble with you than with all the rest of them put together."

"I reckon I can't help it neither," I said. "But maybe it will run a few years longer and I can get there. Maybe someday I will jest walk in on you."

"I hope not," Pete said. "Folks don't go to wars for fun. A man don't leave his maw crying just for fun."

"Then why are you going?" I said.

"I got to," he said. "I just got to. Now you go on to sleep. I got to ketch that early bus in the morning."

"All right," I said. "I hear tell Memphis is a big place. How will you find where the Army's at?"

"I'll ask somebody where to go to join it," Pete said. "Go on to sleep now."

"Is that what you'll ask for? Where to join the Army?" I said.

"Yes," Pete said. He turned onto his back again. "Shut up and go to sleep."

We went to sleep. The next morning we et breakfast by lamplight because the bus would pass at six o'clock. Maw wasn't crying now. She jest looked grim and busy, putting breakfast on the table while we et it. Then she finished packing Pete's grip, except he never wanted to take no grip to the war, but Maw said decent folks never went nowhere, not even to a war, without a change of clothes and something to tote them in. She put in the shoe box of fried chicken and biscuits and she put the Bible in, too, and then it was time to go. We didn't know until then that Maw wasn't going to the bus. She jest brought Pete's cap and overcoat, and still she didn't cry no more, she jest stood with her hands on Pete's shoulders and she didn't move, but somehow, and just holding Pete's shoulders, she looked as hard and fierce as when Pete had turned toward me in the bed last night and tole me that anyway I was all right.

"They could take the country and keep the country, so long as they never bothered me and mine," she said. Then she said, "Don't never forget who you are. You ain't rich and the rest of the world outside of Frenchman's Bend never heard of you. But your blood is good as any blood anywhere, and don't you never forget it."

Then she kissed him, and then we was out of the house, with Pap toting Pete's grip whether Pete wanted him to or not. There wasn't no dawn even yet, not even after we had stood on the highway by the mailbox, awhile. Then we seen the lights of the bus coming and I was watching the bus until it come up and Pete flagged it, and then, sho enough, there was daylight—it had started while I wasn't watching. And now me and Pete expected Pap to say something else foolish, like he done before, about how Uncle Marsh getting wounded in France and that trip to Texas Pap taken in 1918 ought to be enough to save the Unity States in 1942, but he never. He done all right too. He jest said, "Good-by, son. Always remember what your ma told you and write her whenever you find the time." Then he shaked Pete's hand, and Pete looked at me a minute and put his hand on my head and rubbed my head durn nigh hard enough to wring my neck off and jumped into the bus, and the feller wound the door shut and the bus begun to hum; then it was moving, humming and grinding and whining louder and louder; it was going fast, with two little red lights behind it that never seemed to get no littler, but jest seemed to be running together until pretty soon they would touch and jest be one light. But they never did, and then the bus was gone, and even like it was, I could have pretty nigh busted out crying, nigh to nine years old and all.

Me and Pap went back to the house. All that day we worked at the wood tree, and so I never had no good chance until about middle of the afternoon. Then I taken my slingshot and I would have liked to took all my bird eggs, too, because Pete had give me his collection and he holp me with mine, and he would like to git the box out and look at them as good as I would, even if he was nigh twenty years old. But the box was too big to tote a long ways and have to worry with, so I jest taken the shikepoke egg, because it was the best un, and wropped it up good into a matchbox and hid it and the slingshot under the corner of the barn. Then we et supper and went to bed, and I thought then how if I would 'a' had to stayed in that room and that bed like that even for one more night, I jest couldn't 'a' stood it. Then I could hear Pap snoring, but I never heard no sound from Maw, whether she was asleep or not, and I don't reckon she was. So I taken my shoes and drapped them out the window, and then I clumb out like I used to watch Pete do when he was still jest seventeen and Pap held that he was too young yet to be tomcatting around at night, and wouldn't leave him out, and I put on my shoes and went to the barn and got the slingshot and the shikepoke egg and went to the highway.

It wasn't cold, it was jest durn confounded dark, and that highway stretched on in front of me like, without nobody using it, it had stretched out half again as fer jest like a man does when he lays down, so that for a time it looked like full sun was going to ketch me before I had finished them twenty-two miles to Jefferson. But it didn't. Daybreak was jest starting when I walked up the hill into town. I could smell breakfast cooking in the cabins and I wished I had thought to brought me a cold biscuit, but that was too late now. And Pete had told me Memphis was a piece beyond Jefferson, but I never knowed it was no eighty miles. So I stood there on that empty square, with daylight coming and coming and the street lights still burning and that Law looking down at me, and me still eighty miles from Memphis, and it had took me all night to walk jest twenty-two miles, and so, by the time I got to Memphis at that rate, Pete would 'a' done already started for Pearl Harbor.

"Where do you come from?" the Law said.

And I told him again. "I got to git to Memphis. My brother's there."

"You mean you ain't got any folks around here?" the Law said. "Nobody but that brother? What are you doing way off down here and your brother in Memphis?"

And I told him again, "I got to git to Memphis. I ain't got no time to waste talking about it and I ain't got time to walk it. I got to git there today."

"Come on here," the Law said.

We went down another street. And there was the bus, jest like when Pete got into it yestiddy morning, except there wasn't no lights on it now and it was empty. There was a regular bus dee-po like a railroad dee-po, with a ticket counter and a feller behind it, and the Law said, "Set down over there," and I set down on the bench, and the Law said, "I want to use your telephone," and he talked in the telephone a minute and put it down and said to the feller behind the ticket counter, "Keep your eye on him. I'll be back as soon as Mrs. Habersham can arrange to get herself up and dressed." He went out. I got up and went to the ticket counter.

"I want to go to Memphis," I said.

"You bet," the feller said. "You set down on the bench now. Mr. Foote will be back in a minute."

"I don't know no Mr. Foote," I said. "I want to ride that bus to Memphis."

"You got some money?" he said. "It'll cost you seventy-two cents."

I taken out the matchbox and unwropped the shikepoke egg. "I'll swap you this for a ticket to Memphis," I said.

"What's that?" he said.

"It's a shikepoke egg," I said. "You never seen one before. It's worth a dollar. I'll take seventy-two cents fer it."

"No," he said, "the fellers that own that bus insist on a cash basis. If I started swapping tickets for bird eggs and livestock and such, they would fire me. You go and set down on the bench now, like Mr. Foote—"

I started for the door, but he caught me, he put one hand on the ticket counter and jumped over it and caught up with me and reached his hand out to ketch my shirt. I whupped out my pocketknife and snapped it open.

"You put a hand on me and I'll cut it off," I said.

I tried to dodge him and run at the door, but he could move quicker than any grown man I ever see, quick as Pete almost. He cut me off and stood with his back against the door and one foot raised a little, and there wasn't no other way to get out. "Get back on that bench and stay there," he said.

And there wasn't no other way out. And he stood there with his back against the door. So I went back to the bench. And then it seemed like to me that dee-po was full of folks. There was that Law again, and there was two ladies in fur coats and their faces already painted. But they still looked like they had got up in a hurry and they still never liked it, a old one and a young one, looking down at me.

"He hasn't got a overcoat!" the old one said. "How in the world did he ever get down here by himself?"

"I ask you," the Law said. "I couldn't get nothing out of him except his brother is in Memphis and he wants to get back up there."

"That's right," I said. "I got to git to Memphis today."

"Of course you must," the old one said. "Are you sure you can find your brother when you get to Memphis?"

"I reckon I can," I said. "I ain't got but one and I have knowed him all my life. I reckon I will know him again when I see him."

The old one looked at me. "Somehow he doesn't look like he lives in Memphis," she said.

"He probably don't," the Law said. "You can't tell though. He might live anywhere, overhalls or not. This day and time they get scattered overnight from he—— hope to breakfast; boys and girls, too, almost before they can walk good. He might have been in Missouri or Texas either yestiddy, for all we know. But he don't seem to have any doubt his brother is in Memphis. All I know to do is send him up there and leave him look."

"Yes," the old one said.

The young one set down on the bench by me and opened a hand satchel and taken out a artermatic writing pen and some papers.

"Now, honey," the old one said, "we're going to see that you find your brother, but we must have a case history for our files first. We want to know your name and your brother's name and where you were born and when your parents died."

"I don't need no case history neither," I said. "All I want is to git to Memphis. I got to git there today."

"You see?" the Law said. He said it almost like he enjoyed it. "That's what I told you."

"You're lucky, at that, Mrs. Habersham," the bus feller said. "I don't think he's got a gun on him, but he can open that knife da—— I mean, fast enough to suit any man."

But the old one just stood there looking at me.

"Well," she said. "Well. I really don't know what to do."

"I do," the bus feller said. "I'm going to give him a ticket out of my own pocket, as a measure of protecting the company against riot and bloodshed. And when Mr. Foote tells the city board about it, it will be a civic matter and they will not only reimburse me, they will give me a medal too. Hey, Mr. Foote?"

But never nobody paid him no mind. The old one still stood looking down at me. She said "Well," again. Then she taken a dollar from her purse and give it to the bus feller. "I suppose he will travel on a child's ticket, won't he?"

"Wellum," the bus feller said, "I just don't know what the regulations would be. Likely I will be fired for not crating him and marking the crate Poison. But I'll risk it."

Then they were gone. Then the Law came back with a sandwich and give it to me.

"You're sure you can find that brother?" he said.

"I ain't yet convinced why not," I said. "If I don't see Pete first, he'll see me. He knows me too."

Then the Law went out for good, too, and I et the sandwich. Then more folks come in and bought tickets, and then the bus feller said it was time to go, and I got into the bus just like Pete done, and we was gone.

I seen all the towns. I seen all of them. When the bus got to going good, I found out I was jest about wore out for sleep. But there was too much I hadn't never saw before. We run out of Jefferson and run past fields and woods, then we would run into another town and out of that un and past fields and woods again, and then into another town with stores and gins and water tanks, and we run along by the railroad for a spell and I seen the signal arm move, and then I seen the train and then some more towns, and I was jest about plumb wore out for sleep, but I couldn't resk it. Then Memphis begun. It seemed like, to me, it went on for miles. We would pass a patch of stores and I would think that was sholy it and the bus would even stop. But it wouldn't be Memphis yet and we would go on again past water tanks and smokestacks on top of the mills, and if they was gins and sawmills, I never knowed there was that many and I never seen any that big, and where they got enough cotton and logs to run um I don't know.

Then I seen Memphis. I knowed I was right this time. It was standing up into the air. It looked like about a dozen whole towns bigger than Jefferson was set up on one edge in a field, standing up into the air higher than ara hill in all Yoknapatawpha County. Then we was in it, with the bus stopping ever' few feet, it seemed like to me, and cars rushing past on both sides of it and the streets crowded with folks from ever'where in town that day, until I didn't see how there could 'a' been nobody left in Mis'sippi a-tall to even sell me a bus ticket, let alone write out no case histories. Then the bus stopped. It was another bus dee-po, a heap bigger than the one in Jefferson. And I said, "All right. Where do folks join the Army?"

"What?" the bus feller said.

And I said it again, "Where do folks join the Army?"

"Oh," he said. Then he told me how to git there. I was afraid at first I wouldn't ketch on how to do in a town big as Memphis. But I caught on all right. I never had to ask but twice more. Then I was there, and I was durn glad to git out of all them rushing cars and shoving folks and all that racket for a spell, and I thought, It won't be long now, and I thought how if there was any kind of a crowd there that had done already joined the Army, too, Pete would likely see me before I seen him. And so I walked into the room. And Pete wasn't there.

He wasn't even there. There was a soldier with a big arrerhead on his sleeve, writing, and two fellers standing in front of him, and there was some more folks there, I reckon. It seems to me I remember some more folks there. I went to the table where the soldier was writing, and I said, "Where's Pete?" and he looked up and I said, "My brother. Pete Grier. Where is he?"

"What?" the soldier said. "Who?"

And I told him again. "He joined the Army yestiddy. He's going to Pearl Harbor. So am I. I want to ketch him. Where you-all got him?" Now they were all looking at me, but I never paid them no mind. "Come on," I said. "Where is he?"

The soldier had quit writing. He had both hands spraddled out on the table. "Oh," he said. "You're going, too, hah?"

"Yes," I said. "They got to have wood and water. I can chop it and tote it. Come on. Where's Pete?"

The soldier stood up. "Who let you in here?" he said. "Go on. Beat it."

"Durn that," I said. "You tell me where Pete—"

I be dog if he couldn't move faster than the bus feller even. He never come over the table, he come around it, he was on me almost before I knowed it, so that I jest had time to jump back and whup out my pocket-knife and snap it open and hit one lick, and he hollered and jumped back and grabbed one hand with the other and stood there cussing and hollering.

One of the other fellers grabbed me from behind, and I hit at him with the knife, but I couldn't reach him.

Then both of the fellers had me from behind, and then another soldier come out of a door at the back. He had on a belt with a britching strop over one shoulder.

"What the hell is this?" he said.

"That little son cut me with a knife!" the first soldier hollered. When he said that I tried to git at him again, but both them fellers was holding me, two against one, and the soldier with the backing strop said, "Here, here. Put your knife up, feller. None of us are armed. A man don't knife-fight folks that are barehanded." I could begin to hear him then. He sounded jest like Pete talked to me. "Let him go," he said. They let me go. "Now what's all the trouble about?" And I told him. "I see," he said. "And you come up to see if he was all right before he left."

"No," I said. "I came to—"

But he had already turned to where the first soldier was wropping a handkerchief around his hand.

"Have you got him?" he said. The first soldier went back to the table and looked at some papers.

"Here he is," he said. "He enlisted yestiddy. He's in a detachment leaving this morning for Little Rock." He had a watch stropped on his arm. He looked at it. "The train leaves in about fifty minutes. If I know country boys, they're probably all down there at the station right now."

"Get him up here," the one with the backing strop said. "Phone the station. Tell the porter to get him a cab. And you come with me," he said.

It was another office behind that un, with jest a table and some chairs. We set there while the soldier smoked, and it wasn't long; I knowed Pete's feet soon as I heard them. Then the first soldier opened the door and Pete come in. He never had no soldier clothes on. He looked jest like he did when he got on the bus yestiddy morning, except it seemed to me like it was at least a week, so much had happened, and I had done had to do so much traveling. He come in and there he was, looking at me like he hadn't never left home, except that here we was in Memphis, on the way to Pearl Harbor.

"What in durnation are you doing here?" he said.

And I told him, "You got to have wood and water to cook with. I can chop it and tote it for you-all."

"No," Pete said. "You're going back home."

"No, Pete," I said. "I got to go too. I got to. It hurts my heart, Pete."

"No," Pete said. He looked at the soldier. "I jest don't know what could have happened to him, lootenant," he said. "He never drawed a knife on anybody before in his life." He looked at me. "What did you do it for?"

"I don't know," I said. "I jest had to. I jest had to git here. I jest had to find you."

"Well, don't you never do it again, you hear?" Pete said. "You put that knife in your pocket and you keep it there. If I ever again hear of you drawing it on anybody, I'm coming back from wherever I am at and whup the fire out of you. You hear me?"

"I would sure cut a throat if it would bring you back to stay," I said. "Pete," I said. "Pete."

"No," Pete said. Now his voice wasn't hard and quick no more, it was almost quiet, and I knowed now I wouldn't never change him. "You must go home. You must look after Maw, and I am depending on you to look after my ten acres. I want you to go back home. Today. Do you hear?"

"I hear," I said.

"Can he get back home by himself?" the soldier said.

"He come up here by himself," Pete said.

"I can get back, I reckon," I said. "I don't live in but one place. I don't reckon it's moved."

Pete taken a dollar out of his pocket and give it to me. "That'll buy your bus ticket right to our mailbox," he said. "I want you to mind the lootenant. He'll send you to the bus. And you go back home and you take care of Maw and look after my ten acres and keep that durn knife in your pocket. You hear me?"

"Yes, Pete," I said.

"All right," Pete said. "Now I got to go." He put his hand on my head again. But this time he never wrung my neck. He just laid his hand on my head a minute. And then I be dog if he didn't lean down and kiss me, and I heard his feet and then the door, and I never looked up and that was all, me setting there, rubbing the place where Pete kissed me and the soldier throwed back in his chair, looking out the window and coughing. He reached into his pocket and handed something to me without looking around. It was a piece of chewing gum.

"Much obliged," I said. "Well, I reckon I might as well start back. I got a right fer piece to go."

"Wait," the soldier said. Then he telephoned again and I said again I better start back, and he said again, "Wait. Remember what Pete told you."

So we waited, and then another lady come in, old, too, in a fur coat, too, but she smelled all right, she never had no artermatic writing pen nor no case history either. She come in and the soldier got up, and she looked around quick until she saw me, and come and put her hand on my shoulder light and quick and easy as Maw herself might 'a' done it.

"Come on," she said. "Let's go home to dinner."

"Nome," I said. "I got to ketch the bus to Jefferson."

"I know. There's plenty of time. We'll go home and eat dinner first."

She had a car. And now we was right down in the middle of all them other cars. We was almost under the busses, and all them crowds of people on the street close enough to where I could have talked to them if I had knowed who they was. After a while she stopped the car. "Here we are," she said, and I looked at it, and if all that was her house, she sho had a big family. But all of it wasn't. We crossed a hall with trees growing in it and went into a little room without nothing in it but a nigger dressed up in a uniform a heap shinier than them soldiers had, and the nigger shut the door, and then I hollered, "Look out!" and grabbed, but it was all right; that whole little room jest went right on up and stopped and the door opened and we was in another hall, and the lady unlocked a door and we went in, and there was another soldier, a old feller, with a britching strop, too, and a silver-colored bird on each shoulder.

"Here we are," the lady said. "This is Colonel McKellogg. Now, what would you like for dinner?"

"I reckon I'll jest have some ham and eggs and coffee," I said.

She had done started to pick up the telephone. She stopped. "Coffee?" she said. "When did you start drinking coffee?"

"I don't know," I said. "I reckon it was before I could remember."

"You're about eight, aren't you?" she said.

"Nome," I said. "I'm eight and ten months. Going on eleven months."

She telephoned then. Then we set there and I told them how Pete had jest left that morning for Pearl Harbor and I had aimed to go with him, but I would have to go back home to take care of Maw and look after Pete's ten acres, and she said how they had a little boy about my size, too, in a school in the East. Then a nigger, another one, in a short kind of shirttail coat, rolled a kind of wheelbarrer in. It had my ham and eggs and a glass of milk and a piece of pie, too, and I thought I was hungry. But when I taken the first bite I found out I couldn't swallow it, and I got up quick.

"I got to go," I said.

"Wait," she said.

"I got to go," I said.

"Just a minute," she said. "I've already telephoned for the car. It won't be but a minute now. Can't you drink the milk even? Or maybe some of your coffee?"

"Nome," I said. "I ain't hungry. I'll eat when I git home." Then the telephone rung. She never even answered it.

"There," she said. "There's the car." And we went back down in that 'ere little moving room with the dressed-up nigger. This time it was a big car with a soldier driving it. I got into the front with him. She give the soldier a dollar. "He might get hungry," she said. "Try to find a decent place for him."

"O.K., Mrs. McKellogg," the soldier said.

Then we was gone again. And now I could see Memphis good, bright in the sunshine, while we was swinging around it. And first thing I knowed, we was back on the same highway the bus run on this morning—the patches of stores and them big gins and sawmills, and Memphis running on for miles, it seemed like to me, before it begun to give out. Then we was running again between the fields and woods, running fast now, and except for that soldier, it was like I hadn't never been to Memphis a-tall. We was going fast now. At this rate, before I knowed it we would be home again, and I thought about me riding up to Frenchman's Bend in this here big car with a soldier running it, and all of a sudden I begun to cry. I never knowed I was fixing to, and I couldn't stop it. I set there by that soldier, crying. We was going fast.

Children's Complaints

GEORGE JEAN NATHAN

A PARTICULARLY bitter pill to children is their parents' insistent resolve that they should have musical training of one sort or another, whether they are able remotely to distinguish between a piano and a go-cart or not, or whether they are in full possession of all ten digits or have had six of them shot off by the neighbor boy's grandfather's blunderbuss. I mention the piano specifically because, although there are many other instruments to choose from, among them a number that might be more pragmatically profitable in after years, it is generally the art of the pianoforte with which parents confront and challenge their progeny, nine-tenths of whom are destined to end up as insurance salesmen, shyster lawyers, bus boys, or wives of men who venerate the phonograph.

It is the parental theory in the case of male offspring that an acquired ability to play even the simple scales, followed possibly by a one-finger mastery of "Coming Through the Rye," will inevitably contribute a touch of high refinement to the offspring in later years and that, in the case of girls, it will enhance their sweet womanliness and desirability in the eyes of the male of the species. Let a cynical boy contravene his parents' fond belief by casually pointing out to them that, with the sole exception of Paderewski, the world's greatest pianists from de Pachmann to Moriz Rosenthal had not been inoculated by their art with a personal refinement any more voltaic than that enjoyed by the average stockbroker, or let a realistic little girl try to explain that it seems that the average female who pounds a piano drives her husband into the arms of the first woman he can find with a severe case of digital rheumatism—let a boy or girl attempt to do any such thing and it's bed without supper. . . .

It would, as has been noted, accordingly be much better if parents looked the situation unsentimentally and realistically in the face and surrendered their prejudice against other and theoretically more vulgar musical instruments that their offspring are generally attracted to and that presently make even a father and mother who can't differentiate between the tone of a piccolo and that of a harp gnash their æsthetic teeth and openly ventilate the fear that their offspring will grow up to be bums.

Let a child suggest that his predilection runs to the saxophone, the cornet or the drum, for example, and parents customarily comport themselves as if they had just received news that their own mothers and fathers, who used to beat the pants off them for devoting themselves musically to hair combs wrapped in toilet paper, had been killed in a bomb raid. While it is to be freely allowed that the sounds emanating from a saxophone, cornet and drum are, when those instruments are negotiated by the untutored and overly enterprising young, hardly conducive to the household peace and tranquillity, it is also to be meditated that they are scarcely more painful than the piano banging. But that is not the point, although truth argues it is a pretty good one. The point is that there is nothing particularly *infra dignitatem* in the instruments in question and that, all things considered, it is better, if a child has an unmistakable urge to do so, that he grow up to be a good saxophone or cornet player or drummer than a pianist so bad he will have beer bottles heaved at him.

There are, God wot, artistic professions and even light diversions somewhat superior to the saxophone, cornet and drum, but—the professions aside and the diversions considered—I, for one, am not altogether sure that playing a saxophone is any more derogative of self than dissipating time on cards, tooting a cornet any more ignominious (except maybe in the ears of the deafened and indignant residents in the block) than turning the radio dial to soap operas, male blues singers and the Indianapolis Symphony Orchestra, or beating a drum any more demeaning than playing what is called "the game," which consists in figuring out the word a participant who grimly gets down on the floor and bends himself like a corkscrew is pantomimically trying to interpret.

What is more, as has been suggested, there may often be some ultimate money in it, which is more than can be said for the piano in the overwhelming majority of cases. And the affronted parental sensibilities may take further comfort in the palliative thought that the very orchestras they most highly esteem in the concert halls would not be all they are if the parents of certain of their most essential constituent elements had denied the latter as children the low instruments under discussion.

It is always well to bear in mind what interests a child and what does not, and this brings us to the question of his general education. The indignation of parents when their offspring bring home from school low marks in certain studies and when the low marks continue is ill taken. Most often, if parents will take the trouble to study the low marks in relation to the higher ones, they will gradually gain the knowledge not that a child is necessarily backward or lazy in the particular studies but simply that he is not interested in them and is accordingly inattentive, and that no amount of forced study will, however high the grades he achieves, ever make him regard them as other than dismal chores.

Looking back on my own childhood, I recall that I thus always brought home such abysmal marks in arithmetic, for instance, that my father, getting to the bottom of the card, had to look on the other side to find them, and then couldn't believe his eyes. My explanations that arithmetic didn't interest me failed to persuade him and I was forced to continue my study. But though I did continue—it was necessary in those days to offer mathematics later on for college entrance—and though at college itself it was demanded of me further to pursue the cursed subject, I was always more or less a bored dud at it, never profited by it either then or since, and still today cannot, for all my acclaimed and staggering talents in other directions, even multiply seven by nine without putting seven down nine times and adding up the sevens singly.

There is altogether too much parental shortsightedness and misapprehension in the matter of the education of their young. Teachers who, for example, cram the latter's little heads with innumerable historical dates, not one out of fifty of which they can remember a day afterward, should be taken right out into the yard and be drawn and quartered. They waste children's time and, worse, make the kids regard school as a doubly irksome institution. The average youngster, even when he reaches the age of fifteen, remembers hardly more than three or four dates out of all the wholesale dose that has been fruitlessly and, in all good truth, unnecessarily imposed upon him—1492, 1775, 1861 and, possibly, 1898. And these, added to the obvious January 1, February 12, February 22, March 17, May 30, July 4, the last Thursday in November, and December 25 are to all intents and purposes sufficient. Not one child in thirty thousand ever finds it immediately or subsequently profitable to be in rapt possession of the exact knowledge that the British surrendered at Yorktown on October 19, 1781, or that it was on May 2, 1863, that Stonewall Jackson was mortally wounded during the battle of Chancellorsville. Such knowledge is commodious only to children doomed to grow up to be eighteen-dollar-a-week school-teachers and to the depressing species of youngsters who offensively disport themselves on radio quiz programs. . . .

One of the deepest concerns of parents is the safeguarding of their young from what they are pleased to regard, in their own terminology, as bad associates. These bad associates are usually indigenous to the same neighborhood and it is a notable paradox that one of the deepest concerns of *their* parents in turn is the safeguarding of *them* from association with the first mentioned little Machiavellis.

Just how parents, in their infinite wisdom, arrive at the low estimate of their children's favorite companions remains something of a rebus to the kids, since the latter are not long in appreciating that their suspected and condemned boon buddies are no worse in conduct, morals, tastes and dog-tail can-tying than they themselves are, but are, in point of fact, often a heap better.

Looking back upon my own childhood, I remember three specific little boys whom my parents were especially solicitous in cautioning me against. One—and I mention real names—was a youngster hight Charles Buchanan Stuart, popularly known in our gang as Buck. This Buck was a powerfully built boy of some one hundred and fifty pounds whose strength was the marvel of the rest of us. His feats of physical prowess, such as single-handedly upsetting the phaeton in the family stable, batting a baseball through the window of the clergyman's house in the next block, and wrassling the much bigger laundry delivery boy onto his backside, were our gaping awe and admiring envy. Yet it was Buck's parents' frequently expressed conviction that he was a delicate child and that his association with the rest of us, all but one of whom weighed under ninety and none of whom failed regularly to catch his death of cold merely from having stepped into a minor rain puddle, was something to be regarded as inimical to his health, social well-being, and high æsthetic interests. "You know, boys," I well recall his mother admonishing us, "Charlie isn't as strong as you are, and he can't do the things you do, so I must ask you either to stay away and let him rest or, if you are with him, to watch out for him carefully." Whereupon the shamefaced Charlie would shuffle into the house behind his protective mother and, the moment she turned her head, would sneak out the back door into the back yard and delicately entertain himself heaving large hunks of brick at the milk cans in the yard next door and, that done and the contents of the cans duly upset, busting open the stable door with his shoulder and sending the family surrey rolling hell-bent down the side drive.

The second stern warning was directed against a boy named Randall Crawford, known to the gang as Butch. The parental criticism of this Butch was, one gathered, that he was on the lewd side and given to pulling the girls' pigtails, rubbing noses with the more personable ones, and thus otherwise competing with the doom of Casanova and suchlike loafers. The truth about this Butch was, however, as we soon found out, that he was scared to death of girls and would run a block to avoid contact with one of them. The low opinion that my parents had of him was based solely upon my own ignoble explanation, when some little girl came in crying that I had mussed her up, that it was Butch who was the guilty party. As I delivered such explanations no less than three times a week and as the other boys indulged in similar shameless evasions to their parents, it was poor Butch who suffered the blame and gained the reputation of being an adolescent synthesis of Kyrle Bellew, Jim Fiske and Jack-the-Ripper.

The third boy, association with whom alarmed my parents to the point of aghast horror, was one Billy Morris. Billy, it appeared to be their self-persuasion, was what they designated a "sport." For some reason or other, logical antecedents unknown, they viewed him as one alone given to crap shooting for stakes, Sweet Caporal inhaling, sophisticated whistling at passing puellæ, and like attributes and divertissements of a practitioner of the gay life. It was true that Billy had a passion for craps, but it was no less true that he was a sucker at the game and that the rest of us sacrosanct angels regularly took him at it for what nickels and dimes he could dredge up. It was also true that he relished Sweet Caporals, if and when he was able to beg them from the rest of us. And it was again true that he would whistle loudly at the girls, yet such whistling was imposed upon him by the rest of us, none of whom could maneuver his lips beyond a feeble whew, and for his services always had to be recompensed with one of the nickels we had achieved from him via the dice.

A Young Boy's Love

HAVELOCK ELLIS

LOVE COMES normally to a child through what we call the soul rather than through the body. In this and, indeed, throughout—with whatever wide variations from the most common types—I was normal. The young boy's love is a spiritual passion generated within by any stray spark from the real world, and so far as his own consciousness extends, even without any sensory, still less any sensual, elements whatever, easy as it might be to detect such elements. A chance encounter of life sets free within him a vision which has danced within the brains of his ancestors to remote generations and has no relation whatever to the careless girl whose playful hand opens the dark casement that reveals the universe.

I was twelve years old, and the summer holidays, after my last term at Merton College, had just begun. Half a century earlier (as I discovered five years afterwards in Australia when reading his attractive *Autobiography*), at the same age, in this same village of Merton, a man of letters more famous than I am ever likely to be, Leigh Hunt, had met his first love. Here I was now to meet mine.

My mother, though on occasion hospitable, cared little to have strangers staying in the house; a girl or boy cousin would sometimes be invited to spend a week, and left no impress on my imagination. The first stranger not of my kin to stay in the house was a girl of sixteen, the only daughter of my mother's step-brother, who was in a well-to-do position. Agnes, then, for that was her name, was invited to spend a summer week or two with us at Wimbledon in 1871. She was a dark pretty vivacious girl, with long black ringlets, of something the same type, I can now see, as her grandmother, the second Mrs. Wheatley, whom I distinctly remember. Old enough to be a woman in my eyes, and yet young enough to be a comrade and equal, she adapted herself instinctively to the relationship and won my heart immediately. I took not the slightest liberty with her, and never had the slightest impulse to do so, but she, on her part, treated me with an easy familiarity which no woman had ever used with me before, and that fact, certainly, though its significance was then beyond me, undoubtedly had its influence. She would play and romp with me in all innocent unreserve, and when we went out together for long walks, as often happened, she would sometimes make me offer her my arm and treat her as a lady, then again asserting her superiority by treating me to lemonade and at the best places she could find. One day as we strolled arm in arm through the poppied cornfields which then lay between Merton Station and the College —it was in these fields that I first knew the beauty of poppies—my severe little schoolmaster suddenly came round the corner on to us. Timid though I habitually seemed, I raised my cap without flinching or withdrawing my arm under my master's stern eye, and have ever since prided myself on that early little act of moral courage. He doubtless smiled to himself at thus seeing a handsome girl hanging on his quiet pupil's arm, and he subsequently asked my father who she was, but without, I think, mentioning that detail. Agnes returned home, and, strangely enough, I have never seen her since. I lent her Keats's Poems when she left and she lent me *The Wide, Wide World;* we exchanged a few notes but our correspondence speedily withered, without protest on my part, and probably aided by the fact that, through a trivial circumstance connected with this very visit of Agnes—she had once offered to help in the domestic work and been given some peas to shell which her mother resented as too menial a task for her daughter—a certain permanent coldness developed between her mother and mine, each feeling aggrieved. She is still alive, and though she was even then looking forward to marriage as a near probability (for I heard her talk to our servant to that effect) she still remains single, an only child who has devoted her life to the care of her aged parents.

I never saw Agnes again; I never made any effort to see her; I never mentioned her name; no one knew that I even thought of her. But for four years her image moved and lived within me, revealing myself to myself. I had no physical desires and no voluptuous emotions; I never pictured to myself any joy of bodily contact with her or cherished any sensuous dreams. Yet I was devoured by a boy's pure passion. That she should become my wife—though I never tried to imagine what that meant—was a wild and constant aspiration. I would lie awake in bed with streaming eyes praying to God to grant that this might some day be. I have often felt thankful since that our prayers are not heard.

Under the stress of this passion I became a person, and, moreover, in temper a poet. I discovered the beauty of the world, and I discovered a new vein of emotion within myself. I began to write verse. I began to enjoy art, and, at the same time, Nature. In a still vague and rudimentary way, all my literary activities slowly took on a new character. Hitherto they had been impersonal, displaying indeed a certain research, a certain orderly and systematic spirit, perhaps inborn, yet not definitely personal. Now the personal element took shape. The touch of this careless vivacious girl had placed within me a new ferment which began to work through every fibre of my being. It was an epoch-making event in my life.

Intimations of Philosophy in Early Childhood

IRWIN EDMAN

It is possible, I suspect, for most people at all interested in philosophy to put their finger on the time and the book that first introduced them to the "subject." Philosophy in my own mind will always be associated with Bakewell's *Source Book in Ancient Philosophy,* which contains fragments remaining from the early Greeks: Thales, Anaximander, Heraclitus, and Empedocles. The names themselves sounded like incantations. I had an early impression (from which I have not yet recovered) that Greek philosophers in the Ionian Peninsula for some strange reason *wrote* in fragments. As a freshman, too, I vaguely had the idea that Bakewell had with his own hands gathered together these fragments at Yale, or had composed them there, and that the learned professor was himself somehow the source of Greek philosophy. I shall also associate my first bookish relations with philosophy with that great grey volume, translated from unintelligible German into formidable English: Paulsen's *Introduction to Philosophy.* There I gathered that philosophy consisted of an astounding number of isms, with innumerable sub-isms, and that somewhere in that ismatic jungle lay the Truth. Finally, by myself, outside of class, I discovered the little yellow book in the Home University Library, J. A. Thomson's *Introduction to Science,* which opened up the various branches of knowledge and their interrelations and made me feel that with sufficient time and diligence I could become one of the masters—in outline—of all that was to be known.

But there is a moment, or kind of moment, harder to identify. It occurs usually, I suspect, before one knows what the word "philosophy" is, or when one vaguely associates the word "philosophical" with Red Indians burning in stubborn and dignified fortitude at the stake, or with a man watching the ruins and embers of his house, or hearing of the death or elopement of his wife, with grave serenity. Some experience, some word, or some odd fancy crossing one's inexperienced mind—and one is in the presence of, and feels, the delicious, puzzling incitement (without knowing either phrase) of philosophical issues and ultimate things. I have friends who occasionally report instances of such early speculative awakening in their small children, and I know that, from John Locke down, the baby has been a favourite illustration of philosophers—the baby putting together the colour and sound and taste and smell and feel of an orange and saying: "Lo! it is an object, it is an orange!"

Being childless, I have only the smallest stock of illustrations of this philosophical awakening among children, though I gather from my friends that their infant sons are all metaphysicians. I know, for instance, that Ian, aged nine, reads Gibbon, and I hear from his father that his mind is as sceptical and circumspect as that of Hume. I did once take a walk with a child who asked suddenly: "Who made the world?" For the sake of brevity I replied: "God." "Who made God?" was the next question. To reply that God was a First Cause, the Uncreated Creator of all things seemed a stiff dose for a child and would only bring on further questions. I said I would tell him later. But for the awakening of the philosophical impulse in children I can only refer to one autobiographical instance, and I shall try to keep out of my remembrance such sophisticated gloss as a later education in philosophy gave me. I am convinced, as I look back, that all the great issues, Freedom and Determinism, God, Immortality, the reality of the external world, and the nature of reality itself are first stumbled upon when one is very young. I can even imagine that some day a psychiatrist will prove that speculative interests are early childhood fixations and that the metaphysician is an infant trailing clouds of inglorious complexes from the nursery.

Time is certainly the pet theme of much contemporary thought, and I had as certainly not read the modern physicists or Einstein's early work at the age of thirteen. But it was then, if I remember, that I myself first hit upon that perplexity, current in philosophy since Plato defined Time as the moving picture of eternity, a phrase itself puzzle enough. I remember one day coming to my older sister and saying I was bothered about Time. She was, as she is still, full of sound sense and human perception and has never allowed herself to be distracted by nonsense, however elaborate and imposing. She is a philosopher free from cobwebs.

"What do you mean," she said, "you are bothered by time?"

"Well," I said, "take today, for instance. It's really here right now, this very minute, for instance, isn't it?"

"Yes, of course," she said, and turned back to the piano on which she was playing one-half of Beethoven's *Fifth Symphony* arranged for four hands.

"But wait a minute," I said, "tomorrow today will be yesterday, won't it? It will be gone. And tomorrow is not here yet, and it really *isn't* at all. It's all very puzzling. What *is* Time?"

"Time for you to go to bed," she said briskly and, refusing to be entangled any further in aerie irrelevance and childishness, she turned back again to the Andante.

I did go to bed, but I did not sleep. For I was obsessed by the awful unreality of something I had hitherto taken for granted. There was, I mused, last summer on the Jersey coast—the long summer afternoons, the tang of the salt spray as the breakers broke round one as one waded into the surf, the agreeable burning warmth of the sun as one basked on the beach. But *that* was last summer, and it no longer was. It was, I suddenly realized with awe, the Past. But what was the Past? And where was it? And now and here, as I lay in bed this winter evening in a New York apartment, listening to my sister playing the piano, Time itself moved on, and tomorrow this dreaming about the past would be the Past, too. It made me feel uneasy. I got no further before I fell asleep.

I thought about it often in the next weeks. Thought is too systematic a word for what I actually did, I am sure. I did not try to solve the problem. I displayed no precocious dialectic virtuosity. I "thought" about it in that I felt about it seriously. I repeatedly had a sense of the dreamlike though intense quality of time past and remembered, the odd unreality of time sure to come but not yet here, the wavering evanescence of the present. Or, as I put it to myself, yesterday is gone; today is going, always going; tomorrow is coming but it *hasn't* come. I used to try to explain it all to people, to the Negro elevator boy, particularly; he seemed to be the only one who would listen, though he said: "You shouldn't worry yo' head about that!" I don't think I found out until five or six years later that I was far from the only one who had been bemused and bepuzzled by the theme. I had a secret feeling that there was something special, private, and abnormal about being worried about such things, just as a child may go on a long time thinking he is the only one bemused and bepuzzled by sex.

But Time was not the only philosophical problem of which I had an early intimation. I was to learn at college, by way of Paulsen's book, of something called the epistemological problem. How do we *know,* and how do we know that we know? I was to learn of metaphysics, the attempt to define scrupulously what was really real. But epistemology and metaphysics came by anticipation into my ken long before I knew the words or the professional arguments about them, or knew that there were grown men who spent their whole lives debating such issues and were paid by universities for doing so and for teaching others how to do it. I cannot lay claim myself to having hit upon the intimations of these things. It was Julian L., now, I am told, a much sought after pediatrist in New York, who was the agent to bring epistemology and metaphysics (though he, too, did not know the words) to my fourteen-year-old attention from out of his fourteen-year-old observation. The fact he pointed at, I discovered much later, is time and again used as a conventional illustration in philosophical treatises.

It was in the mountains on the afternoon of a hot July day. We had been talking drowsily under a tree by the side of a brook. I was almost asleep. Julian was stirring a stick in the water.

"The stick looks broken, doesn't it?" he said.

I looked up vaguely. "Yes; what of it?" I said. I sometimes shared my sister's realism.

"But it isn't; that's only the shadow in the water; it's *unreal*," said Julian. He lapsed into silence, still stirring the stick. "But there's a *real* shadow," he said; "the shadow itself is *real,* all right."

"Yes," I said. "I'm going to sleep for a while."

Julian's remark made little immediate impression. The reality of a shadow, the unreality of a broken stick did not seem to matter very much amid this sunlight on this summer green. But days later, walking by the brook again with Julian and happening to stir a stick in it myself, my friend's comments of the other day suddenly came back with unexpected cogency and vividness into my mind.

"The shadow in a way *is* real," I suddenly said to Julian. Then two fourteen-year-old epistemologists, sitting by a mountain stream, wrestled dialectically, within the limits of their abilities, with the Real and the Unreal, how we knew anything really, and whether seeing was believing. I soon wearied of the controversy—as I have often done since. The whole problem, I somehow felt even then, was artificial, as I now think I have sound reasons for believing it to be. But the theme haunted me, and often that summer I reverted to it. Dreams, too, were like shadows, and the things one remembered were like dreams. I tried, without success even by my own fourteen-year-old standards, to write a poem about it. Indeed, even now it seems to me that the whole matter is a better theme for poetry than inquiry, and is poetic in its origins and fruits rather than primarily a genuine problem for analysis. The net effect for the time being was to make me a solitary solipsist—how I should have loved the words had I known them!—and I would pretend for as long as I could, till I was too hungry or too tired, that our house, my bed, the meat and milk and eggs at supper, the other summer visitors, Julian himself, were merely shadows or dreams in my mind, and that I myself perhaps was a dream. I seem to remember my mother found me particularly and annoyingly absent-minded the next week or two. It was fun to treat the world round about me as apparitions to my understanding and imagination. Many years later Santayana invented for such dreams, such passing appearances, such momentary objects of intuition, the term "essences." I had not realized until I began to recall these early explorations of epistemology that I had come upon essences long ago.

It was through Julian, too, at the same time, that I first began to think about Freedom and Determinism, Fate and Chance, Necessity and Accident, though, of course, not remotely in those terms. My friend and I used to discuss occasionally the accident that had brought us together in a friendship that, we were certain, would never end. It was a lucky accident, we decided. But the very luck of it, we redecided, *proved* that it was something more than luck; that it *could* not have been an accident. For look, we unanimously agreed, our parents, who had not known each other, must first have decided to come to the same place and, all unknown to each other, to rent houses directly opposite each other. It was not an accident. It was an inevitable chain; it was *intended*. It was Fate. And it was part of Fate, we warmly agreed, that we should be friends forever. Fate and Freedom, these are the familiar preoccupations of theologians from St. Paul and St. Augustine down. So are death and immortality. Many philosophical conceptions, I was to learn later, have their origins in the mind of the child and the mind of the savage. There is a whole library about primitive conceptions of the soul. The appearance of dead men in dreams, if I remember, is supposed to lead the primitive warrior to believe that his dead friends and enemies live in another world. I cannot say that I can recall having been concerned very early with the nature of the soul or the problem of immortality. Nor early to have brooded upon death. Death was what happened to *old* people, people in their forties and fifties or seventies; to people's grandparents, not to anybody one really knew or played with. The death of a boy in our group—Herbert, the fat, good-natured, not very literary member of our Benjamin Franklin Club—first gave me pause and led me to think of the quite incredible fact of death. When older people died, it was as if they had simply gone off or moved away. And in any case one had never known them very well, and adults, besides, did strange things. But Herbert, the liveliest of all, simply gone, stretched out in a coffin and carried away and buried! It was far more upsetting than when Mr. S., the father of one of my friends, died. That was sad and sudden. He came home from a trip, had pneumonia; they brought an oxygen tent for him to breathe in, and three days later he was gone. But *he* was bald-headed and had always seemed incredibly old; he was fifty. It seemed odd not to see him emerge at the aristocratically late hour of a quarter to nine and in his top hat leisurely set off for the local rather than the urgent express train on the Elevated. His son, my chum, wore a black tie and mourning-band and was not allowed to go to the theatre and acquired for a while a special dignity and importance. But that was different. The death of one of us, a contemporary, was another matter. The very young believe not in immortal life, but in eternal life here on earth; it struck me as incredible that anyone, any young person, should really die, simply cease to be. And yet I am convinced that one's adult philosophical opinions are formed in embryo very early, if one is going to have them at all. For it never seemed to me that my friend was living as an angel in some other world. He had ceased simply to be. Death was the end, and there both the incredibility and the sadness of it lay. Death, like birth, was a fact of existence, as inevitable and as natural. I vaguely felt that as a child; I definitely think that now.

But the intimations of immortality that Wordsworth speaks of have, of course, nothing to do with an after-life. They have to do with a sense of something "far more deeply interfused," a presence of something permeatingly beautiful in the crass or exquisite surface of things. Like every child I felt, especially, I think, in the art of music, an adumbration of something acute in its poignancy and intensity, yet other-worldly in its distance from ordinary objects. It doesn't matter much that it was nothing more musically profound than "Angel's Serenade" or *Kammenoi Ostrov* or the *Tannhäuser* Bacchanale that gave me this sense, or that it seldom came from anything commonly called real. If it did not come from music, it came from poetry, and the poetry, too, did not have to be too profound.

I think I know now precisely where I received my introduction to mystical and transcendental philosophy, I think it was again the accident of knowing Julian that introduced to me the genre of thought that regards this world as simply the half-veil, half-revelation of a world beyond phenomena. Julian's father was a businessman by day, by night one of those philosophers without portfolio whom I have earlier described in this book.*

* The author refers to *Philosopher's Holiday.*

In his leisure he played with philosophical ideas. He saw in me a possible initiate. Initiate is a rightly chosen word, for it was to a "secret wisdom" that he introduced me. He proceeded to enlighten me, since he had apparently given his son up as uninterested, concerning theories which I could only vaguely understand, though they seemed to me impressive, and about which to this day I do not think Mr. L. was very clear. I did cloudily gather from him what he had gathered from the purple-bound volumes of a writer whose initials alone appeared upon his work, "T. K." I did not, nor did he, know who the mysterious T. K. was, and never since have I been able to find T. K.'s works in any library. I have since, often enough, encountered ideas not unlike, as I remember them, those of that retiring author, at least as they were mediated to me by my friend's theosophical-minded father. Mr. L. lent me one of T. K.'s books, but I found the words and the sentences too long and too many. The main themes, however, were relatively clear to me as they were transmitted with grave enthusiasm by T. K.'s disciple. The world of matter about us was not the real world. It was the shadow of a world far truer and deeper and more real than that which we meet through the senses. The real (or the divine) world consisted of spiritual beings whose choral dance of Truth and Beauty constituted the order and beauty of our visible world, so far as through virtue or wisdom or genius we could touch them. The important thing for us was to put ourselves in touch with these invisible spiritual beings, with this order of Truth beyond phenomena. Mr. L. used some of these words, and though I did not quite know what they meant (and am not sure I know now), they sounded grand and serious. Only much later did I read the same thing—more or less—but put more clearly and cogently in the writings of Plotinus, the second-century Greek mystic and dialectician. Not until many years later did I realize that the doctrine of T. K. and of Julian's father had its roots in Plato and Plotinus and Augustine and in India's immemorial past.

Some imp or angel of common-sense used to prompt me to argue with T. K.'s prophet. Something in me then warned me, as it articulately does now, to distrust all such high breathlessness in thought. And I made as good a case as I could for the reality of the world of the senses and the distrust of any alleged world beyond it. But even then I was moved, as I am still moved, by the suasion of any such poetic speculations, and I have always been grateful that a businessman amateur interpreting a theosophist should thus early have awakened a feeling in me, a sympathy with "the light that never was on sea or land." I felt then, as I feel now, that the mystics are talking about a world practically "unreal," and spiritually more real than common-sense allows.

Not until I came to college did I find out that philosophy, in the hands of its greatest practitioners, often arose in a search for, often resulted in a programme or a set of principles of, the Good Life, and that when a philosophy is taken seriously it is or becomes a Moral Philosophy. Morals in our neighbourhood in my childhood, and I suspect in most neighbourhoods of the period, had to do with sex chiefly, and immorality meant just one thing and it was better not to say out loud what that was. I don't think I was ever greatly troubled by the question, "What is the Good?" The good was defined by the standards of one's own family and the families that one knew. Moral philosophy arises historically, one is led to believe, when the conventional codes are collapsing, and rival theories of good and evil, competing standards of value, come in conflict with each other. No rival and competing standards seemed to be clashing in our neighbourhood, though I read now that it was a period of transition. There were the toughs in the tenements only two blocks away, but that was another world.

The only very early social scepticism I can recall developing came from the high-school classmate whose family was bitterly poor and who had to work hard and long after school at odd jobs. The neat world of accepted values, the decorous respectability of middle-class life and its economic foundations, all were called into question for me by the fact that this friend of mine had to work after school and that he had to stay in the city in the summer. But it was not only his example; it was his instruction that made me query the operations of right and wrong in the small world I knew. Ben F. was an Austrian immigrant, two or three years older than myself; he seemed to me to look quite grown up. He certainly had read grown-up books. Within a year I was pattering after him a denunciation of the capitalist system, and I accompanied him to Madison Square Garden to cheer, for twenty minutes, Eugene V. Debs. I did not quite know anything about Marx's labour theory of value, but I knew people were underpaid, that the rich exploited the poor, that society must be made over, that there must be equality of opportunity and reward for all. Then, among other things, Ben wouldn't have to work afternoons and could spend his summer vacations in the country, like me, perhaps with me. My economic understanding was primitive enough, and my enthusiasm for social justice as vague as it was enthusiastic. But such as they were, they led me to the portals of moral philosophy. Perhaps, I began to suspect, all that I thought just and proper was itself a middle-class family prejudice. There must be other ways of living, other ways of looking at right and wrong in the world.

I suspect many moral philosophers have begun through being thus accidentally disquieted at about the age of thirteen, and the search for the Good had begun usually because some boy somewhere discovered early that there was something wrong with the *good* people he knew and found people outside his own family who had other standards of good than he had ever dreamed of. But in my own case, the reflection upon the good life had a long intermission and I was not consciously aware that there was such a thing as moral philosophy until long after I had stumbled upon it. Just about this time I discovered poetry, and then I quite forgot the Good Society, and the evils of the one in which I comfortably, and Ben uncomfortably, lived.

It turned out that I was not to think much more about "philosophy" in the strict sense until my freshman year in college. Such general ideas as a high-school pupil gets in America come, I think, largely from literature and history. There is a superstition even among college administrators that philosophy is a subject too "deep" and too "hard" for the underclassman. I picked up (most high-school pupils do) such logic as I got from geometry or outlining Burke's Speech on Conciliation, and such moral philosophy as filtered through in the *Sir Roger de Coverley Papers* and the *Idylls of the King* and the *Rubaiyat of Omar Khayyam*. But as I recall these early intimations of philosophical thought, I wonder why, as in France, philosophy cannot be begun earlier. The themes of reality and unreality, of good and evil, of fate and necessity, of determinism and freedom, the method of thinking itself, the being or the illusion of time are surely themes that early haunt the imagination of all but the most dull among adolescents. Once in the Public Library I browsed among the "100" books, where the inventor of the Dewey decimal system long since elected to place philosophy. The librarian put me off onto *The Three Musketeers* and *Les Misérables*. But I rather wish now that youngsters were brought to philosophy when it naturally springs upon their imaginations. When they come upon it in college it is a subject to be studied. But I am sure many of them, like myself, come upon it much earlier. The stick broken in water, the sense of something deep and far, felt by the sea or in the hills on a summer day, the puzzle and the pathos of time, the uneasiness about the good, have raised questions that one ought not to have to wait until late in one's college career to hear treated as questions worthy of being answered—or of being asked.

The Broken Wheel

WILLIAM SAROYAN

We had a small house on Santa Clara Avenue, in the foreign district where everyone moved about freely and where conversations were carried on across yards and alleys and streets. This house had been the home of a man who had been in the business of roasting and marketing all kinds of nuts. We found small and large pieces of his machinery in the two barns, and in the cracks of the floors we sometimes found nut-shells and bits of nut-meats. The house had a clean wholesome smell. There were a number of crickets somewhere near the kitchen sink and quite a few house spiders, the kind that are called daddy-long-legs. There was also a cat. The cat was there when we moved into the house, so we took it for granted. It was a big black tom with a proud demeanor, an aristocratic air of superiority and indifference. At first it lived under the house in the dark, but later on when it got cold it moved into the house. We never bothered to give it a name, but referred to it simply as the *Gadou,* which is cat in Armenian.

Our trees were two sycamores at the side of the house, by the alley; an English walnut tree in the back yard that was perhaps twenty years old; a small olive tree; and three lilac trees that were growing close to the front porch. The porch was shaded by a thick honeysuckle plant. There were also geraniums and Bermuda grass and other weeds. After a while we planted two peach trees, a cactus tree, and a castor plant. The peach trees happened accidentally; we hadn't meant to plant them, we had only thrown peach-pits in the back yard and the trees had come up by themselves and we hadn't transplanted them. They were growing much too close to one another but they were either very lucky or very stubborn and after three years the leaves that fell from them in the fall were enough to rake into a pile and burn. They were growing just outside our yard but since we had no fence and no close neighbors, except for the family immediately across the alley, we considered the peach trees our trees. It wasn't a question of fruit; we could buy peaches cheaper than they could be grown; it was rather a question of being responsible for the growth of something fine or perhaps a question of blossoms in the spring. Once a year my sister Naomi would bring some of the pink blossoms into the house and place them in a black vase.

We used to see the blossoms in the black vase and suddenly we used to feel that it was all splendid. It seemed to mean that we were alive and we used to laugh about it. In the winter we laughed a great deal. We would be sullen and sorrowful for weeks at a time and then suddenly all of us would begin to laugh. We would laugh fifteen or twenty minutes and then we would be sullen and sorrowful again. It was all splendid and at the same time we felt that it must be pretty sad because it was in us to feel bewildered and futile.

My brother Krikor was responsible for the cactus tree. He came home one afternoon with a piece of thorny-cactus in his hand. He said to me, Did you know that all of this country was desert once and that cactus was growing everywhere?

Do you mean, I asked, no one was living here?

Yes, said Krikor. No one but the lizards, I guess, and the snakes and the horny-toads and the chicken-hawks and things like that. No people.

I thought of our valley without people and streets and houses and I thought it was very strange, very irregular.

Do you mean, I said, all the way to Selma and all the way to Clovis and away over to Kerman, past Skaggs Bridge?

I mean the whole valley, Krikor replied. I mean all this level land between the Coast Ranges and the Sierra Nevadas. All this country where the vineyards are growing now. It was dry here in those days, so they began to bring in the water in canals and irrigation ditches.

Krikor planted the cactus that afternoon and by the time I was ten it was producing splendid red blossoms and a fruit no one knew how to eat; and it was taller than a tall man.

The castor tree happened accidentally too. An old castor tree was growing in the yard of our neighbors across the alley and one summer some of its seeds got into our yard and the following summer we had a small castor tree of our own. It was a spurious sort of a tree, growing much too rapidly and being much too delicate for a tree. A small boy couldn't climb it and the least little storm that came along would tear some of its branches away. But it had a nice leaf and a clean growing-odor and it made a lot of shade. We hadn't planted it, but as long as it started to grow we were glad about it. Everyone hated castor-oil but we thought the tree itself was innocent enough.

In the summertime it would be very hot and we would have to get up early in the morning to feel a cool breeze. Every summer the city sent out a long tractor to plow into the tar of Santa Clara Avenue and improve the condition of the street. This tractor made a monotonous noise, pounding steadily and hollowly, approaching and going away from our house. In the morning we would begin to hear its far-away *boom-boom-boom* and as it came closer to our house we would hear the noise louder and louder and we used to think that this coming and going was like something in life but we couldn't tell just what. We used to say in Armenian, *Yegav noren,* Here it is again. We had no definite basis for our objection, but we sometimes asked what difference it made if the street was a little uneven. No one uses it, anyway, we said. Casparian, the man who sold watermelons each summer, passed over the street every afternoon with his old horse and his wobbly wagon, crying watermelon in Armenian, but there wasn't much other traffic. Those who wanted to get around in a hurry rode bicycles.

One year my uncle Vahan, then a young man, drove down from San Francisco in a brand new Apperson roadster and stopped in front of our house.

How do you like it? he asked. There are only eleven Appersons in America and only one red one. His was the red one. We felt splendid and we all laughed and my uncle Vahan smoked cigarettes. He took his sister, my mother, for a ride to Roeding Park. It was her first ride in an automobile and she felt very proud of her brother. We all thought he was splendid. It wasn't only the Apperson, it was also his nervousness and his energy and the way he laughed and talked. When he came back with my mother he took my sisters, Lucy and Naomi, for a ride to town. My brother Krikor sat on the front porch with a book, waiting nervously for his turn to ride. Krikor said the automobile could go fifty miles per hour. Rouben, our neighbor, was sitting on the porch with us and he said his uncle Levon had a Cadillac which was a more expensive car than an Apperson and could go sixty miles an hour.

Yes, I said, but is it red? He admitted sadly that it was black. There is only one red Apperson in America, I said. It was like saying that one's great-grandfather had seen Lincoln or that one's ancestors had come over on the *Mayflower;* only it was more impressive. You knew that a great big piece of red junk on wheels would come around the corner, thundering, and stop before your house, and you felt that it was a big thing. This is the machine age, and *Over in Europe they are using machine-guns in the War,* and, *They are inventing all sorts of things that turn swiftly, saving time.*

My uncle Vahan came home with Lucy and Naomi and went inside for a cup of Turkish coffee. We could hear him telling his sister how splendidly he had been getting along in San Francisco. He had passed his bar examination and was now an attorney-at-law, but he had made most of his money selling watermelons wholesale. Eventually he hoped to open an office in the Rowell Building right here at home. My mother was very happy about her young brother and we could hear her laughing with him and asking him questions.

Krikor was very ill at ease because his uncle Vahan had not offered to take him for a ride and because he was too proud or too polite to ask for a ride, but I felt, There is a lawyer in our family and he has a red Apperson. We are an enterprising people. I was so happy about this that I couldn't sit still and kept walking on the porch-railing and jumping down.

When my uncle Vahan came out of the house Krikor was standing a few feet from the automobile, admiring it. He was admiring it so humbly, with so much youthful adoration, that my uncle understood what it was that was eating him and said, Come on, you fellows. I'll give you a ride.

Our neighbor Rouben and Krikor got into the car first, and I sat on Krikor's lap. My uncle Vahan started the motor and we went off, making much smoke and a terrific noise. I remember that my mother and Lucy and Naomi stood on the front porch and waved to us. We had an exciting ride through town and felt very elated. When we returned, my mother had cut two cold watermelons and we all sat in the parlor, eating watermelon and talking. It was very hot and we were all perspiring but it was a clear moment in our lives.

My uncle Vahan said, We do not know how fortunate we are to be in such a country as this. Opportunities are unlimited here. Every man is free and he can go as far as he is able. He spoke in Armenian because it was easier for him. He had been thirteen when he came to America and now he was twenty-two. He asked Krikor if he had yet decided on a career for himself and Krikor became embarrassed and began to eat watermelon very rapidly. I hope, my uncle Vahan said, you will decide to study law. And my mother replied, Of course. I thought, Krikor wants to be a musician because he told me, but I didn't say anything. In a day or two my uncle Vahan drove away in his red Apperson and we began to remember all the little details of his visit that we hadn't paid much attention to at first.

Everything was solid and permanent at our house and we didn't notice the time that was passing. One afternoon Krikor came home with a small black satchel. He placed the satchel on the table in our dining-room and we all gathered around to see what was in it. We never knew what Krikor was likely to do and we were always prepared for anything. Krikor was very excited and silent. He placed a small key into the key-hole of the satchel and turned it and opened the satchel, and we saw that it contained a cornet. My mother asked in Armenian, What is that, Krikor? and Krikor replied in Armenian that it was called a cornet.

As far back as I could remember we had always had a piano wherever we had lived. There would be times when no one would go near the piano for months and then suddenly all of us would be playing it. My sister Lucy had taken lessons and could play by note. She played serious music like the works of Chopin and Liszt and Mozart. Naomi played by ear and she played the songs that seemed to be without printed music and that seemed to be the songs of the people, *Keep the Home Fires Burning, I Love You, California, There's a Long Long Trail, Smiles, Dardanella, Oh, What a Pal Was Mary,* and songs like that. I couldn't play by note and I couldn't play by ear but I had managed to invent a few melodies from which it seemed I could never escape and to which I seemed always to be returning, a bit sullenly, as it were. In my despair I used to beat the keys of the piano, employing all the variations of tempo and volume I could devise, and I was always being driven away from the piano by one of my sisters. They said I played as if I were half-crazy. I didn't know why I had to try to play the piano but it seemed to me that I had to. We were all living and it seemed to me that something should happen. I believed this fiercely and when it always turned out that everything remained the same and we kept on doing things over and over again I would be frantic and I wouldn't know what to do with myself. And then once again we would all be laughing.

And now we were to have another musical instrument in our house. Krikor's cornet was a blunt and tangled affair, more a piece of plumbing than a musical instrument. He brought home a music stand and a book on how to play the cornet. By Christmas, he said, I'll be playing *Barcarole*. He blew into the horn and his lips became swollen and sore. Somehow he taught himself to play a very mediocre version of *America* and an even worse version of *My Old Kentucky Home,* and he always insisted that I stand up when he tried to play *America*.

He practiced a long time and we began to accept the horn as something permanent around the house, like the cat or the crickets or the English walnut tree; but he never learned to play *Barcarole*. Krikor had a very bad time of it from the beginning and gradually his ardor cooled and he began to be suspicious. He would fidget with his music and make a valiant effort to play only the printed notes and then suddenly he would go off and make all sorts of noises, and we knew that he could be heard as far south as the brewery and as far north as the Court House Park because we had been told. After a while he would be too tired to blow any more and he would sit down and look very miserable. He would say, I don't know what's the matter. I have done everything the book says to do and I have practiced regularly. He would look at the horn bitterly and ask, Do you think it's because this horn is so old or is it just that I haven't any talent for cornet-playing? I wouldn't know what to think but I would understand how he felt because I felt the same way. There was something to be done, something perfect and precise and graceful, but we hadn't found out what it was.

Everyone for blocks around knew that Krikor had a cornet and when he passed people in the street they would whisper to one another, There he goes. The boy who is making all that noise. He has a cornet and he is trying to learn to play. We thought it was those street cats, but cats don't make that noise in the daytime.

Each summer the long tractor came back and filled the days with its dismal hollow pounding, the nuts from the English walnut tree fell to earth and we gathered them into boxes. Imperceptibly the change was always going on and each spring my sister Naomi placed peach blossoms in the black vase.

One day Krikor said, I have decided to give up the cornet. I can't play it. He spoke deliberately and, I thought, bravely. Less than a week later he came home on a bicycle, riding under the cross-bar because he couldn't reach the pedals from the seat. He was almost twelve but he was small for his age. When my mother saw him coming up our street, pumping under the cross-bar, his body all out of shape, she ran down the front porch steps to the sidewalk. What is this you've brought home? she said. Get out of that crazy thing. Do you want to cripple yourself for life?

Krikor took the bicycle to the back yard and began trying to lower the seat. He worked hard and after a while he got the seat down as far as it would go, but even at that the bicycle was too big for him and he had to go on riding it from under the bar. My mother carried the bicycle into the house one evening and locked it in a closet. Your father, she told Krikor, was an erect man and your mother is an erect woman and I am sure I am not going to let you make a cripple of yourself. If you must ride a bicycle you had better get one you can ride from the top.

Krikor had been selling the *Evening Herald* after school almost two years and he had been saving money. My mother encouraged him to save his earnings but she did not object to his spending as much as he felt he ought to spend. On his twelfth birthday he came home with a cake which had cost him seven dollars and fifty cents. When we asked why he had gone to such an unreasonable expense and why he had brought home such a large cake when there were only five of us to eat it, he said, This was the first cake the baker showed me and I hadn't ever bought a birthday cake before. I thought it was about the right size. Is it too big?

Lucy said, Why, we couldn't eat this cake in a month.

We had cake at every meal for a whole week and we never stopped laughing about it.

So Krikor took the big bicycle back to the shop and traded it in for a smaller one. He had very little talent for making bargains and the only reason he had bought the big bicycle in the first place was that Kebo, the bicycle man, had insisted on selling it to him. He came home on a smaller bicycle, sitting on the seat where he belonged and my mother said, That's more like it. You look like something now.

It wasn't long before I was riding the bicycle more than Krikor was, and finally we got into a fight over it. We had had fights before, but this was our biggest fight because we had grown bigger. Krikor chased me around the house and then suddenly I turned and chased him around the other way. We were wrestling and doing everything we could to be properly angry and at the same time not really to hurt one another when my mother separated us and said that we could not have the bicycle at all if we could not keep from fighting over it. I knew, and I think Krikor knew, it wasn't the bicycle. We would have fought over something else. The bicycle just happened to be there. It was because we were brothers and because we loved one another and because we had been together through so many different things. One day when Krikor and I were fighting silently in the back yard old man Andreas, who was passing through the empty lot next to our house, ran up to our front door and cried in Armenian, Ester, Ester, your sons are killing one another.

Somehow we began to use the bicycle together, hiking one another. Sometimes I hiked Krikor but most of the time he hiked me. There were lots of brothers in the town who were doing this. We had made a path across the lot and at the end of the lot there was a steep bank of three or four feet. We used to start from our back yard and after picking up some speed we used to go down this bank.

One Sunday afternoon in November we decided to ride out to the County Fair Grounds. There was no fair and no baseball game but we wanted to go out there and get on the dirt track with our bicycle. We had done this before and we had enjoyed being in the deserted Fair Grounds because it was different from being out there when all the people were there. It was finer and more private and we had lots more fun being alone. We liked the quiet and the enormity of the place, the strangeness of the empty grandstands. We used to take turns riding the bicycle around the mile track. Krikor had a watch and he would time me and then I would time him and we had a small book in which we kept a written record of our speed.

The castor plant had grown a lot and the peach trees had spread out. Easter and Christmas and Raisin Day had come around, we had thinned the honeysuckle plant to give it new life, we had bought new shoes and new clothes, we had got ill with the flu, but we hadn't noticed and we hadn't remembered. There were a few photographs of us in the family album, but to look at them it didn't seem as if we had changed. We had gone on quietly, sitting through the winter evenings, doing our school lessons, playing the piano, talking with one another, and laughing loudly for no reason. It had all happened and it was all there but we hadn't remembered about it and now we wanted to get on our bicycle and go out to the County Fair Grounds again.

I sat on the cross-bar and Krikor got on the seat and we went across the lot. Now for the big dip, Krikor said. We came to the bank and went down it but while we were going down it something happened. The fork of our bicycle cracked and broke and the front wheel sank on its side. It happened almost too slowly to be real and while it was happening, while the fork was cracking and the wheel was sinking, we seemed to be coming out of an endless dream and we seemed to feel that this trivial occurrence was a vast and a vital thing. It ought to have been amusing and we ought to have laughed about it, but it wasn't at all amusing and we didn't laugh. We walked back to the house without saying a word.

My mother had seen what had happened from the window of Naomi's room and when we went into the house, bewildered and frantically awake, she said, Don't you boys realize you've grown? You're much too big for one bicycle now.

We didn't speak of the matter all afternoon. We sat around the house trying to read, trying to feel that everything was the same and that only the fork of our bicycle had broken but we knew that everything was not the same. It seemed to me that we had forgotten our lives and that now because of this little incident we were remembering all the little details that marked the stages of our growth. I remembered the time Krikor and I made a canoe of plaster laths and burlap and tar, because we wanted to go down a stream, and walked with it six miles to Thompson Ditch through a burning sun and saw it sink.

I remembered the time I nearly drowned in Kings River and Krikor swam after me shouting frantically in Armenian. The time Lucy lost her job at Woolworth's and cried for a week. The time Naomi was ill with pneumonia and we all prayed she wouldn't die. The time Krikor came home with a small phonograph and two records: *Barcarole* and *O Sole Mio.*

And I remembered with a sickening sensation the day my uncle Vahan came to our house in a soldier's uniform and played *Johnny Get Your Gun* on his violin; my mother's cheerfulness when he sat at our table and her sobbing when he went away in a train. I remembered all the days she sat in the parlor reading the *Asbarez* and telling us about the misery and the pain and the dying in the old country.

And I remembered the day we learned that my uncle Vahan had been killed in France and we all sat at the supper table and couldn't eat and went to bed and couldn't sleep because we were all crying and talking about him.

I remembered that I had run down to the *Herald* office each noon for the extra edition about the War and had run through the streets shouting. I remembered the day it ended and the *Herald* printed a front-page etching of our Lord and the words *Peace on Earth, Good Will Toward Men.* How I came home, hoarse from shouting and sick in my soul because it was all over and my uncle Vahan was out there dead. I remembered the times I had walked alone, seeing things and being alive and thinking of my uncle Vahan, and suddenly burst into tears because life was so bright and clean and fierce.

All afternoon and almost all evening there was no talking in our house. My sister Lucy played the piano for a few minutes and my sister Naomi hummed *Smiles* until she remembered that my mother had asked her never to hum that song because her brother Vahan had sung it. We all felt sullen and bewildered. We were getting ready to go to bed when Krikor said, Wasn't it funny the way the bicycle broke under us?

My mother and my sisters said it was the funniest sight they had ever seen and they began to laugh about it. They laughed softly at first. They would stop laughing for a moment and then remember how funny it had been and then they would start laughing again, only louder. Krikor began to laugh with them and it almost seemed as if everything in our world was all right and that we had nothing to feel sad about. I couldn't decide what to do and I didn't think the incident had been funny at all, but after a while I began to laugh, too. All those things had happened and yet we were still living together in our house and we still had our trees and in the summer the city would send out the long tractor again and we would hear it and old Casparian would pass before our house in his wagon, crying watermelon in Armenian. I didn't feel at all happy but I laughed until tears came from my eyes.

Then suddenly something strange happened; it happened inside of me, and at the same time it seemed to be happening all over the world, in the cities, on the surface of the earth everywhere, wherever there were men. I felt that at last I was a part of life, that at last I knew how all things ended. A strange, desolating sadness swept through the earth and for the first time in my life I was feeling it definitely, personally. It seemed as if I had just been born, that I had at that moment become aware of the earth, of man on it, of life, of the beauty and the pain, the joy and the fear and the ugliness. It was all very clear to me and I knew why I had always sat at the piano pounding the keys, why I had fought with my brother Krikor, and why we had laughed together. And because I had been laughing, and because tears had come from my eyes, I sat on my bed and began to cry.

Without saying a word, Krikor began to cry, and after him my sisters began to cry.

My mother said in Armenian, It is no use to cry. We have always had our disappointments and hardships and we have always come out of them and always shall.

When we were all supposed to be asleep, I got up from my bed and went to the door that opened on our parlor and opened it an inch or two. I saw that my mother had taken her brother's photograph from the piano. She had placed it before her on the table and I could hear her weeping softly, and I could see her swaying her head from side to side the way people from the old country do.

Examinations at Harrow

WINSTON S. CHURCHILL

I HAD SCARCELY passed my twelfth birthday when I entered the inhospitable regions of examinations, through which for the next seven years I was destined to journey. These examinations were a great trial to me. The subjects which were dearest to the examiners were almost invariably those I fancied least. I would have liked to have been examined in history, poetry and writing essays. The examiners, on the other hand, were partial to Latin and mathematics. And their will prevailed. Moreover, the questions which they asked on both these subjects were almost invariably those to which I was unable to suggest a satisfactory answer. I should have liked to be asked to say what I knew. They always tried to ask what I did not know. When I would have willingly displayed my knowledge, they sought to expose my ignorance. This sort of treatment had only one result: I did not do well in examinations.

This was especially true of my Entrance Examination to Harrow. The Headmaster, Dr. Welldon, however, took a broad-minded view of my Latin prose; he showed discernment in judging my general ability. This was the more remarkable, because I was found unable to answer a single question in the Latin paper. I wrote my name at the top of the page. I wrote down the number of the question '1'. After much reflection I put a bracket round it thus '(1)'. But thereafter I could not think of anything connected with it that was either relevant or true. Incidentally there arrived from nowhere in particular a blot and several smudges. I gazed for two whole hours at this sad spectacle: and then merciful ushers collected my piece of foolscap with all the others and carried it up to the Headmaster's table. It was from these slender indications of scholarship that Dr. Welldon drew the conclusion that I was worthy to pass into Harrow. It is very much to his credit. It showed that he was a man capable of looking beneath the surface of things: a man not dependent upon paper manifestations. I have always had the greatest regard for him.

In consequence of his decision, I was in due course placed in the third, or lowest division of the Fourth, or bottom, Form. The names of the new boys were printed in the School List in alphabetical order; and as my correct name, Spencer-Churchill, began with an 'S' I gained no more advantage from the alphabet than from the wider sphere of letters. I was in fact only two from the bottom of the whole school; and these two, I regret to say, disappeared almost immediately through illness or some other cause.

The Harrow custom of calling the roll is different from that of Eton. At Eton the boys stand in a cluster and lift their hats when their names are called. At Harrow they file past a Master in the school yard and answer one by one. My position was therefore revealed in its somewhat invidious humility. It was the year 1887. Lord Randolph Churchill had only just resigned his position as Leader of the House of Commons and Chancellor of the Exchequer and he still towered in the forefront of politics. In consequence large numbers of visitors of both sexes used to wait on the school steps, in order to see me march by; and I frequently heard the irreverent comment, 'Why, he's last of all!'

I continued in this unpretentious situation for nearly a year. However, by being so long in the lowest form I gained an immense advantage over the cleverer boys. They all went on to learn Latin and Greek and splendid things like that. But I was taught English. We were considered such dunces that we could only learn English. Mr. Somervell—a most delightful man to whom my debt is great—was charged with the duty of teaching the stupidest boys the most disregarded thing—namely, to write mere English. He knew how to do it. He taught it as no one else has ever taught it. Not only did we learn English parsing thoroughly, but we also practised continually English analysis. Mr. Somervell had a system of his own. He took a fairly long sentence and broke it up into its components by means of black, red, blue and green inks. Subject, verb, object: Relative Clauses, Conditional Clauses, Conjunctive and Disjunctive Clauses! Each had its colour and its bracket. It was a kind of drill. We did it almost daily. As I remained in the Third Fourth (B) three times as long as anyone else, I had three times as much of it. I learned it thoroughly. Thus I got into my bones the essential structure of the ordinary British sentence—which is a noble thing. And when in after years my schoolfellows who had won prizes and distinction for writing such beautiful Latin poetry and pithy Greek epigrams had to come down again to common English, to earn their living or make their way, I did not feel myself at any disadvantage. Naturally I am biased in favour of boys learning English. I would make them all learn English: and then I would let the clever ones learn Latin as an honour, and Greek as a treat. But the only thing I would whip them for would be for not knowing English. I would whip them hard for that.

I first went to Harrow in the summer term. The school possessed the biggest swimming-bath I had ever seen. It was more like the bend of a river than a bath, and it had two bridges across it. Thither we used to repair for hours at a time and bask between our dips eating enormous buns on the hot asphalt margin. Naturally it was a good joke to come up behind some naked friend, or even enemy, and push him in. I made quite a habit of this with boys of my own size or less. One day when I had been no more than a month in the school, I saw a boy standing in a meditative posture wrapped in a towel on the very brink. He was no bigger than I was, so I thought him fair game. Coming stealthily behind, I pushed him in, holding on to his towel out of humanity, so that it should not get wet. I was startled to see a furious face emerge from the foam, and a being evidently of enormous strength making its way by fierce strokes to the shore. I fled, but in vain. Swift as the wind my pursuer overtook me, seized me in a ferocious grip and hurled me into the deepest part of the pool. I soon scrambled out on the other side, and found myself surrounded by an agitated crowd of younger boys. 'You're in for it' they said. 'Do you know what you have done? It's Amery, he's in the Sixth Form. He is Head of his House; he is champion at Gym; he has got his football colours.' They continued to recount his many titles to fame and reverence and to dilate upon the awful retribution that would fall upon me. I was convulsed not only with terror, but with the guilt of sacrilege. How could I tell his rank when he was in a bath-towel, and so small? I determined to apologise immediately. I approached the potentate in lively trepidation. 'I am very sorry' I said. 'I mistook you for a Fourth Form boy. You are so small.' He did not seem at all placated by this; so I added in a most brilliant recovery, 'My father, who is a great man, is also small.' At this he laughed and after some general remarks about my 'cheek' and how I had better be careful in the future, signified that the incident was closed.

I have been fortunate to see a good deal more of him, in times when three years' difference in age is not so important as it is at school. We were afterwards to be Cabinet colleagues for a good many years.

It was thought incongruous that while I apparently stagnated in the lowest form, I should gain a prize open to the whole school for reciting to the Headmaster twelve hundred lines of Macaulay's 'Lays of Ancient Rome' without making a single mistake. I also succeeded in passing the preliminary examination for the Army while still almost at the bottom of the school. This examination seemed to have called forth a very special effort on my part, for many boys far above me in the school failed in it. I also had a piece of good luck. We knew that among other questions we should be asked to draw from memory a map of some country or other. The night before by way of final preparation I put the names of all the maps in the atlas into a hat and drew out New Zealand. I applied my good memory to the geography of that Dominion. Sure enough the first question in the paper was: 'Draw a map of New Zealand.' This was what is called at Monte Carlo an *en plein* and I ought to have been paid thirty-five times my stake. However, I certainly got paid very high marks for my paper.

I was now embarked on a military career. This orientation was entirely due to my collection of soldiers. I had ultimately nearly fifteen hundred. They were all of one size, all British, and organised as an infantry division with a cavalry brigade. My brother Jack commanded the hostile army. But by a Treaty for the Limitation of Armaments he was only allowed to have coloured troops, and they were not allowed to have artillery. Very important! I could muster myself only eighteen field-guns—besides fortress pieces. But all the other services were complete—except one. It is what every army is always short of—transport. My father's old friend, Sir Henry Drummond Wolff, admiring my array, noticed this deficiency and provided a fund from which it was to some extent supplied.

The day came when my father himself paid a formal visit of inspection. All the troops were arranged in the correct formation of attack. He spent twenty minutes studying the scene—which was really impressive—with a keen eye and captivating smile. At the end he asked me if I would like to go into the Army. I thought it would be splendid to command an Army, so I said 'Yes' at once: and immediately I was taken at my word. For years I thought my father, with his experience and flair had discerned in me the qualities of military genius. But I was told later that he had only come to the conclusion that I was not clever enough to go to the Bar. However that may be, the toy soldiers turned the current of my life. Henceforward all my education was directed to passing into Sandhurst, and afterwards to the technical details of the profession of arms. Anything else I had to pick up for myself.

I spent nearly four and a half years at Harrow, of which three were in the Army class. To this I was admitted in consequence of having passed the preliminary examination. It consisted of boys of the middle and higher forms of the school and of very different ages, all of whom were being prepared either for the Sandhurst or the Woolwich examination. We were withdrawn from the ordinary movement of the school from form to form. In consequence I got no promotion or very little and remained quite low down upon the school list, though working alongside of boys nearly all in the Fifth Form. Officially I never got out of the Lower School, so I never had the privilege of having a fag of my own. When in the passage of time I became what was called 'a three-yearer' I ceased to have to fag myself, and as I was older than other boys of my standing, I was appointed in my House to the position of Head of the Fags. This was my first responsible office, and the duties, which were honorary, consisted in keeping the roster of all the fags, making out the list of their duties and dates and placing copies of these lists in the rooms of the monitors, football and cricket champions and other members of our aristocracy. I discharged these functions for upwards of a year, and on the whole I was resigned to my lot.

Meanwhile, I found an admirable method of learning my Latin translations. I was always very slow at using a dictionary: it was just like using a telephone directory. It is easy to open it more or less at the right letter, but then you have to turn backwards and forwards and peer up and down the columns and very often find yourself three or four pages the wrong side of the word you want. In short I found it most laborious, while to other boys it seemed no trouble. But now I formed an alliance with a boy in the Sixth Form. He was very clever and could read Latin as easily as English. Caesar, Ovid, Virgil, Horace and even Martial's epigrams were all the same to him. My daily task was perhaps ten or fifteen lines. This would ordinarily have taken me an hour or an hour and a half to decipher and then it would probably have been wrong. But my friend could in five minutes construe it for me word by word, and once I had seen it exposed, I remembered it firmly. My Sixth-Form friend for his part was almost as much troubled by the English essays he had to write for the Headmaster as I was by these Latin cross-word puzzles. We agreed together that he should tell me my Latin translations and that I should do his essays. The arrangement worked admirably. The Latin master seemed quite satisfied with my work, and I had more time to myself in the mornings. On the other hand once a week or so I had to compose the essays of my Sixth-Form friend. I used to walk up and down the room dictating—just as I do now—and he sat in the corner and wrote it down in long-hand. For several months no difficulty arose; but once we were nearly caught out. One of these essays was thought to have merit. It was 'sent up' to the Headmaster who summoned my friend, commended him on his work, and proceeded to discuss the topic with him in a lively spirit. 'I was interested in this point you make here. You might I think have gone even further. Tell me exactly what you had in your mind.' Dr. Welldon in spite of very chilling responses continued in this way for quite some time to the deep consternation of my confederate. However the Headmaster, not wishing to turn an occasion of praise into one of cavilling, finally let him go with the remark. 'You seem to be better at written than at oral work.' He came back to me like a man who has had a very narrow squeak, and I was most careful ever afterwards to keep to the beaten track in essay-writing.

Dr. Welldon took a friendly interest in me, and knowing that I was weak in the Classics, determined to help me himself. His daily routine was heavy; but he added three times a week a quarter of an hour before evening prayers in which to give me personal tuition. This was a great condescension for the Headmaster, who of course never taught anyone but the monitors and highest scholars. I was proud of the honour: I shrank from the ordeal. If the reader has ever learned any Latin prose he will know that at quite an early stage one comes across the Ablative Absolute with its apparently somewhat despised alternative 'Quum with the pluperfect subjunctive!' I always preferred 'Quum'. True he was a little longer to write, thus lacking the much admired terseness and pith of the Latin language. On the other hand, he avoided a number of pitfalls, I was often uncertain whether the Ablative Absolute should end in 'e' or 'i' or 'o' or 'is' or 'ibus', to the correct selection of which great importance was attached. Dr. Welldon seemed to be physically pained by a mistake being made in any of these letters. I remember that later on Mr. Asquith used to have just the same sort of look on his face when I sometimes adorned a Cabinet discussion by bringing out one of my few but faithful Latin quotations. It was more than annoyance, it was a pang. Moreover Headmasters have powers at their disposal with which Prime Ministers have never yet been invested. So these evening quarters of an hour with Dr. Welldon added considerably to the anxieties of my life. I was much relieved when after nearly a whole term of patient endeavour he desisted from his well-meant but unavailing efforts.

I will here make some general observations about Latin which probably have their application to Greek as well. In a sensible language like English important words are connected and related to one another by other little words. The Romans in that stern antiquity considered such a method weak and unworthy. Nothing would satisfy them but that the structure of every word should be reacted on by its neighbours in accordance with elaborate rules to meet the different conditions in which it might be used. There is no doubt that this method both sounds and looks more impressive than our own. The sentence fits together like a piece of polished machinery. Every phrase can be tensely charged with meaning. It must have been very laborious, even if you were brought up to it; but no doubt it gave the Romans, and the Greeks too, a fine and easy way of establishing their posthumous fame. They were the first comers in the fields of thought and literature. When they arrived at fairly obvious reflections upon life and love, upon war, fate or manners, they coined them into the slogans or epigrams for which their language was so well adapted, and thus preserved the patent rights for all time. Hence their reputation. Nobody ever told me this at school. I have thought it all out in later life.

But even as a schoolboy I questioned the aptness of the Classics for the prime structure of our education. So they told me how Mr. Gladstone read Homer for fun which I thought served him right; and that it would be a great pleasure to me in after life. When I seemed incredulous, they added that classics would be a help in writing or speaking English. They then pointed out the number of our modern words which are derived from the Latin or Greek. Apparently one could use these words much better, if one knew the exact source from which they had sprung. I was fain to admit a practical value. But now even this has been swept away. The foreigners and Scotch have joined together to introduce a pronunciation of Latin which divorces it finally from the English tongue. They tell us to pronounce 'audience' 'owdience'; and 'civil' 'keyweel.' They have distorted one of my most serviceable and impressive quotations into the ridiculous booby 'Wainy, Weedy, Weeky.' Punishment should be reserved for those who have spread this evil.

It took me three tries to pass into Sandhurst. There were five subjects, of which Mathematics, Latin and English were obligatory, and I chose in addition French and Chemistry. In this hand I held only a pair of Kings—English and Chemistry. Nothing less than three would open the jackpot. I had to find another useful card. Latin I could not learn. I had a rooted prejudice which seemed to close my mind against it. Two thousand marks were given for Latin. I might perhaps get 400! French was interesting but rather tricky, and difficult to learn in England. So there remained only Mathematics. After the first Examination was over, when one surveyed the battlefield, it was evident that the war could not be won without another army being brought into the line. Mathematics was the only resource available. I turned to them—I turned on them—in desperation. All my life from time to time I have had to get up disagreeable subjects at short notice, but I consider my triumph, moral and technical, was in learning Mathematics in six months. At the first of these three ordeals I got no more than 500 marks out of 2,500 for Mathematics. At the second I got nearly 2,000. I owe this achievement not only to my own 'back-to-the-wall' resolution—for which no credit is too great; but to the very kindly interest taken in my case by a much respected Harrow master, Mr. C. H. P. Mayo. He convinced me that Mathematics was not a hopeless bog of nonsense, and that there were meanings and rhythms behind the comical hieroglyphics and that I was not incapable of catching glimpses of some of these.

Of course what I call Mathematics is only what the Civil Service Commissioners expected you to know to pass a very rudimentary examination. I suppose that to those who enjoy this peculiar gift, Senior Wranglers and the like, the waters in which I swam must seem only a duck-puddle compared to the Atlantic Ocean. Nevertheless, when I plunged in, I was soon out of my depth. When I look back upon those care-laden months, their prominent features rise from the abyss of memory. Of course I had progressed far beyond Vulgar Fractions and the Decimal System. We were arrived in an 'Alice-in-Wonderland' world, at the portals of which stood 'A Quadratic Equation.' This with a strange grimace pointed the way to the Theory of Indices, which again handed on the intruder to the full rigours of the Binomial Theorem. Further dim chambers lighted by sullen, sulphurous fires were reputed to contain a dragon called the 'Differential Calculus.' But this monster was beyond the bounds appointed by the Civil Service Commissioners who regulated this stage of Pilgrim's heavy journey. We turned aside, not indeed to the uplands of the Delectable Mountains, but into a strange corridor of things like anagrams and acrostics called Sines, Cosines and Tangents. Apparently they were very important, especially when multiplied by each other, or by themselves! They had also this merit—you could learn many of their evolutions off by heart. There was a question in my third and last Examination about these Cosines and Tangents in a highly square-rooted condition which must have been decisive upon the whole of my after life. It was a problem. But luckily I had seen its ugly face only a few days before and recognised it at first sight.

I have never met any of these creatures since. With my third and successful Examination they passed away like the phantasmagoria of a fevered dream. I am assured that they are most helpful in engineering, astronomy and things like that. It is very important to build bridges and canals and to comprehend all the stresses and potentialities of matter, to say nothing of counting all the stars and even universes and measuring how far off they are, and foretelling eclipses and the arrival of comets and such like. I am very glad there are quite a number of people born with a gift and a liking for all of this; like great chess-players who play sixteen games at once blindfold and die quite soon of epilepsy. Serve them right! I hope the Mathematicians, however, are well rewarded. I promise never to blackleg their profession nor take the bread out of their mouths.

I had a feeling once about Mathematics, that I saw it all—Depth beyond depth was revealed to me—The Byss and the Abyss. I saw, as one might see the transit of Venus—or even the Lord Mayor's Show, a quantity passing through infinity and changing its sign from plus to minus. I saw exactly how it happened and why the tergiversation was inevitable: and how the one step involved all the others. It was like politics. But it was after dinner and I let it go!

The practical point is that if this aged, weary-souled Civil Service Commissioner had not asked this particular question about these Cosines or Tangents in their squared or even cubed condition, which I happened to have learned scarcely a week before, not one of the subsequent chapters of this book * would ever have been written. I might have gone into the Church and preached orthodox sermons in a spirit of audacious contradiction to the Age. I might have gone into the City and made a fortune. I might have resorted to the Colonies, or 'Dominions' as they are now called, in the hopes of pleasing, or at least placating them; and thus had, à la Lindsay Gordon or Cecil Rhodes, a lurid career. I might even have gravitated to the Bar, and persons might have been hanged through my defence who now nurse their guilty secrets with complacency. Anyhow, the whole of *my* life would have been altered, and that I suppose would have altered a great many other lives, which in their turn, and so on . . .

* The author refers to *A Roving Commission.* (In Canada, *My Early Life.*)

III. EARLY SPRING

Easter Egg

FRANK BROOKHOUSER

Once he was going with a girl named Helen.

He was a sophomore in high school then, and she was a freshman. She was a very pretty girl, with lustrous brown eyes that she lowered demurely whenever he told her anything nice but which looked squarely at him and became shimmering and misty as early morning dew whenever she told him anything nice. Her hair was brown, too, and in the summertime the sun tinted it with red. Her hands were little and very white. Whenever they kissed, he can remember, she held on to his arm with her fingers tightly and yet tenderly, as though she were afraid he would leave her any minute, forever, and that the second she took them away, everything would be ended.

She did not have the brightness and light-heartedness of most high-school girls. She laughed very often when they were alone but when there was anyone around them, she was meek and quiet. She wasn't very good at parties. She would stay close to him, watching the others playing. And he never looked at her, no matter how loud or uproarious the party was, that she wasn't smiling softly at him, her eyes wrinkling wistfully, as though she were totally unaware that others were around.

She was a very poor girl and she lived in a little house down at the lower end of town where mostly foreigners lived—the Poles and Slavs who worked in the mill. The house was weather-beaten and the paint had been peeling off it slowly for many years. Long ago her mother had stopped thinking about the paint peeling off because she had so many other things to think about, like Helen and Helen's father. Old Hank, her father, was known, benevolently, as the "not steady" kind. This meant, of course, that he was a drunk. He was a good mechanic when he was sober but he was not sober very much so he did not get many jobs. And Helen's mother took in washings. The furniture in the house was of many varieties, but alike in its oldness. The cushions on the couch were worn, drab and colorless. He and Helen usually sat on the porch swing.

"I'm sorry I can't take you to a nicer place," she always said.

"What do you mean?" he would say. "I'm with you. Gee, what more would a fellow want than that?" That was one of the times she would lower her eyes. And he really didn't mind the furniture or the lack of paint or old Hank. He didn't even notice these deficiencies, then. Or he ignored them because they were so unimportant.

Helen was always conscious of her clothes because her mother made all of her dresses. And when he told her that she looked swell—and she did—she would never answer him. She would press her head into his shoulder, snuggling it there, and reach up for his face and touch it gently with her finger tips. Except for kisses, she never asked for anything except an ice-cream cone. Once in a while, when she knew he had more money than usual, she would suggest an ice-cream cone. They would walk along the street eating the cones and she would eat hers very slowly. She would have it long after he had finished.

"Gee, you're slow," he would kid her.

"I guess I am. But girls eat slower, that's all. Do you want some of mine?"

"No, of course not." And he would enjoy watching her take the little bites out of her cone, glancing sideways at him.

He was much richer than Helen. He passed papers after school and got a dollar a week for that. And when he had reached the fifth grade, his father started his sister and himself on an allowance so they would learn about responsibility and handling money. They were started at fifty cents and when they got into high school, it was advanced to a dollar because the needs were greater. This money was for church, movies, candy, miscellany, etc. It covered a lot of things, from baseball gloves to smuggled lipstick. His sister, despite the lipstick, was a better saver than he and always had some left at the end of the week, so he often had to wash dishes for her to come out right on the budget. When he got the paper job, his father and mother conferred one night and decided to continue the allowance despite the windfall because he was getting to be a "young man."

He started going with Helen in January and he saw her almost every night. They were kidded by their families—old Hank used the old word "sparking"—because it was their first love affair. And because it was that, too, both of them knew all about love and they were amazed at how little the old people knew about it. In the kidding, they found mutual strength.

"They could never understand anything like how wonderful our love is," Helen would say.

"We just have to not pay any attention to them, that's all."

"I don't anyway."

He started weeks before Easter to save for the Easter egg. It was the first time he had ever saved in his life (his sister was quite annoyed because she never got out of doing the dishes) and he hasn't saved much since, never for an Easter egg. Each week he put away a quarter or fifty cents because he wanted to get Helen the biggest egg you could buy—a five-pounder.

The Saturday before Easter he went down to the Sweet Shoppe with his money folded safely and securely in a little lump in his watch pocket. For a long time he stared in the window at all the beautiful eggs, resting in the green grass, sitting austerely against the lids of their boxes. He looked at the different decorations on the chocolate, the swans and flower designs and pretties of all kinds. All the time he kept feeling the $4 in his pocket to make sure it was still there. All the time he kept peeking in the store because there were many people inside, congregated around Looie's candy counter, and he was afraid to have them all see he was buying the egg. It was the first egg and the first gift he had ever bought for a girl.

He would think people were noticing him staring in the window and so he would walk up and down the street every once in a while, returning to look inside the store and see how the crowd was. He wished, in his anguish, that he had bought the egg early, before the last-day rush. He damned himself for not having thought of that. Finally, when it was nearly suppertime and the crowd had thinned out, he summoned all his courage, all his manhood, and stalked in, stalked straight up to the candy counter, trying not to see the watching eyes, trying to ignore them.

"Oh, oh, I'll bet Helen's gonna get something," Joe Simmons murmured to three other boys. He ignored it. He stared at Looie, his features strained, his stomach weak.

"I want to get an Easter egg, Looie."

"Fine thing. We got all kinds. What kind you like?"

"Well, I was thinking of a five-pounder."

"Ah, we got the best. We got beauties. You want a name on it, huh? We put the name on for no extra charge."

"Yeah, I was thinking of getting a name on it."

"We fix you up a nice job."

"How much are the five-pounders, Looie?" He knew that. He knew that very well. They were $4. Exactly.

"Four dollars. Finest egg in the store. You make no mistake, Dick. You make good buy."

"That's what I want. Nothing but the best, huh?" They laughed together.

"Yeah, nothing but the best. What you want on the egg?"

" 'To Helen, with love.' " He leaned over the counter to whisper it, so the boys wouldn't hear.

The boys heard, anyway, or surmised. They began to titter and laugh. Looie bit his lower lip and his black eyes were angry.

"Move on," he told the boys, gesturing to the door with his arm. "Go some place else you want to loaf. All the time you loaf and stop good customers from coming in." The boys slouched, smirking, toward the door.

"You don't get no more of our business," one said.

"You ain't business. I should care about your business, anyway. You keep good customers out." (Looie said this regularly, and just as regularly, treated the crowd when the high-school basketball team won an important game.)

"Don't listen to them," Looie told him. "They don't know nothing from nothing. Cheap skates. No wonder they loaf. They ain't got no nice girls."

That made him feel better. It made him feel proud and important. He took out the wad of bills with a flourish, unrolled it, and handed the $4 to Looie.

The egg was big all right, and satisfyingly heavy. He loved the weight of it under his arm. He hurried home so not many people would see him. At night, when he took the egg to Helen, it would be dark and he could cut through the alleys down by her house, so this trip was the only one requiring courage.

His mother was in the parlor darning socks. She had a pile of them on her lap and when he came in the door with the big box under his arm, she hopped up from the chair and the socks fell to the floor.

"My goodness, Richard, what in the world have you got there?" she asked, brushing down her skirt and coming toward him.

"Just an Easter egg."

"An Easter egg?"

"Yeah, an Easter egg for Helen."

"But my God, what kind is it? It's so big."

"It's . . . it's a five-pound one."

"Richard!" She placed her hands on her hips akimbo, staring at him, lips pursed. She said nothing, waiting for him to speak.

"Well, I had the money saved . . . that's how I got it. I saved the money."

She clicked her lips. "What in the world ever made you go and do a foolish thing like that? You'll have to take it back, that's all there is to it. You'll have to take it right back. Your father would hit the roof if he ever heard about it. Two pounds is plenty. Five pounds, my God. . . ." She clicked her lips again.

"I can't take it back now. And two pounds isn't enough. Gee, a two-pounder you get for just anyone. This is for Helen. . . ."

"If I know Helen, she'd like a two-pound one just as much. She'd appreciate it just as much. She knows you don't have a lot of money. Helen knows the value of money, indeed she does, living down there and with that father of hers. I don't like to mention it, Richard, but your father doesn't like the idea of your going to *that* house any too well. Of course, it's not Helen's fault but . . . well. . . ."

"Old Hank's all right. He treats me fine. He never did nothing bad that I saw. I never seen him do a single thing mean."

"But his poor family, Richard. He has no thought for them. Mrs. Wilson taking in washings, working herself to the bone."

"Gee, you're always harping on that, Mom. Can't you forget it, just once?"

His mother's face clouded with feigned hurt. "All right, son. But you are going to take the egg back now. Your father will make you if I don't, and he'll be a lot worse than I am about it. How much *did* it cost?"

"Four dollars."

"Oh my God, Richard. Four dollars. Your father will hit the roof. Two pounds is plenty. It's the thought that counts, Richard. It's not like you were engaged or serious . . . or anything. You're young. And just foolish."

"I'm not foolish. I love Helen. She's a swell girl. There isn't a nicer girl in the world. So why isn't it right I should buy her the best egg I can get. Why isn't it, Mom?"

"You're too young to understand some things, Richard. I'm older and I know. I know Helen's a nice girl . . . although I don't think quite the type for you. . . ."

"Why not?"

"We won't go into that now but I do want to talk to you . . . soon. The thing now is to get that egg back before your father gets home."

"I can't take it back now. I'm not going into Looie's again. Gee, I'd be ashamed ever to go near the place after doing a thing like that." The thought made him weak, his legs even tired. "He'd think I was a big baby . . . or something."

"Looie would be glad to change it. He knows everyone can make a mistake."

"All right, I won't take it at all. I won't take anything to Helen. Even if it is Easter and everything. But I'm not going back to Looie's." He flung the box into a chair and flounced down beside it. He pushed the box away, twisting his hands helplessly, struggling to keep back the tears that were forming with the ache in his throat. His mother walked over to him and brushed her hand against his shoulder.

"Now, son, don't take it that way. I'm just trying to help you do the best thing. The right thing. Suppose I take it back? I know how you feel about taking it back. Would that be better?"

This in itself was such a relief that he began to think maybe he had gone overboard . . . a little. After all, he was young and *not* actually engaged . . . yet.

"I guess that's best." He wanted to relax and not think of it any more, not think of anything.

"Fine." She kissed him lightly on the cheek and went upstairs for her coat.

When she came back from Looie's, she handed him the two-pound egg and the change. She was quiet and altogether different from when she had left.

"Was it all right?"

"Of course."

She stood over him, patting him gently, strangely on the shoulder. He didn't say anything. The two-pound egg, so little and light compared to the other, lay neglected on his lap.

"Richard. . . ."

"Yeah, Mom."

"I really think it was sweet of you to want to give Helen a big egg. You have a good heart. Only it was too much, it really would have been foolish. And your father would have been fit to tie. Now why don't you take her to a movie with some of the extra money. I think she'd like that, don't you? Sort of a double treat."

"That's a swell idea." He suddenly felt better about everything. He put his arm around his mother and she smiled wistfully at him. Then she went upstairs to take off her coat and she didn't come down again until it was time to put the potatoes on.

Helen was very happy with the two-pound egg.

"Oh, Dick," she said, "it's so pretty. And it was so thoughtful and sweet of you." She kissed him on the lips and then many times on the cheek. And they sat on the couch with the worn cushions, the egg in its box between them. Then she said she was going into the kitchen to get a knife so they could eat some.

She came out waving a big butcher knife, gayly, laughing, her eyes bright.

She held the egg on her lap and she kept staring at it and touching the pretties on it and saying how nice it was and how she hated to cut it and spoil it. And then she looked at him and said she was the happiest girl in the world tonight and all because of him.

Finally, she cut two pieces off the end. "I don't want to spoil the words on it yet, not for a long time," she said. "Here's the first piece for you."

They ate the pieces together, watching each other. It was a very good egg.

Then they went out to the swing and she carried the egg with her and set it down beside her on the swing. They ate some more of it without spoiling the words and she was very happy. And sitting there with the egg between them, just talking and eating, they seemed to know each other very well. He seemed to know her as well as he could ever possibly know her in all his life, even though they lived a million years. And he blurted out the story of the five-pound egg and she smiled and pressed his hand tightly.

"Of course, your mother was right, darling," she said. "It *would* have been foolish. And buying it for me, why that's the same as if you gave it to me. Honest, it is. . . ."

"I don't know, Helen. . . ." he said.

And he still doesn't know. Because he loved her very much and he wanted her to have the biggest Easter egg you could buy.

And the next Easter he wasn't going with Helen any more and she was a very poor girl and she married a poor man and will probably never have a big five-pound Easter egg all her life. And he had the four dollars, you see. He had the money for a five-pounder.

The Best Things Come in Small Packages

SALLY BENSON

DINNER ON Christmas Eve was a tasteless affair, and it was a relief to everyone when it was over. Judy Graves even forgot to ask if she could pick up her lamb chop to eat it, and she cut the meat from the bone and pushed the pieces indifferently around her plate with a fork. The feeling of anticipation that had carried her lightly along for the past two weeks had suddenly become concentrated and had settled like a cold, heavy weight in her stomach. She swallowed the last of her milk in a gulp. "I'll help Daddy bring the tree down," she offered.

Mr. Graves pushed back his chair. "Yes," he said, "we might as well get started."

The tree had been selected three days before and carried to a corner of the apartment-house roof so that it would keep fresh in the cold air. Lois and her mother had carefully chosen it for its shape. Now, as Mr. Graves and Judy left the table, Lois spoke. "It isn't so awfully *big*. I mean it's not one of those mammoth things that Daddy usually gets, but it's nice and thick and a *lovely* shape. You'll see what I mean when it's set up."

There were a dozen or more trees on the roof. The air smelled of them. Judy hopefully glanced at the tag on the tallest one. "I don't think this is it," she said. "This one has a long name on it."

At the end of the row, in a corner protected from the wind, a small tree lay against the railing, its branches tied with string. "This must be it," Judy said. She pulled it upright and it swayed toward her. The top branches touched her cheek and the scent of it filled her nostrils. She put her arms around it and held it close. "It isn't so very big," she said, defiantly, "but it's a beautiful little tree. A perfectly *beautiful* little tree. I'll carry it."

They walked back toward the elevator.

Lois was waiting for them by the door, and she looked anxious. "It's *darling*," Judy told her quickly. "It isn't small at all. There were some larger trees on the roof, but they looked scrawny. *Really*."

She carried the tree to the living room and laid it on the clean sheet that had been spread between the windows. Her hands were sticky from the sap and dark green needles clung to her sweater.

Lois's face lost its anxious look. She had slipped a smock over her dress and it gave her an efficient appearance. "I have sort of an idea," she said. "I think it might be unusual if we picked out just blue and silver ornaments and did the whole thing in blue and silver. I mean, there would be plenty of them because the tree is so much smaller."

"Not use all the ornaments!" Judy exclaimed. "You're nuts!"

"Oh," Mrs. Graves protested, "I think it would be better to use all the ornaments. We always have, and I'm fond of them."

"Really," Lois said, "you all act like a lot of reactionaries. You just won't listen to any new suggestions, *ever*."

Mr. Graves fastened the tree in its stand and cut the string from the branches. "I'll tell you what," he said. "When you're eighteen, Lois, you can trim the tree the way you want it, and when Judy's eighteen, she can trim it the way she wants it. How's that?"

He walked over to the table where the Christmas-tree ornaments lay in their boxes. Deliberately he chose a red-and-gold striped ball and hung it on the tree. His action stripped the authority from Lois and her smock and lifted the apprehension from Judy's heart.

"I'm going to put the cat face on for my first one," she said.

It took them over an hour to trim the tree and arrange the crèche on strips of cotton underneath it. Judy, kneeling to set a small celluloid reindeer near a tiny pine tree, suddenly remembered last year and how Bilgy, the cat that had died last summer, had knocked the whole scene over after they had arranged it. Her eyes smarted with tears and she shook her hair over to hide her face.

"It does seem strange without one single toy," Mrs. Graves said sadly. "It really looks bare without any toys under the tree."

"Speaking of toys—" Lois stopped abruptly and giggled.

"Speaking of toys what?" Judy asked.

"Oh, nothing," Lois told her. "You're too old for toys, of course."

"When I was twelve," Mrs. Graves said, "I was still playing with dolls."

"Dolls!" Lois exclaimed. "Oh, Mother!"

"It's living in New York," Mr. Graves said. "And that fool school."

"Well, get your stockings out, girls, and let's hang them," Mrs. Graves put in hurriedly.

Lois's stocking was silk and slim, with a small foot, and Judy brought a wool knee-length sock with a darn in the toe. "Turn your back, Judy," Lois said. She slipped a small package into the toe of Judy's sock.

"Just weight them with the candlesticks," Mrs. Graves told them. "I'll fix them later."

She went to her room and came back with her arms full of packages. "No poking at these," she said.

The Cogswell chair was for Judy's things, the wing chair for Lois's, and the couch for Mr. and Mrs. Graves' presents. Until this year Judy's chair had been almost empty, as her toys had been arranged under the tree after she had gone to bed. This year her chair looked the same as Lois's. Judy, glancing at the packages, wondered if the biggest one could be the jade-green lounging pajamas.

She got the gifts for her father, mother, and Lois from the shelf in her closet. She had bought her father a gadget called a Scotch Bartender, which measured an exact jigger of whiskey, and a practical and charming present for her mother. It was an ashtray, and attached to it was a frog's head. You inserted a cigarette in a place in the mouth, and the ashes fell in the tray. A silk-covered rubber tube extended from the inside of the frog's head and ended in a dainty amber cigarette holder. The idea of the whole thing was to be able to smoke in bed without fear of dropping ashes on the blankets and perhaps going up in flames. For Lois, she had bought a pair of red gloves fastened at the back with a gilt Christmas bell. She had wrapped her packages with care and covered them with stickers that called out, "Season's Greetings," "Joyeux Noël," "Merry Christmas," or warned, "Do Not Open Until Christmas" and "Hands Off Until Dec. 25th."

Lois had wrapped her gifts in blue cellophane and tied them with silver ribbon. Her stickers were silver stars.

It was almost midnight by the time the room was straightened and the carols were sung. Activity had thawed the lump in Judy's stomach somewhat, and she was surprised to find that she was a little sleepy. "I'll never close an eye," she said.

When Lois and Judy were in bed, Mrs. Graves came in to kiss them good night. "I never can realize that you two will never believe in Santa Claus again," she sighed.

"Judy pretended she did until she was almost *eight*," Lois said.

"I did not."

"I beg to differ."

Mrs. Graves uncurled Judy's fingers. "You didn't even wash."

"I did," Judy said, "all but this hand. That isn't dirt, it's sap and it smells good."

She turned on her side and snapped out the light over her bed. For almost five minutes, it seemed as though morning would never come.

The next thing Judy knew, it had come and gone in a swirl of white tissue paper, red ribbons, excited exclamations, and kisses. The big package had contained the jade-green lounging pajamas, which were a little too short and had to be exchanged. There were six pairs of silk stockings of a new shade called Woodsmoke, a pair of pink silk pants with lace edges, a silk nightgown that trailed on the floor, monogrammed writing paper, a new charm bracelet with fourteen charms on it, a bottle of 4711 eau de cologne, white kid gloves that fastened with a zipper, a tiny bottle of real perfume (lily of the valley), bedroom slippers with white fur tops, and, from Lois, a blue satin stocking box. The big present, of course, was the lounging pajamas, but the thing that Lois had tucked in the toe of her stocking was the funniest; it was a small crib with twin dolls in it, bought from the five-and-ten. The dolls were wrapped in tiny cheap blue blankets. Judy screamed with laughter when she saw it.

"That's why," Lois explained, "I very nearly died when Mother said what she did about toys last night."

"I don't wonder," Judy answered. She set the crib under the tree. "There, Mother, that should make you feel better."

She arranged her presents carefully in her chair. "I think I'll go over and give Fuffy hers," she said. Fuffy was her best friend and lived two blocks away.

In her room, she took off her wool socks and slid her new silk stockings over her legs. They felt strange and cold, and her shoes, when she put them on, slid up and down at the heels. Although her knees were plump, the stockings wrinkled around them and she had trouble keeping them up. She put on her new white gloves, her charm bracelet, scented a clean handkerchief with a drop of the lily-of-the-valley perfume, and started toward Fuffy's house. She held the package stiffly, as her hands were pinched in the new gloves. Halfway down the block she met Fuffy. One glance told her that Fuffy was wearing silk stockings, and though Fuffy wore her old wool mittens, Judy could see the peach-colored collar of a new blouse showing over the top of her double-breasted coat. Fuffy was also carrying a package, identical in shape with the one Judy held. She pressed it into Judy's arms. "Here," she said. "Merry Christmas."

"Same to you," Judy replied. "And here."

They walked toward the corner and stood by a large metal basket, into which they carefully threw the tissue-paper wrappings. "I got yours green," Judy said.

"I got yours red, *naturally*."

They had given one another pocketbooks of colored imitation leather, handsomely outfitted with lipstick, powder and rouge compact, comb, and cigarette case.

"I *love* mine," Fuffy said.

"Me, too."

They swung the pocketbooks over their arms and started toward the Park. The streets were alive with children—little children in bright woollen snow suits, five- to ten-year-olds whizzing by on skates and scooters. There were mere babies pushing toys with bells that rang as the wheels turned or riding in shiny red wagons. Smug little girls wheeled English coaches and fussed with dolls' blankets. Judy dangled her charm bracelet. "Look," she said. They stopped while Fuffy admired the charms. "Oh, a little ice pick and a pair of tongs! And a lantern and a wheelbarrow! Honestly, it's absolutely the cutest one I've ever seen!"

"Daddy picked it out all by himself," Judy told her. There was pride in her voice, as though she were speaking of a backward child who had suddenly and amazingly refused to fit a square peg into a round hole.

They talked about what they had received. As they had made almost identical lists during recess at school, the conversation lacked variety.

"Goodness," Judy said, dodging a little girl on roller skates, "it's as much as your life's worth to walk on the street today!"

"Remember when you got the little automobile?" Fuffy asked. Her eyes were wistful. "I don't think I ever had as much fun any Christmas as the year you got that automobile. It was the year I got my Pogo stick."

"The way we tore around in it!" Judy smiled tolerantly. "I was late for dinner."

"How old were we when we got our tricycles?"

"Oh, we must have been *little*," Judy answered. "Five or six, I guess."

"I remember it perfectly."

They tacitly avoided walking in the Park and stayed on Fifth Avenue. The air was filled with the noises children make: screams, whistles, the sound of wheels on cement, the soft thud of balls, and laughter so shrill and mirthless that it could be heard over all the other sounds. Judy's hands grew cold in her new gloves and the seams of her stockings twisted on her legs. They walked on and on, waiting sedately at corners for the lights to change, swinging their new bags from their arms. At Sixtieth Street they started back uptown. Judy's heels hurt where her shoes had rubbed against them and several times Fuffy stopped to adjust her stockings.

By the time they had reached the door to Fuffy's apartment on Seventy-ninth Street, they had grown silent. "Well, Merry Christmas *encore,* and thanks loads for the bag," Judy said.

Judy was surprised to see that it was not even noon when she reached home. The apartment was silent. Lois and her mother had gone out and her father lay on the living-room couch, asleep.

She took off her coat and hat and hung them in the hall closet and went into the living room. The little tree stood between the windows, heavy with ornaments. In the daylight it looked overburdened, as though its branches were not strong enough to carry the weight of so many things. She began rearranging her presents. There didn't seem to be so many now; the gloves were in her coat pocket, she was wearing the bracelet and one of the pairs of stockings, and she had taken the perfume to her room. She decided to put her things away and found that she could easily make them into one load. She put the stocking box Lois had given her in her bureau drawer and arranged the stockings in the compartments. Her new nightgown and silk pants she spread over the top of her old underwear.

Closing the drawer, she left the rest of her things lying on the bed and walked back to the living room. For a while she stood looking out of the window, jingling her bracelet against the glass. Then she walked over to the tree once more. Stooping down, she picked up the little crib with the twin babies. And then she sank to the floor. She could almost get under the lowest branches of the tree by ducking, and she edged closer to it.

Bits of silver rain touched her hair and the boughs overhead gave her a closed-in feeling, like being in a small house. She put the crib in her lap and unpinned the blankets, smoothed them out, and pinned them more tightly under the babies' chins. "Go to sleep," she said softly, and rocked the cradle lightly with her finger.

Thanksgiving Hunter

JESSE STUART

"Hold your rifle like this," Uncle Wash said, changing the position of my rifle. "When I throw this marble into the air, follow it with your bead; at the right time gently squeeze the trigger!"

Uncle Wash threw the marble high into the air and I lined my sights with the tiny moving marble, gently squeezing the trigger, timing the speed of my object until it slowed in the air ready to drop to earth again. Just as it reached its height, my rifle cracked and the marble was broken into tiny pieces.

Uncle Wash was a tall man with a hard leathery face, dark discolored teeth and blue eyes that had a faraway look in them. He hunted the year round; he violated all the hunting laws. He knew every path, creek, river and rock cliff within a radius of ten miles. Since he was a great hunter, he wanted to make a great hunter out of me. And tomorrow, Thanksgiving Day, would be the day for Uncle Wash to take me on my first hunt.

Uncle Wash woke me long before daylight.

"Oil your double-barrel," he said. "Oil it just like I've showed you."

I had to clean the barrels with an oily rag tied to a long string with a knot in the end. I dropped the heavy knot down the barrel and pulled the oily rag through the barrel. I did this many times to each barrel. Then I rubbed a meat-rind over both barrels and shined them with a dry rag. After this was done I polished the gun stock.

"Love the feel of your gun," Uncle Wash had often told me. "There's nothing like the feel of a gun. Know how far it will shoot. Know your gun better than you know your own self; know it and love it."

Before the sun had melted the frost from the multicolored trees and from the fields of stubble and dead grasses, we had cleaned our guns, had eaten our breakfasts and were on our way. Uncle Wash, Dave Pratt, Steve Blevins walked ahead of me along the path and talked about the great hunts they had taken and the game they had killed. And while they talked, words that Uncle Wash had told me about loving the feel of a gun kept going through my head. Maybe it is because Uncle Wash speaks of a gun like it was a living person is why he is such a good marksman, I thought.

"This is the dove country," Uncle Wash said soon as we had reached the cattle barn on the west side of our farm. "Doves are feeding here. They nest in these pines and feed around this barn fall and winter. Plenty of wheat grains, rye grains, and timothy seed here for doves."

Uncle Wash is right about the doves, I thought. I had seen them fly in pairs all summer long into the pine grove that covered the knoll east of our barn. I had heard their mournful songs. I had seen them in early April carrying straws in their bills to build their nests; I had seen them flying through the blue spring air after each other; I had seen them in the summer carrying food in their bills for their tiny young. I had heard their young ones crying for more food from the nests among the pines when the winds didn't sough among the pine boughs to drown their sounds. And when the leaves started turning brown I had seen whole flocks of doves, young and old ones, fly down from the tall pines to our barnyard to pick up the wasted grain. I had seen them often and been so close to them that they were no longer afraid of me.

"Doves are fat now," Uncle Wash said to Dave Pratt.

"Doves are wonderful to eat," Dave said.

And then I remembered when I had watched them in the spring and summer, I had never thought about killing and eating them. I had thought of them as birds that lived in the tops of pine trees and that hunted their food from the earth. I remembered their mournful songs that had often made me feel lonely when I worked in the cornfield near the barn. I had thought of them as flying over the deep hollows in pairs in the bright sunlight air chasing each other as they flew toward their nests in pines.

"Now we must get good shooting into this flock of doves," Uncle Wash said to us, "before they get wild. They've not been shot among this season."

Then Uncle Wash, to show his skill in hunting, sent us in different directions so that when the doves flew up from our barn lot, they would have to fly over one of our guns. He gave us orders to close in toward the barn and when the doves saw us, they would take to the air and we would do our shooting.

"And if they get away," Uncle Wash said, "follow them up and talk to them in their own language."

Each of us went his separate way. I walked toward the pine grove, carrying my gun just as Uncle Wash had instructed me. I was ready to start shooting as soon as I heard the flutter of dove wings. I walked over the frosted white grass and the wheat stubble until I came to the fringe of pine woods. And when I walked slowly over the needles of pines that covered the autumn earth, I heard the flutter of many wings and the barking of guns. The doves didn't come my way. I saw many fall from the bright autumn air to the brown crab-grass-colored earth.

I saw these hunters pick up the doves they had killed and cram their limp lifeless bleeding bodies with tousled feathers into their brown hunting coats. They picked them up as fast as they could, trying to watch the way the doves went.

"Which way did they go, Wash," Dave asked soon as he had picked up his kill.

"That way," Uncle Wash pointed to the low hill on the west.

"Let's be after 'em, men," Steve said.

The seasoned hunters hurried after their prey while I stood under a tall pine and kicked the toe of my brogan shoe against the brown pine needles that had carpeted the ground. I saw these men hurry over the hill, cross the ravine and climb the hill over which the doves had flown.

I watched them reach the summit of the hill, stop and call to the doves in tones not unlike the doves' own calling. I saw them with guns poised against the sky. Soon they had disappeared the way the doves had gone.

I sat down on the edge of a lichened rock that emerged from the rugged hill. I laid my double-barrel down beside me, and sunlight fingered through the pine boughs above me in pencil-sized streaks of light. And when one of these shifting pencil-sized streaks of light touched my gun barrels, they shone brightly in the light. My gun was cleaned and coiled and the little pine needles stuck to its meat-rind-greased barrels. Over my head the wind soughed lonely among the pine needles. And from under these pines I could see the vast open fields where the corn stubble stood knee high, where the wheat stubble would have shown plainly had it not been for the great growth of crab-grass after we had cut the wheat; crab-grass that had been blighted by autumn frost and shone brilliantly brown in the sun.

Even the air was cool to breathe into the lungs; I could feel it deep down when I breathed and it tasted of the green pine boughs that flavored it as it seethed through their thick tops. This was a clean cool autumn earth that both men and birds loved. And as I sat on the lichened rock with pine needles at my feet, with the soughing pine boughs above me, I thought the doves had chosen a fine place to find food, to nest and raise their young. But while I sat looking at the earth about me, I heard the thunder of the seasoned hunters' guns beyond the low ridge. I knew that they had talked to the doves until they had got close enough to shoot again.

As I sat on the rock, listening to the guns in the distance, I thought Uncle

Wash might be right after all. It was better to shoot and kill with a gun than to kill with one's hands or with a club. I remembered the time I went over the hill to see how our young corn was growing after we had plowed it the last time. And while I stood looking over the corn whose long ears were in tender blisters, I watched a ground-hog come from the edge of the woods, ride down a stalk of corn, and start eating a blister-ear. I found a dead sassafras stick near me, tiptoed quietly behind the ground-hog and hit him over the head. I didn't finish him with that lick. It took many licks.

When I left the cornfield, I left the ground-hog dead beside his ear of corn. I couldn't forget killing the ground-hog over an ear of corn and leaving him dead, his grey-furred clean body to waste on the lonely hill.

I can't disappoint Uncle Wash, I thought. He has trained me to shoot. He says that I will make a great hunter. He wants me to hunt like my father, cousins and uncles. He says that I will be the greatest marksman among them.

I thought about the way my people had hunted and how they had loved their guns. I thought about how Uncle Wash had taken care of his gun, how he had treated it like a living thing and how he had told me to love the feel of it. And now my gun lay beside me with pine needles sticking to it. If Uncle Wash were near he would make me pick the gun up, brush away the pine needles and wipe the gun barrels with my handkerchief. If I had lost my handkerchief, as I had seen Uncle Wash often do, he would make me pull out my shirt-tail to wipe my gun with it. Uncle Wash didn't object to wearing dirty clothes or to wiping his face with a dirty bandanna; he didn't mind living in a dirty house—but never, never would he allow a speck of rust or dirt on his gun.

It was comfortable to sit on the rock since the sun was directly above me. It warmed me with a glow of autumn. I felt the sun's rays against my face and the sun was good to feel. But the good fresh autumn air was no longer cool as the frost that covered the autumn grass that morning, nor could I feel it go deep into my lungs; the autumn air was warmer and it was flavored more with the scent of pines.

Now that the shooting had long been over near our cattle barn, I heard the lazy murmur of the woodcock in the pine woods near by. Uncle Wash said woodcocks were game birds and he killed them wherever he found them. Once I thought I would follow the sound and kill the woodcock. I picked up my gun but laid it aside again. I wanted to kill something to show Uncle Wash. I didn't want him to be disappointed in me.

Instead of trying to find a rabbit sitting behind a broom-sedge cluster or in a briar thicket as Uncle Wash had trained me to do, I felt relaxed and lazy in the autumn sun that had now penetrated the pine boughs from directly overhead. I looked over the brown vast autumn earth about me where I had worked when everything was green and growing, where birds sang in the spring air as they built their nests. I looked at the tops of barren trees and thought how a few months ago they were waving clouds of green. And now it was a sad world, a dying world. There was so much death in the world that I had known: flowers were dead, leaves were dead, and the frosted grass was lifeless in the wind. Everything was dead and dying but a few wild birds and rabbits. I had almost grown to the rock where I sat but I didn't want to stir. I wanted to glimpse the life about me before it all was covered with winter snows. I hated to think of killing in this autumn world. When I picked up my gun, I didn't feel life in it—I felt death.

I didn't hear the old hunters' guns now but I knew that, wherever they were, they were hunting for something to shoot. I thought they would return to the barn if the doves came back, as they surely would, for the pine grove where I sat was one place in this autumn world that was a home to the doves. And while I sat on the rock, I thought I would practice the dove whistle that Uncle Wash had taught me. I thought a dove would come close and I would shoot the dove so that I could go home with something in my hunting coat.

As I sat whistling a dove call, I heard the distant thunder of their guns beyond the low ridge. Then I knew they were coming back toward the cattle barn.

And, as I sat whistling my dove calls, I heard a dove answer me. I called gently to the dove. Again it answered. This time it was closer to me. I picked up my gun from the rock and gently brushed the pine needles from its stock and barrels. And as I did this, I called pensively to the dove and it answered plaintively.

I aimed my gun soon as I saw the dove walking toward me. When it walked toward my gun so unafraid, I thought it was a pet dove. I lowered my gun; laid it across my lap. Never had a dove come this close to me. When I called again, it answered at my feet. Then it fanned its wings and flew upon the rock beside me trying to reach the sound of my voice. It called, but I didn't answer. I looked at the dove when it turned its head to one side to try to see me. Its eye was gone, with the mark of a shot across its face. Then it turned the other side of its head toward me to try to see. The other eye was gone.

As I looked at the dove the shooting grew louder; the old hunters were getting closer. I heard the fanning of dove wings above the pines. And I heard doves batting their wings against the pine boughs. And the dove beside me called to them. It knew the sounds of their wings. Maybe it knows each dove by the sound of his wings, I thought. And then the dove spoke beside me. I was afraid to answer. I could have reached out my hand and picked this dove up from the rock. Though it was blind, I couldn't kill it, and yet I knew it would have a hard time to live.

When the dove beside me called again, I heard an answer from a pine bough near by. The dove beside me spoke and the dove in the pine bough answered. Soon they were talking to each other as the guns grew louder. Suddnly, the blind dove fluttered through the tree-tops, chirruping its plaintive melancholy notes, toward the sound of its mate's voice. I heard its wings batting the wind-shaken pine boughs as it ascended, struggling, toward the beckoning voice.

The Song the Soldiers Sang

ALICE FARNHAM

THE SOLDIERS were coming. They came marching down the narrow back street to avoid traffic, and the little girl's heart began to pound the way it always did. She stood quite still, her eyes big and brilliant in her little sallow face, her lips parted. She was trembling.

The little colored children who lived in the block were hilarious, as they always were when it was time for the soldiers. The boys, in their ragged pants, strutted barefoot up the middle of the street with rich gurgles of laughter.

They mimicked, "Hup-hup-hup! *One,* two, three, four!"

The smallest of them, in a half-unfastened sunsuit, jumped up and down the curb beside her in an ecstasy.

"Come the *sodgers,* come the *sodgers*!"

Now the little girl could hear them. Above the noises of the city streets she heard it. First only a beat—then, stronger and stronger, the deep boys' voices as the soldiers came singing home from classes to the hotel that was their barracks.

The little girl's hands were like ice. Would they be singing The Song?

Twice a day the soldiers passed, the wonderful singing soldiers. All the days were glowing and bright and alive now, even though she had no one to play with, no one at all in the big dingy house but herself and Cousin Ella. Things didn't matter so much, now that the soldiers had come—things like not living with your mother, and never having anyone to talk to. Sunday was a lonesome day, but you could make up fine conversations with imaginary soldiers while you looked out the gray lace curtains at the littered street. And you could sing snatches of their rollicking song that you'd never heard before, and try to imagine how it would sound if you could only hear all of it at once.

Word ran down the street ahead of them. The soldiers!

They didn't always sing. Sometimes they just whistled, and sometimes they had a yell that started *R.O.T.C.,* and sometimes they were tired and just marched with their eyes straight ahead. Then all you could hear was the tramp of their feet, a tired, heavy sound. It made you want to cry because you felt that the soldiers couldn't stop, that they must march on like that forever.

But today they were singing, and it was The Song.

The little colored boys marched with them, pompous and swaggering and very serious. The younger children ran beside them as they marched, shrieking with laughter. The little girl wanted to follow the soldiers too, but it was not dignified to make a game of it as the colored children did. She stood there very stiff and straight.

—*"twopence to* spend, *and twopence to* lend, *And twopence to send home to my wife!"* sang the soldiers as they swung past. They pronounced it toopence.

"Poor wife!" sang the soldiers who followed. But the ones in the middle weren't singing, and the boys in the rear ranks had started "Pistol-Packin' Mamma" in opposition to the song up front.

The little girl winked back angry tears. That was always the way. You never got to hear the whole thing at one time, so you could learn it.

When the soldiers had gone, she walked along the curb moodily, teetering off balance now and then because the heels of her open-toed shoes were much too high. Even the sight of her bright-red toenails didn't help.

She wanted someone to talk to about the soldiers. Cousin Ella was old. She didn't care about anything any more. There were other children in the block, but Cousin Ella wouldn't let her play with them. There was only Mrs. Holmstrom.

She was off down the street like an arrow, the soiled, backless white play-shoes clattering over the uneven brick pavement.

At a frowning little house behind an old-fashioned iron railing, she unlatched the gate and clumped noisily up the steps. She rang the doorbell once and then moved anxiously to the window, shading her eyes to peer through.

"Mrs. Holmstrom! Mrs. Holmstrom!" she shouted. "Are you in, Mrs. Holmstrom?"

"It's you then, is it, Katey?" said Mrs. Holmstrom, opening the door.

The little girl had already gone to the scarred piano that stood in a corner of the little living room.

"Did you hear the soldiers today, Mrs. Holmstrom?" Her tone was excited.

"How should I not hear them?" Mrs. Holmstrom shook her head. "They'd wake the dead, them boys would."

The little girl turned from the piano. Her eyes were shining again, and much too large for her face. Her little skinny hand lingered lovingly over the yellow keys.

"But the song, you know, Mrs. Holmstrom—they were singing a different line today. Didn't you notice?"

"I can't say I did. But go ahead and pick out your little tunes on the piano, Katey. You'll get it yet," said Mrs. Holmstrom. "Just close the door behind you when you go out. I got to get back. The mister's waitin' on his supper."

The little girl scarcely heard her. In utter absorption, with the most frowning and concentrated care, she was picking out the disjointed fragments of a little tune. Sometimes she would seem to stop and listen for something, head sharply back and body tense; and then, with a quick gleam of satisfaction, she would bend absorbed over the keys again.

"I *got toopence, jolly, jolly toopence,*" sang the little girl with gusto. "*Toopence to* lend, *and toopence to* spend, *and toopence to send home to my wife.* Poor wife!"

But her face clouded as she slid off the stool. There was more to it than that, lots more—parts about happy is the day, and the silvery mooo-oo-oon, when the boys' voices swooped up into a joyous shout.

But always it eluded her. Always they had gone by before she could fix the words or the tune in her mind, or they'd change songs in the middle of the block, or start whistling and not sing at all. You just couldn't depend on them.

Back in the kitchen, Mrs. Holmstrom said deprecatingly to her husband, "The little motherless one from down the street."

"Don't give a man no peace."

But his grumbling was only perfunctory. He sat awhile over his paper, in his soiled and bedaubed painter's overalls, with his shoes off, and then he said suddenly, "*There's* a mother."

"Hah!" said Mrs. Holmstrom, and slammed the oven door.

When the little girl went home, Cousin Ella didn't notice her, as usual. There was a cold frankfurter in the refrigerator and she ate it, then a pork chop she found on the bottom shelf. The pork chop was greasy but all right.

Slowly she went upstairs. From a bureau drawer she took the enormous, peeling, red patent leather handbag that contained her treasures. A broken charm bracelet, a comb with several teeth missing, a chromo of the Madonna, a ten-cent compact, a card dispensed by the Your Weight and Fortune machine in the five-and-ten: "You possess great energy and determination, and are extremely popular with the opposite sex."

In the money-pocket was a dime. With a forlorn hope she probed the lining, though she knew it would be empty. A dime wouldn't be enough. She closed the pocketbook, her eyes darting to the door.

She stole to the head of the stairs and listened. There was only the rustle of the evening paper, Cousin Ella's occasional cough.

She took off her shoes and tiptoed into Cousin Ella's bedroom. The marble-topped bureau, the dark heavy furniture, all had an accusing look of Cousin Ella. The little girl paid no attention. With quick sure fingers she opened Cousin Ella's pocketbook and took out a quarter. That was all she'd need. She'd priced sheet music before.

"Where you going?" Cousin Ella looked up from the crossword puzzle on the back page.

"Friday night," the little girl said glibly. "Stores all open. I want to walk through the five-and-dime."

The fat old woman grunted, turned back to her puzzle. The little puzzle that was Katey slipped out the door, her heart racing. Now—now she would find it!

The girl at the music counter wouldn't even look. She sat up there at her piano, laughing and flirting with two sailors. She wouldn't even look at the tense little girl who stood there clutching the big red pocketbook.

Finally she heard, or could no longer not hear, a pleading voice. With a frown of annoyance, she turned away from the sailors.

"I never heard of a song about toopence," she said coldly.

The little girl's eyes were stricken. "Jolly, *jolly* toopence?" she quavered.

"Not any kind of toopence," said the salesgirl with finality. She returned to the sailors.

That's it, the child thought dully. It's never any use to steal. You think that maybe God won't notice, just this once; but He always does. Stolen money won't bring you any luck.

She felt a flicker of hope when she heard the man who sold little folders of popular songs hawking his wares at the door as she went out.

"Here they are, folks! Most popular hits of screen and radio, the songs you want to know! Only a dime, here they are, folks!"

The little girl got out her dime with fingers that suddenly trembled. "Mister, have you got a song about toopence? Jolly, jolly toopence?"

"Sis, we got them *all*," said the hawker, with conviction. "Here, run along home with it and see for yourself. Here they are, folks, only a dime!"

The little girl stood by a lighted store window. Her quick eager eyes ran up and down the pages. There was no song about twopence.

Her feet dragged as she scuffed through the dark streets toward home.

She would put the quarter back, when she got there. Stealing is something you pay for, after all.

She didn't want to go home yet. On an impulse she didn't turn at the corner but went on. Straight up Chestnut Street was the hotel where the soldiers stayed.

She walked fast till she came to it, and then she walked very, very slowly. Soldiers were in twos and threes about the door, but she affected not to notice them. A subtle change came over her gait; she swung her flat hips slightly and swayed a little from the shoulders. Mincing along with tiny steps, her gaze was fastened on something intensely interesting, incredibly fascinating, in the middle distance. Her eyes were bright with it, her lips parted in a little smile. Now she was no longer a little girl; she was beauty and sophistication and allure; she was Rita Hayworth and Lana Turner and Hedy Lamarr.

No one recognized her. No one ever did. The soldiers went on laughing and talking just as before. No one even knew she'd passed by.

The little girl gave one lingering, wistful, backward look. With a sigh she turned away again and began kicking her way along in the aimless, moody shuffle peculiar to disconsolate youth.

As she turned the drugstore corner she became erect and tense again. There on a stool at the empty fountain, close to the door, sat one of the soldiers! The tall one, with the freckles and the blue eyes, who always marched on her side of the street on the outside of the fifth row—oh, she'd know him anywhere, that one! He always roared The Song in a cheerful bass that just made you feel good all over, and sometimes he'd grin at you as he went by, so close you could reach out and touch him.

Her walk was self-conscious as she went in, blinking at the lights. She sidled onto the stool beside him with a deprecating cough.

"Hi!" said the soldier, grinning down amiably. "Keep late hours for your size, don't you?"

"I'm eleven," she said, with a touch of hauteur. "I always stay up late. Cousin Ella never minds."

"Well, Katey, what'll it be?" said the proprietor, with a look of disfavor.

She cleared her throat. "Just a—a glass of water, please, Mr. Greenberg."

"Bring the kid a soda," the soldier ordered. "What flavor, kid?"

For a dizzy moment she thought she might fall off the stool. It was like a dream—the beautiful dream that came a thousand times, in a thousand guises—but Mr. Greenberg couldn't be a dream. Nobody would dream Mr. Greenberg.

"Well, tell us about yourself," said the soldier carelessly. He poured out a little more of his milk shake. "So Cousin Ella don't mind you staying out late, huh? What about your old man and your old lady? Don't they care either?"

Katey turned very pale. She put down the straw for a minute, carefully. "They don't—" she swallowed. "They don't—exactly—care either."

She pushed the soda away. Then she turned on the soldier a look of such burning misery that it penetrated even his offhand good humor.

"They don't—want me," she said rapidly. "They're divorced and I live with Cousin Ella because nobody wants me. My father went away. A long time ago, he went away."

"That's tough." The soldier's voice was gentle.

"My *mother* wants me." The little girl held her head up, as though by saying a thing many, many times one could make it so. "I know she wants me. Only she works in a beauty parlor, and has to room downtown. But she comes to see me sometimes," she added defiantly.

"Sure," said the soldier.

"Of course, she's very pretty, and when a person's mother is very pretty, it's natural she should have a lot of gentleman friends, and they take up most of her time. It's only natural."

"*Very* natural," the soldier agreed. He took out a pack of cigarettes from his pocket. There was only one in it, and he crumpled the empty pack and threw it on the floor. "So what do you do with yourself all day?"

She hesitated. "I take walks and pretend I'm people. Or I read movie magazines or look around in the five-and-ten. But mostly," she brightened, "mostly I go calling on Mrs. Holmstrom, because she has a piano."

"Does, eh?"

The little girl nodded several times, her eyes alight.

"I pick tunes out, you know—ones I hear in the movies or on the radio or places. I get so I can play them real good without any music. Mrs. Holmstrom says I'm a wonder," she added modestly.

"I'll bet you are."

The soldier looked at her with amusement. He saw a bony little figure in a cheap, pink rayon slack suit, indifferently ironed; a sallow, wistful, little face and stringy dark hair; a huge red pocketbook, importantly held and displayed.

"I'm *musical*," she explained. "I like to sing better than anything." She opened the handbag and took out the folded sheet of printed song stanzas. "See, here are some of the ones I'm working on now. Right now I'm learning 'East of the Rockies.'"

The soldier whistled. "That's a humdinger. How about—"

All at once she remembered it. The Song!

"Oh, tell me what it is!" The words tumbled out in a breathless rush as she leaned tensely forward. "The song the soldiers sing—oh, you know the one! Every day, on their way back from school—*you* know!" Her face was flushed. "Toopence!"

"*That* one?" The soldier laughed. "Sure—I'll teach it to you." He looked around, and cleared his throat. "Well—er—not here. I'll walk you part way home. It won't take you long to get it."

As she slid down from the high white stool Katey's knees almost buckled under her. She was weak with happiness.

She broke into a giggle when they were out in the street. "The first time I heard it, do you know what I thought? I thought they were saying, '*Two pants!' Two pants to lend, two pants to send home to my wife.*"

"Now, the first part goes like this," said the soldier seriously. "I'*ve got sixpence*—starts out with sixpence, see, and works on down—I'*ve got six-pence—*"

"To last me all my life!" she finished, with an improvised little dance step as she sang.

The soldier took out a harmonica, polished it on his sleeve with loving care. "All right, you sing and I'll give you the tune."

"I'*ve got—*"

There were running footsteps behind them.

"Bill! Hey Gallagher! Telephone, you GI Casanova!"

The soldier put his harmonica away hurriedly. "So long, Katey—see you again sometime. OK, I'm coming!"

She reached desperately for his sleeve. "Tomorrow night? Will you teach me the song tomorrow?"

"OK," he assented hastily. "See you later!"

He sprinted up the street toward the hotel. She stood there a moment under the street light, watching him, till he ran in at the lighted lobby. She started down the dark street toward home, the darkness still warm and bright and quivering with his presence, and then she stopped.

At the door of the drugstore she stood for a moment with bright eyes to reconnoiter. Mr. Greenberg was behind the prescription counter, in back; there was no one else in the store.

With a tremulous rush, she had swooped on something that lay on the floor beside the soda fountain, in triumph bore it away. The discarded cigarette wrapper.

The soldiers marched by again next day, and her heart swelled as she stood on the curb to watch. They sang, "Let Me Call You Sweetheart," and then they sang "Hinky-Dinky Parlez-Vous," and all at once, while they were singing, swaggering past, she wanted to cry with the beauty of them.

They were beautiful, beautiful, all of them. Some of them wore glasses, and some were too short; the little one who was always falling out of step had such a pug nose you could scarcely call it a nose at all. But it didn't matter. They were beautiful. All of them were beautiful.

And then she saw him swinging along in the sunlight, his books under one arm, trench cap balanced on one sunburned eyebrow, and her heart seemed to stop. Her eyes clung adoringly to his face. He saw her. As he went by, he turned his face toward her and winked.

She knew then that he was the most beautiful soldier of all.

Night was very long in coming. The unwanted sun still hung in the sky, the hands of every clock stood motionless. Only the clock in the shoemaker's window held out any hope: he kept it an hour fast.

When it said eight o'clock, she started slowly up the street. She didn't run. There was a funny trembling at the pit of her stomach, and her hands were cold.

It was still too early. She'd known that. That was why he wasn't anywhere around.

She walked past the hotel again. This time she didn't look in. She'd walk by without looking, until the tenth time. No—the fifth. Ten was too many.

The fourth time past she looked in the hotel again. Even now, he might be coming toward her—for a moment she couldn't breathe. No.

She had been walking up and down for almost an hour when at last she saw him. A blonde girl was on his arm, and both of them were laughing as they came.

The child stood there motionless.

The soldier's face wore a look of surprise, just tinged with embarrassment. "Hello, Katey—what are you doing up here?"

She swallowed. That other girl was looking down at her in amusement. "Competition, Bill?"

The little girl ignored her. She took one step toward the soldier, her eyes in desperate beseeching on his face. "You told me to come." Her voice was tremulous, almost inaudible. "You said you'd meet me tonight and teach me the song. You said it last night."

The soldier glanced sidewise at his companion and cleared his throat. "Sure I did, Katey—I remember now. But I didn't realize we'd said tonight. Now be a good girl and run along home. Some other night, huh?"

With great dignity the little girl turned and walked away. Her feet dragged a little and there was a mist over things. Once she walked into a fat man who asked where she thought she was going, but she kept straight on.

Cousin Ella didn't look up when she went in. She went slowly, very slowly, up the stairs. It was as if she bore a tremendous load on her shoulders, bowing them down.

"I'm walking all bent over," she thought in surprise. "I'm walking like Cousin Ella." It scared her a little. Could you really turn old in a single night, in a single hour?

Not till she was safely in the dark bedroom and the door locked between her and all the world, did she break down. She sank beside the bed and buried her face.

How could she live? How do you go on living, when your heart is broken, when in all the busy world there is no one who loves you?

Long was the night, that had been so long in coming.

Katey sat at the piano in Mrs. Holmstrom's neat little parlor. With one hand she picked out a tune she had made up that morning, but her eyes looked through the piano and far away. It was a sad little tune that said over and over, "I'm lonely, I'm so lonely," but no one knew the words but Katey.

There was a beat of music in the distance.

"Here comes the soldiers, Katey," called Mrs. Holmstrom.

"Yes'm," the little girl said listlessly. She sat listening, her sallow face flushing as the beat came closer. For a moment she stood by the window irresolute, and then, as if drawn against her will, went slowly out.

The soldiers were almost there now. It was one of their tired days, and they had stopped singing. They didn't even whistle as they came past her, four abreast.

The sergeant swung smartly along the brick sidewalk.

"Hup! Hup! *Three,* four! Hup!"

Katey didn't want to look. She kept her face turned away. Her chin was quivering.

"Psst! *Katey*!"

Oh beloved, well-remembered voice! She looked up, tremulous, flushed with delight.

Grinning, he tossed a little folded wad of paper at her feet as he went by. She snatched it up and darted away, her whole face alight. The words blurred a little as she read them.

Dear Katey:

I'm sorry about last night. Honest I never meant to disappoint you. Don't be mad, will you?

Here's the words of that song you wanted. You learn them like a good girl and meet me in front of the drugstore tonight. I'll teach you the tune. Honest.

Bill

P.S. Will be alone this time.

Through the endless hours of the day she idled. She mustn't get there too soon. But at sight of the shoemaker's clock she began to run, and so she arrived out of breath after all.

She slowed down before he saw her. With a haughty, a world-weary face she studied the roof lines of the houses opposite. She was a young lady out for an evening stroll, a stroll which just chanced to bring her in this direction of all others, and her mind was detached from the things of the street.

So much so, in fact, that she tripped over a loose brick and went sprawling.

The soldier caught her. "Here, look where you're goin', Star-Dust! Wanta break your neck?"

"Oh!" She looked at him, her eyes wide with a fine amazement. "Why, I really never even thought of *you* being here, Mr. Gallagher! I just happened to be out for a walk—" Her voice was high, her gestures elaborate with airy unconcern.

The corners of the soldier's mouth quirked as he looked at her. "Just happened along, eh?"

"I *often* walk here," she said loftily. "Almost every night. Looking at the stars and things. I forgot all *about* you being here."

"I'm sure of it," said the soldier. "Now that you're here, how about a soda?"

She unbent. "Well—since I *am* here. Choc'lit."

Ambrosia through a straw, ice-cold and heavenly chocolate-flavored and fizzing a little in your nose!

As she sipped, she cast sidelong glances at the soldier's face. He looked like the pictures of the Greek gods in the fifth grade reader. Her throat ached with the beauty and wonder of him, so that she almost choked in her chocolate soda for love.

The soldier was oblivious of his godhood.

"You learn all those words yet, kid?" he asked, lighting a cigarette and looking down at her.

She glowed. "Yes, every single one! *I've got sixpence, jolly, jolly—*"

"OK, OK," he said hastily. "Outside. Not here."

They went across the street. A low wall ran around the Methodist church, and they sat there under the street-light.

"Now, let's hear you. No, wait till I get the Stradivarius oiled up." He took out the harmonica and wiped it with a handkerchief. "Let's go!"

Away they went.

"—to send home to my wife. Poor wife!" sang the little girl joyously. Suddenly she couldn't sit still. She sprang up and danced the rollicking tune as she sang it.

The soldier's feet tapped on the pavement. The harmonica wheezed manfully into the chorus.

> *—by the light of the sil-vurr-rry moo-oo-oon,*
> Hap-*py is the day that we* line *up for our pay,*
> *As we go rolling home!*

"Oh, it's the finest song I ever heard!" the little girl panted. "Isn't it the best song you ever heard too?" And she danced a little more, in the fancy high-heeled shoes that were too big. "I'*ve got sixpence—*"

The soldier was smiling as he looked at her, but there was pity in his eyes too, and a sadness. The little girl felt it, and her song trailed away uncertainly.

She sat down again and looked up at him anxiously. "I sang it all *right*?"

"You sang it swell." The soldier was looking at his harmonica. He wiped it off again with slow thoroughness.

"You know your song now, don't you, kid?"

She nodded mutely, her eyes never leaving his face. Foreboding fluttered in her heart.

"I want you to sing it when I'm gone, Katey." The soldier didn't look at her. The light from the street lamp was lavender as it shone on him, like moonlight in a dream. "They're sending us to camp tomorrow. Tomorrow night. We won't be around any more."

The little girl sat there without speaking for a moment. Her voice seemed to come from a great distance as she said, not very distinctly, "The camp—is your camp far off?"

"Georgia."

The little girl's shoulders sagged. He reached over and put the harmonica in her hand. It felt icy to his touch.

"Look, Katey, I want you to have it while I'm gone. And I want you to play it and sing and be happy, Katey, and not go feeling lonely because things aren't—just the way they oughta be. And remember, Katey," he tilted her chin up, "I'll be back!"

She seized his hand, covered it with kisses, pressed it to her cheek. "Oh, I'll never see you again! I'll never see you again!" she cried in a passion of grief. "You'll be gone and I'll never see you any more! I can't bear it, I can't! I can't!"

The soldier stroked her hair clumsily. "Katey, I'll see you! I'm coming back!"

She raised a dirty little tear-stained face. "Swear it! Swear that you will!"

"OK, so I swear it," said the soldier uncomfortably, looking around to see that no one heard. "And I'll write to you. Every week, if you'll promise to be a good girl and not cry. And I want you to play that harmonica real good when I get back, you hear?"

Feverishly she searched in her bag. "A pencil—write down your address!"

He felt in his pockets. "Damn, I haven't got one either. Never mind, I'll write it out when I get home and toss it to you tomorrow when I go by."

When you go by. When you go by. The last time I'll ever see you. But the feel of the harmonica in her hand gave her comfort.

"You'll be there, won't you?" The soldier glanced at his watch. "To wave good-by."

Her fingers closed round the harmonica.

"I'll be there," she said steadily.

"That's fine." He sounded relieved as he rose. "Be a good girl and keep your chin up. I'll write. There!"

He had hurriedly kissed her forehead and was gone. Gone up to the street to the hotel, where his date sat waiting in the lobby.

The little girl walked home in a dream, a confusion of pain and joy. Around the harmonica her fingers were tight.

He was going, tomorrow he was going. All the singing soldiers would go tomorrow, and the little back street would be gray desolation once more.

But he would write; he had promised. He would come back. He had sworn it. And when he came, it would not be a child Katey who greeted him. No, a woman—beautiful, queenly, poised! *Much* more beautiful than the blonde girl last night.

Starry-eyed, she strained the harmonica to her thin bosom and spoke in an exalted hush. "Oh, I *will* wait for you, my darling! I'll be true! True to the end of time." And despite her heartbreak, she felt a little thrill of pleasure in the phrase.

She went in the door and up the dark staircase in a trance.

"I'll be true!" she murmured, pressing the harmonica to her cheek. "Oh, beloved—true to the end of time!"

She knelt by the window to gaze out at the stars hanging bright over the alley—the same stars that looked down upon him!—and an improvement occurred to her.

Reverently she whispered, "To the end of time—and beyond!"

When Cousin Ella woke her, she knew by the look of the sun on the carpet that the soldiers had already gone by.

"But I'll see him this afternoon," she thought, reaching hurriedly for her shoes. "This afternoon, when they come back. For the last time."

She shivered and took the harmonica out from under her pillow.

Cousin Ella was in the room, showing unusual activity.

"I declare, they might have told a body," she mumbled. Cousin Ella wore tight, black high-buttoned boots, and always walked as if her feet hurt. "Just call on the phone as cool as you please—'coming out for Katey at ten-thirty, please have her ready!' " she mimicked, in a high falsetto.

A giant hand seemed to close round Katey's heart. She sat on the edge of the bed, watching the old woman with frightened eyes. "Who—who called, Cousin Ella? You mean they're coming *today*?"

Cousin Ella handed out her clean underwear from the bureau and straightened up. "Your mother is who I mean, Miss. And that latest friend of hers—Mr. *Mordie,* he calls himself. They're taking you off somewheres for the day. Nonsense, I call it."

When she got home, he'd be gone. Slowly, like a sleepwalker, the little girl dressed in her best clothes. She would miss him, and he'd be gone. Forever, forever he'd be gone.

When her mother came, her new gentleman friend Mr. Mordie expansive and beaming behind her, the little girl pushed away her cereal untouched.

"Hello, sweetie-pie!" Her mother kissed her carelessly. "Gee, you're gettin' big, isn't she, Lew? Come on, hon', finish up and don't keep Mr. Mordie and I waiting. We're going to give you a real treat, aren't we, Mr. Mordie?"

Katey kept her eyes on her plate.

"You bet!" said Mr. Mordie fondly. "We're gonna show the kid a good time. A whole day out at Moonlight Park!"

Cousin Ella sniffed.

"Come on, come on!" said Katey's mother impatiently. "I'm surprised at you, Katey. When a person's going to use his car and give up his whole day to give you a good time, the least you can do is show a little appreciation and not keep them waiting."

She moistened a corner of her handkerchief with her tongue and rubbed a spot from the child's cheek.

"Now what do you say to Mr. Mordie?"

The little girl swallowed. "Thank—you, Mr. Mordie."

She sat between them in the front seat, her eyes glazed with misery. She felt a dull surprise that people could hurt so and live.

Now and then, at her mother's insistence, she would arouse to say mechanically, "That'll be fine, Mr. Mordie," or "Yes, Mr. Mordie, I like the amusements a lot."

"Kids are funny," her mother apologized. "Get so excited they can't hardly talk." She gave Katey an angry look under her mascara-ed lashes.

Once the little girl asked faintly, "Are we—going to stay long, Mr. Mordie? All day, I mean?"

"Of course we are!" Her mother sounded snappish. "We're going to stay here and have supper at the pavilion. For goodness sake, Katey, you might act less like it was a funeral when a person tries to give you a little enjoyment!"

Numb with despair, the child sat silent.

When they reached the park, Mr. Mordie helped them out with heavy joviality. "Now we'll all go for a ride on the roller coaster! How about it, Katey?"

It was on the roller coaster that she began to feel sick. That terrible moment when the car hung poised on the brink, the swoop through space—

"Boy, give me the old roller coaster every time! Couldn't keep me off it when I was a kid!"

"You said it!" Katey's mother laughed gaily. She pinched her daughter's arm. "Wasn't that great, hon'?"

White-lipped, the child managed, "It was swell, Mr. Mordie!"

For lunch they had hot dogs and bottled pop at a stand under the trees—because, as Katey's mother said, they'd have supper at the pavilion and didn't really need much. Dessert was ice cream and popcorn. The little girl ate automatically, scarcely tasting what she swallowed.

Soon now, only two more hours, he would be marching past her house for the last time. The boys would be jolly and laughing, for their classes now were over. And they'd be singing The Song, and it would be for the last time, and all her life she'd remember that she wasn't there to hear it, that she wasn't there to wave good-by.

A huge lump hurt her throat. The people and trees began to blur.

Mr. Mordie looked at her curiously.

He said in a low voice, "Marie, that kid don't look just right to me. You suppose there's anything wrong with her?"

"Forget it!" Katey's pretty mother compressed her lips. "Stubborn spell, that's all! Just don't pay no attention."

On the Tumble-Bug, Katey clung desperately to the sides of the car. The ground was still in motion around her when they got off. She staggered and would have fallen but for Mr. Mordie.

He stared at her. "Hey, this kid's sick! Look at her!"

A pale-green Katey lurched to the nearest tree and proved his point. She leaned her head against the tree. Her thin child's body shook with sobs.

"I want to go home!" she wailed. "I want to go home, I want to go home!"

No one said much during the ride. Katey was handed over at the door in disgrace, to be put to bed by Cousin Ella.

When he was nearly down to the car, Mr. Mordie came back up the steps again. Apologetically he patted her hand. "Here, kiddo, here's a quarter. Buy yourself somethin' when you're feelin' better, see?"

Cousin Ella scolded all the way upstairs, but Katey didn't mind. She had seen the dining-room clock, and it said ten minutes after four. An hour, an hour, an hour!

"Might've known how it would turn out, but no one asks *me*!" Cousin Ella's voice was shrill and vindictive. "Now you'll just lie there, young lady, for the rest of the day. And no supper!" She banged the door behind her.

For a few moments the little girl lay there, weak tears of thankfulness streaming down her face, wetting her hair and her ears. Nothing mattered, nothing mattered! Not mother, not Cousin Ella, nothing. God had brought her safely home, in time to wave good-by. Only God could have done it.

When she had waited for what seemed years, she lifted herself cautiously from the bed. The house was silent. Cousin Ella's voice came faintly from the back yard. Noiselessly she stole down the stairs. In the street, she began to run.

As she made her purchase in the five-and-ten, she looked at the clock. Ten minutes till the soldiers came. "Don't wrap it up," she said quickly. "I want to carry it that way."

Out in the street, she looked down at it lovingly. It was a small, silk American flag, with yellow fringe. Holding it tight, in a hand suddenly wet with perspiration, she hurried through the streets. Soon, soon—

At the corner she stopped to lean dizzily against a telephone pole. The colored children were noisy in the street.

"Yay man, they *comin'*! Hup! Hup!"

Above the city noises came a rhythmic beat that swelled into song, and the sound of marching feet. The soldiers were singing, their voices deep and rich against the sounds of traffic, throbbing, growing, till the air seemed to ring with their song. They were singing The Song.

The little girl's heart beat very loud. She felt as though she would suffocate. She held herself very erect.

On they came. They were laughing as they marched, as they sang. It was their last day. And then she saw him.

The sun touched his head with a special light. He was sunshine itself. Warmth and radiance enwrapped her as he passed.

Unconsciously she reached out her hand. He pressed a fold of paper into it, squeezed her cold fingers with a little special smile—tender, half-rueful—as he looked back. And then he had passed, still in step with the others.

The boys who followed him roared the song in their deep young voices.

No-o cares have I to grie-eve me,
Pretty little girl to decei-eve me—
Happy as a king, belie-eve me,
As we go rolling home!

Still singing, the voices began to die away, to fade in the noise of city traffic. The little girl stood at attention, the twenty-five-cent flag draped across her flat chest.

The voices came faint and fainter. A big truck rumbled by, a news commentator's voice crackled from a radio somewhere in the block. In the distance a far-off beat of music hung in the air and was dispersed.

The soldiers were gone. The beautiful soldiers were gone.

Her First Ball

KATHERINE MANSFIELD

EXACTLY WHEN the ball began Leila would have found it hard to say. Perhaps her first real partner was the cab. It did not matter that she shared the cab with the Sheridan girls and their brother. She sat back in her own little corner of it, and the bolster on which her hand rested felt like the sleeve of an unknown young man's dress suit; and away they bowled, past waltzing lamp-posts and houses and fences and trees.

"Have you really never been to a ball before, Leila? But, my child, how too weird—" cried the Sheridan girls.

"Our nearest neighbour was fifteen miles," said Leila softly, gently opening and shutting her fan.

Oh, dear, how hard it was to be indifferent like the others! She tried not to smile too much; she tried not to care. But every single thing was so new and exciting . . . Meg's tuberoses, Jose's long loop of amber, Laura's little dark head, pushing above her white fur like a flower through snow. She would remember for ever. It even gave her a pang to see her cousin Laurie throw away the wisps of tissue paper he pulled from the fastenings of his new gloves. She would like to have kept those wisps as a keepsake, as a remembrance. Laurie leaned forward and put his hand on Laura's knee.

"Look here, darling," he said. "The third and the ninth as usual. Twig?"

Oh, how marvellous to have a brother! In her excitement Leila felt that if there had been time, if it hadn't been impossible, she couldn't have helped crying because she was an only child, and no brother had ever said "Twig?" to her; no sister would ever say, as Meg said to Jose that moment, "I've never known your hair go up more successfully than it has to-night!"

But, of course, there was no time. They were at the drill hall already; there were cabs in front of them and cabs behind. The road was bright on either side with moving fan-like lights, and on the pavement gay couples seemed to float through the air; little satin shoes chased each other like birds.

"Hold on to me, Leila; you'll get lost," said Laura.

"Come on, girls, let's make a dash for it," said Laurie.

Leila put two fingers on Laura's pink velvet cloak, and they were somehow lifted past the big golden lantern, carried along the passage, and pushed into the little room marked "Ladies." Here the crowd was so great there was hardly space to take off their things; the noise was deafening. Two benches on either side were stacked high with wraps. Two old women in white aprons ran up and down tossing fresh armfuls. And everybody was pressing forward trying to get at the little dressing-table and mirror at the far end.

A great quivering jet of gas lighted the ladies' room. It couldn't wait; it was dancing already. When the door opened again and there came a burst of tuning from the drill hall, it leaped almost to the ceiling.

Dark girls, fair girls were patting their hair, tying ribbons again, tucking handkerchiefs down the fronts of their bodices, smoothing marble-white gloves. And because they were all laughing it seemed to Leila that they were all lovely.

"Aren't there any invisible hair-pins?" cried a voice. "How most extraordinary! I can't see a single invisible hair-pin."

"Powder my back, there's a darling," cried some one else.

"But I must have a needle and cotton. I've torn simply miles and miles of the frill," wailed a third.

Then, "Pass them along, pass them along!" The straw basket of programmes was tossed from arm to arm. Darling little pink-and-silver programmes, with pink pencils and fluffy tassels. Leila's fingers shook as she took one out of the basket. She wanted to ask some one, "Am I meant to have one too?" but she had just time to read: "Waltz 3. *Two, Two in a Canoe*. Polka 4. *Making the Feathers Fly*," when Meg cried, "Ready Leila?" and they pressed their way through the crush in the passage towards the big double doors of the drill hall.

Dancing had not begun yet, but the band had stopped tuning, and the noise was so great it seemed that when it did begin to play it would never be heard. Leila, pressing close to Meg, looking over Meg's shoulder, felt that even the little quivering coloured flags strung across the ceiling were talking. She quite forgot to be shy; she forgot how in the middle of dressing she had sat down on the bed with one shoe off and one shoe on and begged her mother to ring up her cousins and say she couldn't go after all. And the rush of longing she had had to be sitting on the veranda of their forsaken up-country home, listening to the baby owls crying "More pork" in the moonlight, was changed to a rush of joy so sweet that it was hard to bear alone. She clutched her fan, and, gazing at the gleaming, golden floor, the azaleas, the lanterns, the stage at one end with its red carpet and gilt chairs and the band in a corner, she thought breathlessly, "How heavenly; how simply heavenly!"

All the girls stood grouped together at one side of the doors, the men at the other, and the chaperones in dark dresses, smiling rather foolishly, walked with little careful steps over the polished floor towards the stage.

"This is my little country cousin Leila. Be nice to her. Find her partners; she's under my wing," said Meg, going up to one girl after another.

Strange faces smiled at Leila—sweetly, vaguely. Strange voices answered, "Of course, my dear." But Leila felt the girls didn't really see her. They were looking towards the men. Why didn't the men begin? What were they waiting for? There they stood, smoothing their gloves, patting their glossy hair and smiling among themselves. Then, quite suddenly, as if they had only just made up their minds that that was what they had to do, the men came gliding over the parquet. There was a joyful flutter among the girls. A tall, fair man flew up to Meg, seized her programme, scribbled something; Meg passed him on to Leila. "May I have the pleasure?" He ducked and smiled. There came a dark man wearing an eyeglass, then cousin Laurie with a friend, and Laura with a little freckled fellow whose tie was crooked. Then quite an old man—fat, with a big bald patch on his head—took her programme and murmured, "Let me see, let me see!" And he was a long time comparing his programme, which looked black with names, with hers. It seemed to give him so much trouble that Leila was ashamed. "Oh, please don't bother," she said eagerly. But instead of replying the fat man wrote something, glanced at her again. "Do I remember this bright little face?" he said softly. "Is it known to me of yore?" At that moment the band began playing; the fat man disappeared. He was tossed away on a great wave of music that came flying over the gleaming floor, breaking the groups up into couples, scattering them, sending them spinning. . . .

Leila had learned to dance at boarding school. Every Saturday afternoon the boarders were hurried off to a little corrugated iron mission hall where Miss Eccles (of London) held her "select" classes. But the difference between that dusty-smelling hall—with calico texts on the walls, the poor terrified little woman in a brown velvet toque with rabbit's ears thumping the cold piano, Miss Eccles poking the girls' feet with her long white wand—and this was so tremendous that Leila was sure if her partner didn't come and she had to listen to that marvellous music and to watch the others sliding, gliding over the golden floor, she would die at least, or faint, or lift her arms and fly out of one of those dark windows that showed the stars.

"Ours, I think—" Some one bowed, smiled, and offered her his arm; she hadn't to die after all. Some one's hand pressed her waist, and she floated away like a flower that is tossed into a pool.

"Quite a good floor, isn't it?" drawled a faint voice close to her ear.

"I think it's most beautifully slippery," said Leila.

"Pardon!" The faint voice sounded surprised. Leila said it again. And there was a tiny pause before the voice echoed, "Oh, quite!" and she was swung round again.

He steered so beautifully. That was the great difference between dancing with girls and men, Leila decided. Girls banged into each other, and stamped on each other's feet; the girl who was gentleman always clutched you so.

The azaleas were separate flowers no longer; they were pink and white flags streaming by.

"Were you at the Bells' last week?" the voice came again. It sounded tired. Leila wondered whether she ought to ask him if he would like to stop.

"No, this is my first dance," said she.

Her partner gave a little gasping laugh. "Oh, I say," he protested.

"Yes, it is really the first dance I've ever been to." Leila was most fervent. It was such a relief to be able to tell somebody. "You see, I've lived in the country all my life up until now. . . ."

At that moment the music stopped, and they went to sit on two chairs against the wall. Leila tucked her pink satin feet under and fanned herself, while she blissfully watched the other couples passing and disappearing through the swing doors.

"Enjoying yourself, Leila?" asked Jose, nodding her golden head.

Laura passed and gave her the faintest little wink; it made Leila wonder for a moment whether she was quite grown up after all. Certainly her partner did not say very much. He coughed, tucked his handkerchief away, pulled down his waistcoat, took a minute thread off his sleeve. But it didn't matter. Almost immediately the band started, and her second partner seemed to spring from the ceiling.

"Floor's not bad," said the new voice. Did one always begin with the floor? And then, "Were you at the Neaves' on Tuesday?" And again Leila explained. Perhaps it was a little strange that her partners were not more interested. For it was thrilling. Her first ball! She was only at the beginning of everything. It seemed to her that she had never known what the night was like before. Up till now it had been dark, silent, beautiful very often —oh, yes—but mournful somehow. Solemn. And now it would never be like that again—it had opened dazzling bright.

"Care for an ice?" said her partner. And they went through the swing doors, down the passage, to the supper room. Her cheeks burned, she was fearfully thirsty. How sweet the ices looked on little glass plates, and how cold the frosted spoon was, iced too! And when they came back to the hall there was the fat man waiting for her by the door. It gave her quite a shock again to see how old he was; he ought to have been on the stage with the fathers and mothers. And when Leila compared him with her other partners he looked shabby. His waistcoat was creased, there was a button off his glove, his coat looked as if it was dusty with French chalk.

"Come along, little lady," said the fat man. He scarcely troubled to clasp her, and they moved away so gently, it was more like walking than dancing. But he said not a word about the floor. "Your first dance, isn't it?" he murmured.

"How *did* you know?"

"Ah," said the fat man, "that's what it is to be old!" He wheezed faintly as he steered her past an awkward couple. "You see, I've been doing this kind of thing for the last thirty years."

"Thirty years?" cried Leila. Twelve years before she was born!

"It hardly bears thinking about, does it?" said the fat man gloomily. Leila looked at his bald head, and she felt quite sorry for him.

"I think it's marvellous to be still going on," she said kindly.

"Kind little lady," said the fat man, and he pressed her a little closer, and hummed a bar of the waltz. "Of course," he said, "you can't hope to last anything like as long as that. No-no," said the fat man, "long before that you'll be sitting up there on the stage, looking on, in your nice black velvet. And these pretty arms will have turned into little short fat ones, and you'll beat time with such a different kind of fan—a black bony one." The fat man seemed to shudder. "And you'll smile away like the poor old dears up there, and point to your daughter, and tell the elderly lady next to you how some dreadful man tried to kiss her at the club ball. And your heart will ache, ache"—the fat man squeezed her closer still, as if he really was sorry for that poor heart—"because no one wants to kiss you now. And you'll say how unpleasant these polished floors are to walk on, how dangerous they are. Eh, Mademoiselle Twinkletoes?" said the fat man softly.

Leila gave a light little laugh, but she did not feel like laughing. Was it—could it all be true? It sounded terribly true. Was this first ball only the beginning of her last ball after all? At that the music seemed to change; it sounded sad, sad; it rose upon a great sigh. Oh, how quickly things changed! Why didn't happiness last for ever? For ever wasn't a bit too long.

"I want to stop," she said in a breathless voice. The fat man led her to the door.

"No," she said, "I won't go outside. I won't sit down. I'll just stand here, thank you." She leaned against the wall, tapping with her foot, pulling up her gloves and trying to smile. But deep inside her a little girl threw her pinafore over her head and sobbed. Why had he spoiled it all?

"I say, you know," said the fat man, "you mustn't take me seriously, little lady."

"As if I should!" said Leila, tossing her small dark head and sucking her underlip. . . .

Again the couples paraded. The swing doors opened and shut. Now new music was given out by the bandmaster. But Leila didn't want to dance any more. She wanted to be home, or sitting on the veranda listening to those baby owls. When she looked through the dark windows at the stars, they had long beams like wings. . . .

But presently a soft, melting, ravishing tune began, and a young man with curly hair bowed before her. She would have to dance, out of politeness, until she could find Meg. Very stiffly she walked into the middle; very haughtily she put her hand on his sleeve. But in one minute, in one turn, her feet glided, glided. The lights, the azaleas, the dresses, the pink faces, the velvet chairs, all became one beautiful flying wheel. And when her next partner bumped her into the fat man and he said, "Par*don,*" she smiled at him more radiantly than ever. She didn't even recognize him again.

The Brothers Patton

WALT GROVE

I WAS GROWN, of course. I was fifteen and it was turning into spring and my brother Dennis was in the army so I was the oldest. My brother Mike was just a kid, only six, and I had no time for him because I was grown and having dates with Mary Jane Butler. Mike didn't understand that and kept after me all the time to play Superman. Even Friday night when this terrible thing happened to me and I was trying to get dressed, Mike kept pulling on my shirt, saying, "Pat, Pat, play with me, won't you, Pat?"

"For the last time, Mike, no."

"Why not, huh, Pat?"

"I'm busy—can't you leave me alone?"

Mike had on his red Superman cape, an old cowboy hat, and two toy guns and a wooden knife in his belt. He leaned against my twin bed, chin on fist, and looked at me. "That's Dennis's tie and you're wearing it," he said.

"Oh, go away, Mike. Leave me alone."

"That's Dennis's beer tie. Dennis told me it was. He said, Mike this is my beer tie. I always wear it and spill beer on it so while I'm in the army don't let anyone get it." Mike looked darkly at me. "You take off poor Dennis's beer tie, you're bad."

"Come on, Mike, leave me alone."

"Take it off or I'll call Mom."

"Now, Mike, you wouldn't do that."

"Mom, Mom, you better come here!"

"Listen, Mike—"

"Mom, oh Mom!"

Mom came and stood in the doorway, looking at us. "What's all this noise about?"

I felt very embarrassed as I had just come from the shower and had on nothing but my shorts and a shirt. "Mother, please, I'm not dressed. You shouldn't come in like this, I'm grown."

Mom laughed. She just looked at me and laughed, and I got very angry and finished tying the tie and picked up my pants with dignity and put them on. "Very well," I said. "Very well, laugh."

"Is it Dennis's tie?" Mom asked.

"Listen, Mom, I've got to wear this tie."

"Make him take it off, he's bad," Mike said.

"Is it, Pat?"

"Yes, but it's the only thing that goes with this shirt."

"Why, it's dirty," Mom said. "It's old and dirty, Pat."

"Oh, very well," I said. "It's dirty. It's very dirty. *I* have no opinion, no one cares if *my* clothes don't match."

Mom laughed, her eyes laughing the most and making me the maddest, and she picked Mike up and kissed him, though he squirmed, and carried him into the living room where Dad was. I sighed and finished dressing. I put on my coat carefully, pulling it down behind, and put a white handkerchief casually in my breast pocket and combed my hair again. Then I went into Mom's room and looked at myself in the mirror and I certainly was mature except where I stuck out behind. Some people say I am fat, but that is not true; it's only because my physique protrudes in the back. I went into the living room and stood until Dad lowered his paper and gazed blankly at me like he does when he's being funny. His hair was a wisp like a Kewpie doll's, his glasses crooked as usual.

"Why, Pat, you aren't going out at this time of night?"

"Dad, you know I have a date."

"A date? My, my! Mother, is this all right?"

"It's up to you," Mom said.

"Well, *I* certainly didn't have any dates when *I* was a boy."

"Come on, Dad," I said, "stop kidding."

"Well, I'll think it over." He lifted his paper.

"Cut it out, Dad, I'll be late."

He looked blanker than ever. "Something you want, Pat?"

"You know I haven't any money."

"No money? Why I gave you money only last week." He pulls that one every time, he thinks it's funny. But he laughed and got up and slapped me on the shoulder and put his arm around me. I am taller, and he grinned, "Look at us, Mother, this boy is taller than I am."

He handed me his billfold and told me to take what I wanted and I did and he told me to take more. But Mother said I had quite enough; so I put the two bills in my right pants pocket. I had fifty cents in my left pants pocket and in the little pocket in my coat was eighteen cents, but no one knew that but me.

"Well, good night," I said, "I'll probably be in late. . . ."

"No you won't," Mom said. "You know how Mrs. Butler will talk in church Sunday if you keep Mary Jane out after eleven. And you're too young to stay out late yourself."

"Oh, all right," I said. I put my hand on Mike's head but he frowned, moving away from me.

"You're bad. You should be nice to your little brother and play with me. Someday you'll be very sorry about this."

"Now, Mike, don't be like this."

"You won't play Superman, you're bad."

"Here, I'll play Superman," Dad said. "Bang!"

I went out the door and Dad was on the floor on his hands and knees going "Bang!" Mike was running at him, yelling, "That isn't any fair, that isn't any fair, bang!" I walked up the street slowly, trying to keep my behind from sticking out so far. Mary Jane lived ten blocks away and it was a warm night with stars and very dark. I walked past the first street light; the houses were lighted inside, and as I walked along erectly I thought about Dennis.

He was my older brother and people called him That Crazy Dennis Patton because he laughed. But he wasn't crazy; he was happy. He wasn't big, like Dad, and he wanted to be a poet. He worked in the airplane factory and wrote poetry and it wasn't printed anywhere, but he laughed. One time I told him when I got out of high I would get a job and he could just write poetry. He looked at me awfully funny and I felt funny, but he just said, "Okay, it's a deal."

Before he went in the army he sold his car and put the money in the bank. It was a wonderful car and we used to ride around in it with the top down. But they drafted him into the artillery and before he left he burned all his poetry. I came home and there it was, burning, and I felt bad but he only laughed. After he went overseas he wrote a letter saying he was sitting on an ammunition dump, it was raining, no one had shot at him yet, he hadn't even seen a Fascist, all he'd seen was mud, but he wrote a poem. It was just three lines:

Home,
Home;
Home.

I put it away for him in a box I got, just that one crumpled sheet, and every now and then I take it out and read it. Sometimes I think what if Dennis gets killed? What if my brother Dennis gets killed in this war with all his poetry burned and just this one little poem and I've never had a chance to get a job so he can be a poet? I try not to think that, but I'm in high and several seniors have gone and everyday we have this judo class. I learned how to break a guy's neck three different ways, but I still think about Dennis.

That was how I had the first date with Mary Jane Butler. I was in judo class learning how to break a guy's neck by jumping on it the right way and I thought of Dennis sitting on the ammunition dump in the rain and I got so mad I wanted to cry. I walked away and stood by the tennis courts where the girls were playing and I hated everything. Mary Jane was near by and she said, "Hello, what's the matter?"

I just laughed, bitterly. She looked odd and walked over, peering at me. "Don't you feel well, Pat?"

"Listen, go away, will you?"

"I didn't mean to intrude," she said. "I'm sorry."

"That doesn't help, you could bust out in tears and it still wouldn't help."

"Well, come over here and sit down," she said.

I didn't want to go back to the judo class; so I sat with her against the wire fence and she talked until the bell rang when I told her I would walk home with her that afternoon. I did, and later in the week we had our first date. It worried me, but not too much, which was all right because I found there wasn't anything to it at all. You just talk calmly and spend some money.

Anyway, this Friday night when I had on Dennis's beer tie was our fourth date—four week ends straight and it was more or less an anniversary. When I got to Mary Jane's house it was the right time; so I knocked and Mrs. Butler asked who it was and I told her and she let me in. Mrs. Butler is a thin woman and no matter what she has on she always looks like she's going out to cut roses or dig in a flowerbed. She stood with a sweater about her shoulders, hugging herself, so I said it was a nice night and she said yes. Then I said spring is really here and she said yes. She kept looking at me all the time as if she suspected me of something, so when Mary Jane came in I was glad. We smiled and Mrs. Butler put a hand to her mouth, looking sharply at Mary Jane, and then bent down and plucked something from Mary Jane's dress.

"Let's go, Pat," Mary Jane said.

"Kiss Mother," Mrs. Butler leaned a cheek toward Mary Jane and Mary

Jane kissed her and I opened the door and we went out. Mrs. Butler peered after us. "You don't have a car, do you, Patrick?"

"No, ma'am."

"That's good. I worry so about Mary Jane."

"Good night, Mrs. Butler," I said.

"Oh, I'll be up when you come back."

We walked across the porch to the walk and the door closed behind us and I felt better and took Mary Jane's hand. It was always so warm it surprised me and gave me a nice, pleasant feeling. We walked that way to the streetcar tracks. Mary Jane was beautiful, she had brown hair and eyes, and silk stockings and high heels. She was cute. We went downtown and saw a movie about a lieutenant and a girl who had a fight because the girl wanted to live, she said. So the lieutenant left and this other guy who was the casual type did a horrible thing to the girl, only it was very vague and no one ever said what it was. But in the end the lieutenant comes back with a medal and they meet accidentally in an elevator and this song plays all the way through. Afterwards Mary Jane and I went back to our neighborhood to the Hangout where everyone goes and sat side by side in a booth drinking cokes.

"I liked the picture," she said, "did you?"

"No, the lieutenant was silly. Soldiers aren't like that. Dennis and his friends aren't like that."

"Oh, you're just hipped on that subject. Listen, Pat, didn't Dennis have a car?"

"Sure, a convertible, but he sold it."

"Oh," Mary Jane said. "Sam Ott has a nice car."

"It's not as nice as Dennis's was."

"It's the best one at high. It'll do seventy."

"That thing? It couldn't."

"Well, it did," she said. I looked at her and she looked at me and said quickly, "Now, Pat, don't you tell Mother."

"Tell her what?"

"Well, I was with Sam Ott Sunday and we rode in his car."

"Oh," I said.

I didn't feel so good, but we sat there a bit longer and then she looked at her watch and we had to go. We walked to her house and stood at the front door with the light shining through and I held her hand for a moment, both of us very quiet.

"Oh, I forgot," I said. "We're having a barbecue tomorrow night and you're supposed to come."

"I can't, Pat."

"It's all right—my mother will call your mother."

"But I've got a date."

"Oh."

"I'm sorry, Pat."

"Yes," I grinned. "Yes, well, good night."

"Good night, Pat."

I kept grinning and I walked off the porch whistling, then the door closed behind me and I stopped grinning and when I got far enough away I stopped whistling. I didn't want to whistle. I wanted to walk along in the dark feeling bad. Sam Ott and his car. Sam Ott was a senior, a big guy, what if I had a fight with him? It would happen on the front steps at high with everyone looking at me. He was certainly big and a senior. Well, I would fight. We both knew judo so it would probably be terrible and the hospital would call Mom, telling her. But I would fight.

I walked home feeling bad and Dad was still up, reading, with three cigar butts in the ash tray beside him. We had a glass of milk and some cake together in the kitchen, and before he turned off the lights he put a hand on the back of his neck and said, "I wish your brother Dennis had a nice warm bed to sleep in tonight."

The next day was Saturday and I slept late until Mike came in and pulled the sheet off me and yelled "Superman!" three times in my ear. Finally Mom made me get up and eat breakfast; Mike danced around the table, singing, "Old fat Pat's a sissy, old fat Pat's a sissy." Then Mom sent me down to the store and when I got there I read the list and it was for the barbecue and I felt bad again.

I bought the stuff and went home and sat and thought: Dennis in Italy, Mary Jane Butler and Sam Ott. Dad came home for lunch and afterwards he and Mike fixed the barbecue pit. Mike put on his cowboy hat and got two hammers, a screwdriver, and a saw, and they went outside. Dad dug out the pit and Mike hit his foot with the hammer. Mom was asleep in her room and I sat in mine, just thinking.

Before dinner time Dad and Mike came in and woke Mom up and they started getting ready for the barbecue. We always have had barbecues and we sit around the barbecue pit and Dad smokes a cigar and drips the sauce on. Dennis used to lie on the ground and laugh at Dad or play with Mike. I didn't want to go out, but Dad and Mike yelled at me.

"Pat, come out, Dad's going to drip the sauce!"

"Pat, Mike's speaking to you," Dad called.

I went out the back door and walked down to the barbecue pit and sat in a chair. Mom was arranging some things on the table and Mike leaned on the arm of my chair, chin on fist. "Now Dad's going to drip the sauce," he said. "Aren't you, Dad?"

"I shall now drip sauce." Dad took the swab and dipped it into the sauce and ran it over the meat.

"What're you doing, Dad?" Mike yelled.

"Dripping sauce, Mike."

"He's dripping sauce, Pat," Mike said. "Look at Dad!"

"Oh, I can see," I said.

"Do it again, Dad," Mike said. "Now watch Dad, Pat."

"I will now drip sauce again," Dad said, and did.

"Look, Pat, look at Dad!" Mike yelled.

"Mike, I can see, I'm not blind!"

"Now, Pat, don't yell at Mike," Mom said.

"Well, he yelled at me."

"Don't you want to see Dad drip sauce?" Mike said.

"Oh, forget it, forget it."

"What's wrong with dripping sauce?" Dad said. "Why, I have dripped sauce for twenty-four years."

"All right, okay," I said. "Let's forget it."

Mike looked darkly at me. "That's bad. You shouldn't talk to Dad like that. He's your father."

"Okay," I said. "But shut up about it, can't you?"

Mike backed away, shaking his head. "You're bad."

Mom looked at Dad and Dad looked at Mom like they do, and they both looked at me. "What's the matter, Pat?" Mom said.

"What's wrong, son?" Dad asked.

"He's bad," Mike said.

I couldn't sit any longer. I couldn't just sit and listen to all that talk. I stood up and walked toward the house. I had to do something, I had to run or yell or something.

"Now, Pat, don't be childish," Dad said.

I went in the house and laid on my bed. It was twilight and outside I could hear Mom and Dad and Mike talking. I rolled over and looked at the ceiling. The room was dim and I felt very bad. If Dennis were home it would be different, if he were home that Sam Ott would see. Everything in my life was wrong and I knew nothing would ever be as bad. I sat up, wondering why I felt bad. Then I knew and I was scared.

I was in love with Mary Jane Butler.

I stood up and put my hands in my pants pockets. I was fifteen, I stuck out behind, I had had four dates with Mary Jane and had spent exactly seven dollars and twenty-nine cents. But, I was grown and I was in love. I took my hands out of my pockets and sat down. I was afraid for a moment and then I thought: what am I going to do?

I looked out the window. Mom and Dad and Mike were sitting in chairs, the fire in the pit was embers. I went out the side door, up the driveway, and down the walk. It was dark, a nice warm spring night, and I felt a little sick. I walked down to the park, watched the lights around the lake cast reflections. A gang of boys rode their bicycles through, whistling shrilly. I walked by the drive-in where Dennis used to drink beer and quote poetry; a bunch of women were getting out of a car, laughing. I went to the drugstore and stood in front of it and Benny came out and rode his bicycle away on a delivery. Inside a little boy was looking at a comic book and eating a melting ice-cream cone. I walked on until I came to high. It was dark, silent, a lot bigger than in daytime. I went across the grass to the tennis courts and sat against the wire fence, thinking. After a long time I got up and walked to the Hangout. I went by feeling self-conscious with Sam Ott's old car outside, but when I got to the end of the block I turned and looked back at the Hangout and made up my mind. Very well, she has made her choice. I loved her, I had four dates with her, but I am grown, she can have him.

I walked home and everyone else was in bed so I went into the kitchen and ate some cold barbecue and drank almost a quart of milk and went to bed with a calm resignation. You're very calm, I told myself as I got between the sheets. You're very calm and that shows philosophy. And I went to sleep.

Sunday morning there is always Sunday School and the funny papers. I tried to sleep late but Mike paraded around my bed, yelling how good *he* was, that *he* was going to Sunday School, until I was wide awake and then he left. So I got up and hunted for the funny papers, but he had hidden them, so I just ate breakfast. But all day I was calmly resigned. I was grown, of course, so it was natural. I was polite, too. Dad and Mike played Superman all day, yelling "Bang!" and disturbing my peace of mind, but I tolerated it and was quiet. Even when Dad read the funny papers to Mike, acting out all the characters, and saying "Biff, sock, zowie!" I said nothing and did my algebra. Mom asked me to go to church that night and I said yes. She was amazed, so I explained that I was grown and had a philosophy of life and she laughed. But even then I remained calmly resigned.

I felt the same way when I went to school Monday. Calm. All day I was tolerant of the teachers, not arguing when they were wrong as they usually are. I was polite, I listened. Even in study hall when that little girl freshman giggled I did not turn and glare. She had a right to giggle; it was her life.

I did not see Mary Jane Butler all day, not even at physical training when she played tennis. I did see Sam Ott when school let out, walking loudly through the hall to attract attention. But I felt no bitterness toward him. I merely put my books in my locker, stuck my algebra book in my jacket pocket, and walked down the hall carrying my jacket. And there was Mary Jane, sort of standing still and walking at the same time. She smiled so I nodded casually.

"Pat, are you going home? I'll walk with you."

I opened the door and she went outside and I followed. It was a nice afternoon and we walked in the crowd going home, everyone laughing and talking. She said it was very warm; I agreed. We walked past the bus stop, and the crowd thinned out, and we were walking alone. At other times being alone with Mary Jane would have aroused a certain emotion in me, but now I was only very calm. She seemed worried and kept glancing sideways at me and finally said, "How was the barbecue?"

"Nice," I said.

We walked to her corner and she stopped, so I stopped. I could walk home with her or just walk home. She shifted the books in her arms and frowned and said, "I'm sorry I didn't go."

"You'll have to come some time," I said, politely.

"Pat . . . I didn't have a good time with Sam Ott."

I grinned, "Yes, he is an exhibitionist."

"It wasn't that. It's just that some people make you happy."

"Huh?" I said.

"Some people make you happy." She looked at me.

I switched my jacket from one hand to the other. "You mean you're only happy when somebody is around? Can't somebody be happy just by himself, can't he?"

"Some people can. But some people just make me happy without doing anything."

I slung my jacket over my shoulder. "Good-bye, Mary Jane."

"Pat, aren't you coming home with me?"

"Listen, you're the nicest girl I know, but I can't."

"Oh," she said.

She was nice. But I smiled and hurried off and then I stopped smiling and walked as fast as I could without running, thinking: you're not grown, you never were, how could you be grown? When I got to our house I went in the side door and I threw my jacket on my bed and went into the kitchen. Mike was drinking a glass of milk; he had on his toy guns and his Superman cape and his cowboy hat. I jumped behind the icebox, pointed my finger at him, and said, "Bang!"

He looked at me coolly. "You can't shoot me with a finger."

"It's a gun, it's a make-believe gun. Bang!"

"*I* don't see any gun."

I came from behind the icebox and poured a glass of milk and stood beside him drinking it. "It is if you pretend."

"No, it isn't," Mike said. "You can't use your finger. That isn't any fair. When I stick you up and take your gun away how can I take away your finger?" He looked at me darkly. "You don't play fair."

"Well, give me a gun then."

He chewed on the rim of the glass. "We'll play?"

"Yes."

"Like I say?"

"Yes."

"I'll get to be Superman?"

"Yes."

"Very well." He handed me a toy gun. "And it isn't any fair to use your finger."

"All right—what do I do?"

"Well," Mike said, "you just go outside and hide and I'm Superman and I come out and you shoot me only I'm Superman and I take your gun away and throw you over the house because you're bad."

"Then what?"

"I don't know," he said impatiently. "Just go outside."

I went into the back yard and hid behind the rosebushes and in a bit Mike came out the door and stood on the steps. He didn't see me, but he kept looking and finally he said, "Are you hid, Pat?"

"Yes."

He looked at the rosebushes then and saw me and ran down the steps yelling, "Superman, Superman, Superman!" I jumped from behind the bushes and raised the toy gun, looking along the barrel of it, and I thought of Dennis. He is there in all that war, I thought, and I stand with a toy gun in my hand. For a second I hated everything again, I hated the world and all the stupid people, I hated it all very much. Then Mike hit my legs, I fell back, he yanked the gun from my hand. I fell to the ground and he jumped on me, yelling, "Biff, bam, sock!" He got up, but I laid still.

"Pat?"

I moaned softly.

"Pat?" He squatted beside me. "Pat, did I hurt you?"

I moaned again and he put a hand on my chest to lean and look into my face and I grabbed him, rolled him over and held him. He struggled, yelling. "You can't do this to Superman, it isn't any fair!"

"I'm doing it, Superman!"

"It isn't any fair, you aren't playing fair, you're bad!" He squirmed quickly, got away, then flung himself at me and I caught him and fell backwards. "Sock!" he yelled. "Sock, I got you, sock!"

I laid there, Mike sitting on my chest. I looked at him and laughed and he laughed, too. For a moment we were like that, Mike bouncing up and down with my laughs and moving with his own laughs. Then he slid off and laid beside me in the grass in the warm sun.

"I like to play Superman with you, Pat."

"Thank you, Mike." I'm fifteen, I thought, and I'm not grown but I'm growing; in two years I can get in the army and then Mike will be here alone and he will think about me like I think about Dennis; I want him to, I want it very much; it's a good thing and I'll work hard at it.

"Is there mail?" Mike asked.

We walked up the driveway to the front of the house and I held him up and he took a letter from the box. We stood on the sidewalk in the sun and looked at the envelope with its return APO number, its censor's stamp, and Mike said. "It's from Dennis, huh?"

"Yes."

"Well, let's read it then."

"Dad and Mom like to open them—they aren't home now."

He stood moving his jaw, thinking. "Okay, let's wait."

We took the letter inside and put it on the dining-room table where Mom and Dad would see it first, then we went outside. The letter is there now and when Dad and Mom come home we'll all read it, but right now Mike and I are playing Superman.

The Circle of Innocence

JEANNE SINGER

MRS. LOGAN sat at the breakfast table, waiting for her daughter. She had always been the first to breakfast while her husband was alive, and she still preceded Agatha by a good fifteen minutes. In that time, she saw what she wanted to see of the morning mail and the morning headlines, and she was ready, with her cheerful sociability, to discuss the plans of the day with Agatha before she left for school. This morning, however, she ignored the papers. She sucked her lower lip as she stirred her coffee, and she devoted more attention to the one unopened letter that lay beside her daughter's plate than she did to the three letters of her own that she had opened and immediately discarded.

She thought for a moment of putting the letter into her pocket but then she could not do it. She had always respected Agatha's privacy, and she had always respected herself for that respect, although Agatha was a girl with whom even a mother's intimacy would have been extremely difficult. She did not touch the envelope, but contented herself with watching it as she pecked at her roll.

Her intent expression relaxed when she heard her daughter's galumphing footsteps on the stairs. Agatha always went up and down furiously. All of her gestures were too rapid and too large as the gestures of a shy person are so apt to be at the times when they are not feeling shy.

The girl's eyes immediately sought out the letter, and her face changed with pleasure as she plunged it into the pocket of her jacket without pausing on her way to kiss her mother good morning. She seemed to have no aptitude at all for deceit or even for dissimulation. If she had screamed with joy the way some girls do when they are pleased with the appearance of a certain handwriting on an envelope, the letter could not have been more stressed, more completely brought to her mother's attention.

"Why don't you read it, dear, I don't mind," said Mrs. Logan.

"It'll wait. I'm too hungry," she said and she did attack her grapefruit like an ordinary, healthy, happy girl. But her face! Her face made Mrs. Logan's heart turn over within her.

Some girls are already formed at sixteen. It is quite plain what they are to be, and what they consider the good things of the world. With Agatha, you could not even be sure whether she would be beautiful or terribly plain. Sometimes she was so awkward that her mother wanted to cry, and yet there was, occasionally, a touching directness about her movements that promised an authentic grace. Her face, too, would change from day to day, sometimes from one hour to another. Even the features would seem to be different. Her whole face would compose itself into a startling beauty that could not have been prophesied even an hour before. For instance, at breakfast here, with her great eyes paled to a twilight gray and her mouth sweet and compassionate, she was entirely different from the Agatha Logan of, say, last Friday night, who wore her lovely evening dress as if it had been made of wire, humping her shoulders and catching her heel in the skirt three times.

Mrs. Logan considered Agatha difficult, and difficult in a particularly difficult way. She had long ago determined to be a good and enlightened mother. She would never do anything to her daughter that her mother had done to her to make her own youth miserable. She would give her daughter all the freedom she wanted, smile on her beaux, believe her innocent until she was proved guilty. Unfortunately, however this course was made difficult for her, as for so many mothers, by the fact that she had a different child from the one she was prepared for. There were no beaux. Agatha liked to sit indoors all day and read. She was naturally honest and frank, and there had been no maidenly deceptions for Mrs. Logan to wink at, as she had so complacently planned.

Then Mother Maria had summoned Mrs. Logan to school. Mrs. Logan always liked to speak to the nuns. It gave her the pleasantly virtuous feeling that a child has when a favorite teacher has praised her; and there was, added to that satisfaction, a slight consciousness of her own generosity in granting them their superiority. She felt patronizing and blessed at the same time, both wise and forgiven.

That was how most of the nuns made her feel, but her talk with the Mother Superior had a different effect. Mother Maria had been perfectly direct. She said, "There is something you ought to know and I prefer to tell you the facts without comment. I know there is more than one way of thinking about this. You know how I feel myself. My dress tells you what I, myself, have chosen. You must decide what you want to do, if you want to do anything at all."

"If you want to do anything at all!" Of course she wanted to do something. She knew that without a second thought. She had as strong an instinct to pull Agatha back into the world as she would have had if she had seen the girl drowning, or wavering on the edge of an actual, physical abyss. Only for a moment, now, as she looked at her daughter's face transformed with joy, did she pause in her determination.

She had hardly waited for any courteous generalities with the Mother. Hurrying from the room, she jumped into the car and drove it from the side gate to the front to wait for Agatha to come out of school. It required no thought. She was trembling with her own certainty. She waited with a shivering curiosity to see if there were any superficial signs in the girl's manner that she had missed in her ignorance, which would be plain to her now.

Agatha came out of school in a cluster of girls. She looked particularly young among her contemporaries, more noticeably incomplete. When she caught sight of her mother in the car at the gate, she came loping down the path, with her books divided into two piles under her two crooked arms in a manner that made Mrs. Logan say, irritably, in spite of the sudden swelling of affection that she felt for her daughter, "Why on earth do you always have to bring so much home? Nobody else seems to lug home so many books."

Agatha giggled and shrugged her shoulders cheerfully. "Sometimes that's what I ask myself, Mummy. But whenever I leave one in school, that's just the one I need that night, and I spend all my time kicking myself because I don't have it. Wherefore you see."

"Wherefore I see."

"How did you happen to come today?"

"That's a fine thing. Aren't you glad?"

"Sure I'm glad, my darling."

"Oh, Aggie, don't you know you can't hug me when I'm driving. Do you want a drink?"

"If I can have a soda and nuts for my complexion."

"All right. Your complexion has been pretty good lately."

"Any mail when you left, Mummy?"

"I left before lunch. Why so interested? You aren't sending for Clark Gable's picture again, are you?" Mrs. Logan knew at once she had made a mistake, that she had overplayed her own innocence. The girl blushed and yanked off her hat with a gesture of annoyance, and fitted it over the pile of books that lay in her lap.

"Mummy, how you do see through me," she said with exaggerated wonder. But then they had arrived at Schrafft's and the effort of parking distracted them both.

What with the soda and the little shopping that they stopped off for on the way home, Mrs. Logan's excitement quieted down, and gradually the normality of the day and of Agatha's behavior made her feelings at the school gate seem almost hysterical. The Mother Superior was seeing things. Her manner was the manner of wisdom but it must be deceptive. The woman's view of things was bound to be colored by her own propensities, her own feelings, her own way of life. Her opinions must be accepted only with modifications, they must be sifted through the fine net of Mrs. Logan's own worldliness and then re-examined.

But the sight of the letter beside her daughter's plate stirred it all up again, and when she saw her daughter's face, she heard the Mother's voice again, believed it again, every word of it, as she had believed the nuns when she herself had gone to school to them.

"Aunt Emma is coming to lunch," she said then. "But you needn't come home if you don't want to." This consideration could not have been too unusual as Agatha looked pleased but not surprised.

"I'll get a sandwich in the lunchroom," she said, "and I'll pray for both of you before I eat it."

"Save your prayers for church, child. Good-bye."

Mrs. Logan still lingered at the table for a moment after her daughter left the house.

Then she went into her daughter's room and began a systematic search. The room was not entirely familiar to her. They never sat there, and Agatha was so tidy in her habits that there was never any occasion for going over her bureau drawers or her closet. If she wanted a paper clip or a rubber band from the desk, she knew exactly where she could put her hand on it. There had never been any need to rummage around.

There was a print of Bellini's Holy Family over the bed. It was an excellent print. Agatha had astonished her mother by spending all the money she had gotten on her sixteenth birthday on this picture. The room was otherwise unornamented. The top of her bureau was bare. Mrs. Logan had been no more dismayed by this bareness than she had been by the pictures of the screen stars that had formerly ornamented the walls. She knew a phase when she saw one. But now she wondered, now she questioned her own perspicacity; and it was this self-doubt, this need for reassurance, that steadied her for her intrinsically unpleasant task. She was, unfortunately, not a woman who could really enjoy a clandestine search for her daughter's secret.

But she had to know. She found the letters with all of Agatha's other letters, in the bottom drawer of her desk. This openness, this witness to the girl's faith that she would not be spied upon, pulled her up short for a minute, but did not really damage her assurance that she must go ahead, equip herself with all the information that she needed.

The postmarks were all from Ocean Beach. So far Sister Maria had been telling the truth. "I want to be absolutely fair to you and to your point of view, Mrs. Logan, even though it doesn't coincide with my own. That's why I'm telling you this, now. Your daughter is unusually gifted. I have been very fond of her, but I also want to be fair to you."

Each letter was directed in the same lavish hand, the generous loops of the letters reaching up and down to mingle with the words on the lines above and below. She did not see how she could have failed to wonder which one of Agatha's few seaside acquaintances carried on such a rich correspondence. It was a difficult hand to read at first. There was an unpleasant moment when Mrs. Logan thought she was being confronted by a letter in Latin.

"My dear child,

True thirst for holiness is beautiful and rare, difficult to know truly, and often counterfeit. Human beings are constantly subject to emotions they cannot name, racked by the desire for some mist-obscured prize whose very nature is unknown to them. . . ."

Gradually, she acquired ease in reading the dark and complicated script, and as it became easier, she felt her eyes, her whole body, relax. It was pleasant as darkness when the eyes have become accustomed to the shadow.

"My dear child,

May I point out the length of the road you would have to travel, so much longer for you than for many others who have so much less delightful a portion of the world to pass through. . . ."

Mrs. Logan did not leave her daughter's room for several hours. First she picked the pack of letters out of the drawer, and flipped through them as through a pack of cards. A sentence or two to confirm the character of the letters, a glance through the pile to see that they were all alike, that was all that was required, all that she intended; but she read first one and then another and then another. Then she leaned back in her chair, with the letters in her two hands, with no desire to leave the bare and sunny room or the sanctuary which the letters had erected. Then she read them all again, each one in sequence, without haste or impatience, just as if each letter had come to her in the morning mail. Although the hand had been strange to her, she soon recognized the familiar voice.

Mrs. Logan had decided, as soon as she pulled herself out of the sweet, disabling calm which had come over her in Agatha's room, that she must go to Ocean Beach as soon as possible and speak to Father Gregory. At the moment of her decision, she felt the necessary degree of indignation. She was not only angry but aware of the justice of her anger.

But before she could speak to Father Gregory, she had to find a time when her daylong absence would not be questioned by Agatha. She had to think of the probable chill in the air so close to the ocean, and to choose the proper clothes. She had to go down to the station and take a train and sit on the train for two hours, watching the landscape grow flatter and paler and sandier as they approached the shore. When the conductor opened the door at the Tulans stop, the cold air swept through the almost empty car, rich and sharp with the clammy smell of the low tide.

They had only spent their summers at Ocean Beach, but somehow that smell was the smell of home to her, perhaps because it was to Ocean Beach that she had first come as Mrs. Stacey Logan. Agatha was born there and spent the first year of her life there, because Mrs. Logan had almost died in childbirth and could not be moved back to the city for the winter.

It was when they were at the house at the beach that Stacey had had time to spend with her in the first years of their marriage, and now when she thought of him, she almost always thought of him as he was at the beach.

She remembered getting up before dawn to pack him off with Father Gregory on their fishing trips. She drove the two men and their kits down to the dock in the thin, milky light of the dispersing night, sweet with the morning star. The white mist clung to the dark steel-smooth water of the bay, and the fishermen's steps clanked and clogged on the wooden pier with wonderful clarity. As the two men climbed aboard, she could hear them laughing with the excitement of the new day.

She remembered sitting on the porch in the evening, knitting while the two men walked up and down, up and down, the short gravel path. They walked many miles each week, never leaving that path. Peace to her then had been the muffled sound of the sea and the sound of her husband's voice in the dark, as he talked to his friend. Father Gregory's voice was low. She could hear him only when their pacing brought them close to the house, but Stacey's voice she could always hear even when she could not distinguish his words.

It was strange how Father Gregory had been transformed for her, after her husband's death. During Stacey's life, they had never forgotten his priesthood, had always respected both his person and his vocation, but religion had been little more than a ritual to her then; she had been a happy woman for so long that she knew almost nothing of the realities of terror and of worship. But when Stacey Logan was drowned and Father Gregory had given her the news and offered her the comfort not only of his friendship but of the church, she had found in him a new strangeness and a new intimacy.

He was no longer the friend who sat for long hours talking over the dinner table, there was no longer the selfless ease of long association. In place of that, there was a stranger who offered her the peace of sanctuary in her grief, who accepted and understood her sorrow with all of the church's ancient wisdom, added her sorrow to the sum of the sorrows of the world and so deprived her of its full weight.

But he had done more than that. He had remained friend as well as priest in his friendliness to Agatha. He had allowed her to replace her father on his long fishing expeditions and the girl had shown a new placidity that summer which she could only have won from such a companion. Not only had her mother been relieved of the duty of consolation to Agatha, but she had found in her daughter a sudden maturity and companionship.

Of course, that had not lasted longer than the sense of strangeness hung over their little household. Mrs. Logan would not have wanted it to last longer. She was, in fact, made happier by Agatha's subsequent return to her own awkward, cheerful carelessness than she had been by the premature consideration and fellowship; and for that return too, she had silently thanked Father Gregory's wisdom. Her own feeling of piety, of mystic safety, of goodness even—her gradual acceptance of her loss made it seem almost like a voluntary sacrifice—had slowly dissolved. Her gratitude had grown more human again, less strange; but she found herself thinking often of those months of devotion, of seclusion, almost as of a happy time, as she thought of the time when her health came back to her after her long illness, or of the time when Stacey had suddenly decided he had to have a vacation and had made her come off with him on an hour's notice.

Now she was traveling through the long, silver waves of sandgrass toward the deepening sky to reproach her teacher and her friend, and the nearer she came to him, the more difficult it was to maintain her anger at the proper pitch. It was only by thinking of Agatha, by repairing time and again to the picture of the girl, her long legs clattering down the school steps, her long arms awkwardly crooked over the two piles of strapped books and papers; to the picture of Agatha, sullen and impatient at the dressmaker's, perversely beautiful and affectionate at the breakfast table, that she could maintain her resolve, her mother's exasperated point of view.

On the trip back, she found herself exhausted. Father Gregory had been as kind, as understanding, as generous as she had always known him. She had gained all that she had hoped from her visit and that was time. He was willing to give her all the time that she wanted, on almost the terms she had asked, and on the trip back to the city, Mrs. Logan slept, fitfully, all the way. It must have been more of an effort than she had realized to question and to reproach him.

Agatha stayed in her own room until the very minute she was called to dinner and she came out then, with her thumb in her book, mumbling rhythmically to herself, and laid the book, face downward, on the sideboard behind her chair.

"It's the sixty-minute quiz tomorrow. Couldn't we eat a little fast tonight, Mum? I've got such hundreds of pages to do."

"I'm sure you've time for a decent dinner. You'll never remember if you cram so."

"I won't have anything to remember if I don't cram so."

"And, Agatha, don't they tell you it's bad for a book to be put down like that? It breaks their backs."

"My, but it sounds sad when you say it like that—I'll use this knife to keep the place," and she patted the book with exaggerated tenderness, as she closed it over the knife's blade.

"Come on Aggie, your soup's getting cold.—Where's Virginia going this summer?"

"To California, the lucky bum."

"I didn't know you wanted to go to California."

"Well as a matter of fact, I don't particularly, but it does sound swell and far-away with the sixty-min. tomorrow."

"You know I was thinking of Maine for us this summer. You remember that place Aunt Ethel told us about."

"Why I never even heard of such an audacious woman! Maine, after all these years at Ocean Park!"

"Well, somehow the thought of it this year is a little depressing." Now Agatha was not answering. Agatha was letting her go on, listening to her, suddenly too quiet, too astute, thinking her mother faithless and eager to escape from her passing grief. "I don't know, but I thought it might be better for both of us, if we went someplace else for this summer. Don't you think it would be fun to see some new people for a change? Get away from all that sand? I shudder when I think of those damp sheets. I'm probably just admitting my age but I feel as if I could *not* face those soft seashore cigarettes for another season. What do you think?"

"I don't know. I never thought of it. I always begin to get the most enormous yen for the ocean this time of year—but if you. . . ."

"I mentioned it to Father Gregory, when I spoke to him last week, and he said he knew someone who might want the house for the summer."

"Did you tell him you mightn't come?"

"I couldn't exactly tell him, when I didn't know, but I said I was thinking about it."

"What did he say?"

"He said of course he'd miss his fishing partner but that he thought a change would be wonderful for you."

"Mum, did he really say that or did you say didn't he think a change would be wonderful for me and then he said yes?"

Mrs. Logan laughed. "Here's a nice piece of well-done for you, Mr. District-Attorney. Honestly I don't remember just how it came out, but I did get the impression very strongly that he thought it would be good for you to meet some young people."

"That's great. I meet young people every day of my life."

"School's different." She kept looking at the girl, trying to see through her words, appraise the progress she was making, and as she watched, Agatha's intent expression relaxed suddenly, and she stopped playing with her meat.

"Oh well," she said, out of a short, choking laugh at her own momentary confusion, "I won't worry until I see the tickets. You'll go to the beach all right. I forgot we have to go through this practically every year."

"I hope you're as smart on your sixty-minute tomorrow," said Mrs. Logan, half laughing, half reproving, but it was the laugh that Agatha picked up and continued.

"I certainly hope I am, and please could I have another piece of meat?"

As they came around a corner of the climbing road, while there was still nothing to be seen of the inn but its single cupolaed spire, they saw the tennis courts. There was nobody playing at the moment. There was no one in sight but a tall thin man tenderly poking at the clay with his toe, apparently trying to make up his mind whether or not the courts were dry enough to be played on. The pale, sand-colored surface was still mottled with dampness, and he must have decided against playing because he bent down and yanked at a couple of weeds that were growing stubbornly in the alley, and slouched off toward a little shack.

"Say, those courts don't look bad at all," said Mrs. Logan. "In this air, I almost feel tempted myself."

"Why not? I'll take you on any time you say."

"Why don't you take some lessons while you're here? There's probably someone around. Wouldn't you like that?" Agatha was looking back over her shoulder at the courts until they were out of sight. They were surrounded by wire nets up which a few roses were trying to struggle. Tennis was plainly not one of the major interests of the guests at the Old Duke's Inn.

"They're a little weedy but they're not bad," Agatha said. "What makes you think there's a pro around?"

"The booklet! Don't you remember the booklet?"

"Oh, the booklet. I remember," and they both laughed together as their car drew up before the wide inhabited porch of the Old Duke's Inn.

"Well, we're here," said Mrs. Logan. Agatha stood looking up at the complicated window banks of the inn's façade, holding her hat high like a parasol to shade her eyes. Her voice expressed resignation rather than reproof, and her mother felt it necessary to repeat her meaningless phrase in a tone of greater enthusiasm.

"Well, we're here," she said brightly, climbing out of the car and smiling welcome to the porter who came out for their bags. She did really feel good to have arrived. There is always a certain excitement about an arrival of any sort, and the air was most invigorating besides. There had been rain in the early morning, and now the sky had all the brightness of fall, and the luxuriant trees of July shone with an almost autumnal brilliance. Crowds of small, puffy clouds traveled rapidly toward the horizon with a contagious vigor. The bridge table of old ladies in one corner of the porch was a little discouraging but then young people would certainly be off doing something on such a bright afternoon.

It was only when they went into the dining room that evening that Mrs. Logan could see that it was the old ladies at the bridge table, dog-collared for dinner, who set the tone of the inn. As a matter of fact, the only young person in sight sat with two such dowagers at a corner table. It was such a cool evening that the three large fans in the ceiling were silent, and the air moved gently through the large, clean room, pleasantly sunless and gray after the brightness out doors.

Mrs. Logan appraised the room and her neighbors as she quickly followed Agatha and the waitress to the table that had been reserved for them, and as she sat down she looked at her daughter, hopefully. Their eyes met and Mrs. Logan could not suppress a small shamefaced smile. She was not accustomed to artificial enthusiasms and it made her feel lonesome to be false with Agatha. Agatha leaned forward and patted her hand, vigorously.

"Never mind, Mum," she said, "the food looks good."

Neither of them mentioned the boy who sat with his aunts at the corner table. He was a big boy, still stoop-shouldered with his sudden height and he seemed to have worked out a satisfactory technique with his companions. He ate steadily without talking, and they only talked to him to ply him with food. He accepted or refused pleasantly and both generations seemed to have accepted without rancour the impossibility of social intercourse between them. The two women, obviously sisters, had plenty to say to one another, and they did not take the trouble to conceal the fact that they were interested in Agatha.

Mrs. Logan tried to look at Agatha with their eyes—not because she considered their boy suitable, he was too young, possibly no more than fifteen—and she found the exercise encouraging. Agatha looked well, she thought. She had had her hair properly done for her before they left. Her hair was a pretty color, and for the moment at least, looked purposeful and controlled. Her new dress was brilliantly white. At times like this, Mrs. Logan admired in her daughter that same simplicity and directness of manner that were at other times so infuriating and inconvenient.

Immediately after breakfast the next morning, she took Agatha down to the tennis court. That was part of her plan—to keep the girl's days so filled with tennis and riding and swimming that at least a week would pass pleasantly. If things at the inn looked no better after that, they could go elsewhere.

Next to the court, there was a small shack, painted dark green, and smelling hot and woody, even in the cool morning. On the front step of the shack sat the boy they had seen in the dining room. He was reading a book and chewing on his middle finger as he read, but when he heard them coming, he jumped up and over to a bench by the court, without even bothering to unbend himself completely, and called, "Hey, Clem," with hardly a second's pause in his reading.

The faded sign over the door said, "Clement Winn—instruction in tennis, riding and swimming by appointment—racquets restrung." Tennis seemed to be Mr. Winn's present interest as he appeared in the door of the shack in a pair of white canvas slacks and sneakers, with the end of a gut string, from a partially strung racquet, in his teeth. Seeing Mrs. Logan and Agatha, he dropped the racquet back into the house, and picked up a shirt which he made no attempt to put on as he spoke to them. He just held it in his two hands as witness to a potential correctness. The exposed part of his body was completely hairless and so burned from tennis and riding and swimming, that in the shadows of his neck and arms, his brown skin looked almost black. The sun had streaked his light brown hair with straw. He was not, however, very athletic looking, having a narrow frame, and one shoulder higher than the other. He had the look of a person who has been successfully sent out-of-doors for his health. His light gray eyes were clear and insensitive.

Agatha stood looking at the court as her mother arranged for her lessons.

"Mr. Winn can take you now, Aggie. What do you think? While it's nice and cool?"

"Swell, I'll run up to the house for my racquet."

"All right, then, I'll walk back with you and I won't watch today. I'll wait a while, 'til you're ready to show off."

Agatha did not have much to say about the tennis lesson, but she exchanged curt nods with the boy, whose name was Johnny, as they passed in the dining room. The next morning, as soon as the mail had been assorted and distributed, she went off for another lesson, so Mrs. Logan began to feel that everything would work out all right after all.

Agatha went to the tennis courts every day as soon as the mail was in. Mrs. Logan was sure that there would be no letter yet, as Father Gregory had promised that this correspondence would be sparse during the summer, but her breakfast hour was tormented by Agatha's attention to the slow operations of the mail clerk behind the desk in the front hall. Sometimes he would look at an envelope for a full minute before he decided where to put it, almost as if reading were a new and difficult accomplishment for him. She found herself breathless with the girl's controlled suspense, and when the sorting was done, the impatient old ladies dispersed, and Agatha sent off for her lesson, the tension relaxed with an exhausting suddenness, and for the first time in her life, she found herself able to sit perfectly still for an hour at a time. For a few days, Agatha always seemed to return too quickly.

She felt, strongly, a need for ceaseless vigilance, a vigilance that was all the more difficult in that she was guarding against something she could not see, which she could not even properly name or examine for fear of losing her sustaining anger. Her conversation with Father Gregory had accomplished what she had set out to accomplish, but it had not been really satisfying.

He never gave her the opportunity for the worldly scoffing she had planned. His piety included all the worldliness, all the urbanity and cynicism she could muster against him. She could never feel that she had passed beyond him into her present practicality. He seemed to have already traversed a greater, saner practicality than her own to arrive at his present stage of holiness and devotion. He had denied her nothing and yet she had come away with a vague, undirected sense of dissatisfaction that was difficult to keep submerged.

But still she watched over Agatha, and in spite of the questions that kept asking themselves in her mind, in spite of the sensation of doubtfulness that sometimes took her unawares, she never altered her course for a moment, or tried to think of an alternative. All of her energies were devoted to watching Agatha, to keeping her interested, and for the first few days, while Agatha played tennis, Mrs. Logan sat motionless at the far end of the long porch.

Then the tennis sessions grew longer and longer, until one day she had to walk down to the courts to get Agatha to go to the lake for their swim. Agatha jumped up and came promptly enough as soon as she saw her mother, with no special farewell to Johnny who seemed to be still reading in the same position, chewing on the same finger as he had been the first morning they came to the court.

"That boy certainly has wonderful concentration," Mrs. Logan said.

"He says he can do two things at once—you know—read and listen to the radio, or read and keep a score, any number of things like that."

"Quite a boy."

"Yes, I imagine he's quite clever," Agatha agreed without enthusiasm, but also without any perception of her mother's light mockery. "He's only fifteen, but he graduated this June."

Agatha went back to the court almost immediately after lunch. During the second week they were at the inn, Mrs. Logan was charged for five half hours of instruction, but Mr. Winn must have worked several extra hours a day with Agatha and Johnny. When he was busy with his other pupils, Agatha and Johnny would stay somewhere near the court, watching or reading, or practicing backhand strokes without a ball and exchanging criticisms. When Winn played a set or two with one of the bellhops in the late afternoon, Agatha, hunched up in her sweater, seemed to be reading with as much interest as Johnny, but they would take turns running after the balls that were always going through the unmended gaps in the wire netting. They never missed one, or delayed a second, or became confused as to whose turn it was to chase.

Then their companionship began to extend beyond the tennis court. One afternoon that was so hot that Agatha and Mrs. Logan had stayed down at the lake right through lunch and into the afternoon, Agatha suddenly raised her head from her arms, folded on the sand, and asked if they could go in to supper a little early. "Clem's playing golf with a guy from Maple Hollow, and he said we could go around with him. It'll be nice and cool at that time."

"My goodness, does he play golf, too?"

"He could teach that too, I guess, but people would think it was funny. But he could do it."

"What time do you want to eat?"

"Well, if we could be finished by a quarter to seven?—Mum, do you like it here?"

"Why of course, don't you?"

"But you don't have much to do except bridge and the like."

"Well I've been having some good walks in the mornings with Mr. and Mrs. Peters. They're the kind of walkers I like. As a matter of fact, they were planning a trip to Tidenham next week, and they wondered if you wanted to come along."

"Walking?"

"Of course, what did you think?"

"You go, Mum. Don't worry about me, I'll be all right."

"I had no intention of worrying about you."

"Don't you sound a little bitter at this point, Mrs. L. You haven't been feeling neglected, have you?" Agatha raised herself to a half-sitting position on the sand and pointed her head toward her mother in half-frowning examination.

"Don't be silly, child. I'll complain loud enough if anything's wrong. I came for a rest and I'm resting."

She wanted to ask Agatha what they talked about all day, what they found so engrossing all through the long days. They hardly ever laughed, and, until this request, Johnny and Agatha had shown no desire to spend their evenings together. Agatha had seemed content to play family casino, or to watch her mother's bridge game with the Peters until she went to bed at ten o'clock. Johnny sat beside his two aunts on the porch, in the midst of a group of elderly ladies, but their chattering did not distract him from his constant reading. He read until there was hardly a ray of light left, when all of the old ladies would discover at once, with a swooping rush, that they must warn him of the dangers of such a practice, urge upon him rest and better lighting and the use of an eyewash. He accepted their advice calmly, even with a certain graciousness for such a lengthy, awkward lad, and left them, presumably to pick up his book again under the more healthful light of his bedlamp.

Mrs. Logan could not quite understand their relationship but she said nothing about it. She found herself extravagantly anxious not to intrude on Agatha's privacy in any detail, in order to compensate for the major intrusion of her whole summer's course. Besides, Agatha was busy enough, and she seemed happy enough; and, if it were not for the continued regularity of her interest in the irritating, retarded routine of the mail clerk, Mrs. Logan would have gratefully accepted Johnny, without question, as a mother's ideal of the perfect companion for her daughter's vacation—good-natured, athletic, and without disquieting charm of any sort.

After Agatha left for the golf course that evening, Mrs. Logan walked up and down the porch a few times, but it was still so early that she decided to go into the dining room again and have another cup of coffee at the Peters' table. Mr. and Mrs. Peters were a convenient sort of couple for her to have found. Mr. Peters was one of those men who is always pleasant and patient with women because he despises them. He stayed with his wife all the time when he was not playing golf, but he hardly talked to her at all. He seemed pleased when Mrs. Peters took to Mrs. Logan so quickly, and the triangular arrangement that they soon settled into, appeared to satisfy him completely. While Mrs. Logan could not understand Mrs. Peters' attitude to her husband—she could never have treated Stacey like that, left him sitting all scrubbed and tidy after his golf, with just a book, or not even a book, with just a view of the horizon, while she chattered to her friends—still she liked Mrs. Peters; and it was fortunate to be able to feel perfectly comfortable, and not at all intrusive, walking with them, and sitting with them on the porch, and playing cards with them in the evening.

Mr. Peters occasionally showed that he was not entirely deaf to their talk, by giving his wife a look of mock severity when she took too long leaps from the truth to what she considered the probabilities. These severe glances, she would always answer with great particularity, always knowing exactly what he was complaining about. Sometimes when she was searching for the proper word, he would supply her with the one he considered accurate. In this way, he could always derail his wife's train of thought, when he preferred to listen to some new topic.

Mrs. Peters had given Mrs. Logan all the vital statistics on Johnny Storck as soon as she saw him playing tennis with Agatha. He was motherless. His father's two sisters kept house for them in the winter and always took Johnny away for the summer. It was remarkable that he was as manly as he was with those two old women after him all the time. Now Mrs. Logan had only to mention the fact that Agatha and Johnny were walking around the golf course with Mr. Winn, to have Mrs. Peters take off on the topic of the young instructor.

She had not mentioned Agatha's expedition with any such intention. It had not occurred to her that there would be any information about Mr. Winn. His bland eyes and his constant, patient activity on the tennis court had made her look on him almost as an automaton, useful for entertaining the children. After four days of work, Agatha had been so pleased with her new backhand that she had made her mother come down to see it. It had been as good a backhand as she hoped to see, but she could not help being amused at the seriousness of Agatha and Johnny and their instructor. He seemed to be a completely humorless man, and talked about a backhand as earnestly as if it were a key to heaven and the foundation of culture.

This attitude both Agatha and Johnny seemed to find easy to accept.

"You know, Mum, more good players have been ruined by a weak backhand than by anything else."

"I imagine they would. I know it pushed me out of the game entirely."

"No, really, even the best ones, like—Mum, what are you smiling at?"

"You're a great perfectionist, aren't you Aggie?"

"Oh well, not exactly. But you know how it is—you remember, Mrs. L. 'Now if you'd only led up to that king, jack, and if I'd only held off with my ace and if'—"

"Stop. Stop. I don't talk like that, really, do I?"

"No, not you, Angel Face, but I've heard some people who do."

Now it appeared, for instance, that Mr. Winn was much older than she had thought. Mrs. Peters put him pretty close to forty, although Mrs. Logan had assumed that he was a student, like so many of the young men who work at summer hotels. She had been right to this extent; he had been a chemist, but for the last few years jobs as a tennis pro in Florida in the winter and in Maine in the summer had been pleasanter or easier to get than jobs as a chemist. He had been at the Old Duke's Inn for the last eight years that the Peters had been coming there and Mrs. Peters thought that he might have been there even before that.

"You remember, Jim, that Mrs. Roscoe the first year we were here. She seemed to know him quite well, right at the beginning of the season; but of course she did have an intimate sort of a manner, she was even friendly with Jim before the summer was out. She—" Mrs. Peters' talk was constantly running up against some deflecting obstacle like Mrs. Roscoe and shooting off from it in an entirely new direction. There had been no scandal really, although people had been a little . . .

"Hopeful?" Mr. Peters suggested, ducking into the talk, suddenly, from his seemingly deep abstraction. But this time his wife did not allow herself to be deflected.

After several weeks of service as audience, Mrs. Logan now knew how to select the outstanding facts from the mass of ornamental theorizing and comparing and checking of data. From the enthusiastic tangle of Mrs. Peters' unfinished sentences, Mrs. Logan gathered that there had also been a Mrs. Ray, a Mrs. Valini, a Mrs. Kroner and a Mrs. Ingelhof. But there had never been anything wrong that anyone could see. None of these women had returned to the Old Duke's Inn for a second summer.

Mrs. Devlin, the year before, had come closest to being a scandal, and it was Mrs. Peters' theory that Clem had been spoken to, and had decided to take Agatha and Johnny with him on his evening golfing rounds to preserve and entertain and advertise his innocence. He was always wonderful with children, Mrs. Peters said.

It would have been foolish to consider Mrs. Peters' tales anything but reassuring. Their very vagueness showed them to be pure speculation, and Mr. Peters' derogatory glances had had to be rebutted and silenced more often than usual. Moreover, Mrs. Peters had also assumed that Agatha was to be regarded as a child in this matter. Mr. Winn's taste seemed to run to matrons.

So once more, Mrs. Logan marked herself fortunate in her situation at the Inn, and she refused to worry even when Agatha had not turned up, by the time the bridge game ended at eleven o'clock.

She went up to their room and prepared for the night, slowly and carefully, sitting in her slip at the foot of her bed, mending a tiny raggedness at the edge of her white collar, with small patient stitches that allowed her to hear perfectly each tick of her bedroom clock. She had just climbed into bed and put on her glasses to settle to her magazine, when the door was opened cautiously a crack, Agatha cautiously peeped in, and then flung into the room with such violence that she had to plunge after it with both hands, to keep it from banging up against the plaster wall.

"Oh, Mum, I'm so glad you're still up. I couldn't bear to think of creeping around and keeping quiet," Agatha said, and she closed her bureau drawer with the loud bang from which she had just saved the door.

"I'm glad you're glad." Mrs. Logan took off her glasses and poked the corner of her magazine under her pillow to save the place. "But it's just possible that 217 is sleeping, so I'd watch those bangs if I were you."

"O.K., I'll watch it. Oh, Mum, it was so marvelous. Were you out?"

"On the porch for a while, if you call that out. But the moon was nice. . . ."

"Oh the moon was nothing, it wasn't the moon."

"Where were you? I thought you were just going to walk around the golf course?" She could not help being pleased with her tone. This was the first time that Agatha had ever kept her waiting like that. She had managed not to imagine too many disasters during the evening and now she was managing to appear interested but not suspicious. She must have done the right thing because Agatha flung herself down on the bed with her enthusiasm unabated.

"I'm not even going to brush my teeth— It was the Northern Lights. Didn't you really see them at all? Clem said it was a remarkable display."

"You know I might have, at that. We noticed a strange light toward Tidenham, and we thought there might be a fire or some celebration with fireworks. We wondered."

"It was the Northern Lights. The Aurora Borealis. Aurora Borealis. At the South Pole it's the Aurora Australis, but it's not as good there, or no one's ever seen it when it was really big. Haven't you ever seen the Northern Lights?"

"I don't think I ever have. I don't remember really. Of course, I haven't. I've never been any farther North than we are right now."

"We saw the whole thing. We went to the top of that hill near Tidenham where you can see forever and ever. It was fascinating—all flickering—sort of streams of light—and terribly black dark behind the lights. It's a funny greenish sort of color. Clem says that nearer the Pole, they see all the colors of the rainbow.—You should have seen Johnny. He looked as if he'd been electrocuted. . . ."

"Electrocuted!"

"You know—not dead, but full of electricity. You could practically see the sparks. First he rolled over and over on the ground like a ball. Then when he saw that he was all wet, he started shaking off the water like a dog when he comes out of the lake. Then he was cold. We were all a little cold, but he'd got the back of his shirt wet, and he kept flapping his arms around him in the craziest way." This last gesture Agatha demonstrated, slapping herself such loud blows on the back and shoulders that she started to laugh and slapped herself harder and harder.

"Aggie, what's the matter with you? Are you cold? If you're cold why don't you get under the covers?"

"Good idea!" Agatha stopped her absurd gymnastics promptly and climbed into bed, pulling the covers right up to her chin and hugging them close to her, with the same dramatic rapidity and excitement with which she had first flung open the door.

"Would you come up on the roof with us tomorrow, if it's good again? Or it may even be better because the moon will go down earlier tomorrow. That old moon spoiled it a little tonight. It was too bright, and it was so still. We're going to go up about ten tomorrow. Clem knows all about it, he's a scientist, you know. Will you—you really ought to."

"If it's not too cold."

"Oh, it's much best when it's cold. The colder it is the better."

"Well, if it's not too cold. Are you going to sleep late tomorrow?"

"Not particularly. Clem says there's a Mrs. Devlin who came today—who plays about like me. . . ."

"Mrs. Devlin?"

"Yes. I haven't seen her yet, but he knows her game from last year and I promised to play her tomorrow at nine while he gives her little boy a riding lesson." Agatha chucked the covers up to her chin as if she were shivering.

"Are you so cold, Aggie? You didn't take a cold, did you?"

"Oh, no, honestly I didn't. I'm half cold and half excited. Oh, Mum, please don't fuss about it. I'll be all right. Honestly I will."

The next morning, they both had their breakfast up in their room and Mrs. Logan was still in bed when Agatha left for the tennis courts a little before nine. She looked particularly childish in her short white tennis dress with her hair tied back out of her eyes with a blue ribbon, and her morning manner was once more completely matter of fact. She looked out of the window, briefly, when she got up, but only to see about the tennis weather; and, although she said that it did not look as if it could possibly be the same sky, she seemed to accept the change without regret. She left after a dutiful kiss on her mother's cheek, but, after a few minutes, she came back again, breathless from having run up the stairs.

"Would you do me a favor, Mrs. L.? I can't wait for the mail. If there's something for me, would you bring it down to the beach with you? O.K. I'm late now, but positively."

"All right. I'll bring it, and Aggie will you *please* try to go out without slamming." Suddenly she felt irritable, as if she could not bear another loud noise, another sudden gesture, and least of all another sudden hug. Her words sounded short and cranky and Agatha retreated backward and closed the door like an adult. The girl was unbearably confusing. Here she was watching her like a mother in an old-fashioned novel, taking her away so dramatically, as if she were a grown girl capable of feelings and decisions that were important and coherent and possibly permanent; and she acted like an infant. Then as soon as her mother had settled into thinking of her comfortably as an excitable child, she showed that she had not forgotten, even for a day, not for more than a minute or two, the letter she was waiting for, the voice that Mrs. Logan was trying to lead her away from.

Agatha was too faithful, and yet she was not faithful enough. She had not waited. She had handed over to her mother the waiting, the anticipation, the loving attention to the slow maneuvering of the mail clerk. Mrs. Logan got up and dressed and was downstairs when the post came, hastened by a strange eagerness to take up Agatha's devotion, not to miss even one step of the ritual the girl had attended so watchfully every morning of their stay at the Inn.

There was no letter for Agatha. Mrs. Logan was almost worried about Father Gregory. He had said that he would write seldom, not that he would not write at all, and this complete silence, on top of Agatha's childishness gave her a feeling of being lost and not a little foolish, as if she had been struggling with something in a dark room and had had the lights turned on to discover that she was alone and unassailed.

After the last letter had been put into its cubbyhole, and the young clerk had gone for his second breakfast, Mrs. Logan still sat in the wicker chair. She flipped her own letters with her right hand as though they were a deck of cards, and with this gesture she recalled, she experienced again, for a brief moment, the sunny calm of Agatha's room on that spring morning when she had first read through her daughter's letters from Father Gregory. Then she stood up quickly, and, putting the little stack of unopened envelopes into her knitting bag, she started off for the tennis court.

It was a gray, cool morning, with heavy, cottony clouds piling over one another and separating only occasionally to show a portion of brilliant blue sky, but never releasing any sunlight. It was a bad day for tennis, with sudden, sharp little winds traveling across the fields, carrying the smell of the harassed water of the lake. Mrs. Logan buttoned her loose coat up to her neck, tucked her blown hairs underneath one another, and wished that she had worn a hat.

The tennis courts lay in a slight hollow, and were further protected from the winds by the body of the woods that lay behind them. Only an occasional pack of leaves skimmed over the court and gathered in crackling clusters at the foot of the backboards.

Mrs. Logan could see, immediately, as she neared the court, that Agatha was playing well. Her opponent was a small woman, hardly bigger than a child, but plainly a woman, even from a distance. Her hair was almost hidden by a smartly wrapped white turban which completed perfectly the picture of compact, competent neatness she presented, as she snapped the ball up into her hand with the tip of her racquet. When Agatha waved to her mother, Mrs. Devlin nodded toward their visitor, but in such a way as to indicate quite definitely, that she did not care to stop for introductions, although she was prepared to be friendly afterward.

Johnny was standing at Agatha's end of the court, leaning against the netting, holding his book as if he had forgotten it, but with his finger still in its place. He wore an outgrown sweatshirt and jigged from one foot to the other occasionally and slapped at his bare legs as if he wanted to keep warm while wasting as little attention as possible on the task.

When he saw Mrs. Logan approaching, he came over and politely brushed the leaves from the rustic bench and offered it to her, but he did not speak either, assuming in a friendly way, that she shared his interest in the game and his unwillingness to interrupt tennis with conversation. He made no pretense at impartiality. He kept to Agatha's side of the court, occasionally retrieved a ball for her, and said, "Hey," every time she made a particularly good shot. Agatha acknowledged his tribute only occasionally, and then not so much with thanks as with an expression of shared admiration for some outside phenomenon.

Agatha was playing superb tennis. Mrs. Logan could hardly believe that she had improved so much in one month, even though she had been at it every day. She played as if she were very happy, but she was extremely polite to her opponent. She waited for her service until Mrs. Devlin was in perfect position and then even an extravagant portion of a minute after that.

Mrs. Devlin was a good tennis player. Her strokes were full and controlled, and after each error, she looked as if she had just learned something valuable. But she could do nothing with Agatha. Agatha covered the court as if it had contracted under her feet. Her strokes showed no effort at all. She swung her racquet as if that were the only possible way for her to handle it, and the course of the ball was beautiful and swift. She seemed to be choosing not only the place where the ball would land, but the kind of shot with which it would be returned. Her game seemed to her mother, not only more sure, but more devious than she had ever imagined Agatha playing, and yet there was no sign of thought or of concentration on her face. Each stroke seemed to be no more than the perfect expression of her high spirits. She hummed quietly to herself as she collected the balls after each play and she bounced one across the court, in cheerful staccatos, to the service line.

Mrs. Devlin was pleasant about her defeat. She appeared to be almost proud for Agatha as if she herself had taught the skill with which she had been confounded. Agatha, however, once she was off the court, seemed to lose both lightness and manners. She deprecated her victory in a most unconvincing and insincere voice, and then she went off to talk to Johnny about it, leaving the two women to manage their own introductions.

"I'm afraid Mr. Winn flattered me when he said your daughter and I were about equal."

"Well, she's been at it a lot this summer. Probably by the end of the week you'll be well ahead of her." At this, Mrs. Devlin smiled, as if she doubted that it would be worth the trouble, and then changed the subject with a disproportionate air of graciousness.

In the late afternoon, all at once, the sun came out boldly, and the sky that had been hidden all day was brilliantly, vigorously blue. It was too late in the day for the sunlight to give any real warmth, but the unexpected brightness at the end of the day was both cheering and stimulating, and people greeted one another in the lobby before dinner with gaiety and with spirit.

Mrs. Peters was full of conversation. How changeable the weather had been, how hard it was to know what to wear, how chilly she had been on their walk that morning. Then suddenly she stopped herself in the middle of a sentence and gave Mrs. Logan a sharp nudge.

"If that isn't the funniest thing. There's that Mrs. Devlin I was telling you about."

"Yes, I know. Agatha played tennis with her this morning."

"Did you really, Aggie? You *must* be good. I hear she's very good."

"Agatha is good. She beat her."

"I was good this morning, anyhow," Agatha answered with routine modesty. Mrs. Devlin was standing at the foot of the steps looking around the crowded hall. She looked at the people around her the way a mechanic looks at a rack of tools, eager and yet practical, with a selective and yet somehow belittling glance, knowing the tools are excellent and necessary of course but quite useless without the skillful, wielding hand.

She nodded to Agatha and Mrs. Logan smartly but not encouragingly as she walked across the room to the group whose company she had chosen. Agatha's answering nod parodied hers almost too obviously, and the girl seemed to be amused and pleased all over again by her victory that morning.

"I'm glad you beat her," said Mrs. Peters, after her eyes had returned to her own party from their pursuit of Mrs. Devlin across the room. "You can do it for me, three times a week, if you want to."

As soon as they had left the Peters to go into dinner, Agatha said, "It's going to be wonderful tonight. I'm perfectly sure of it. You will come with us, Mummy, won't you? Really you oughtn't to miss it."

"How do you get up on the roof? I never heard of anyone going up there."

"Clem knows how. He'll come and meet us here around half past nine or ten."

It was shortly after nine-thirty when Mrs. Logan noticed Clem standing in the doorway. It was startling to see him there. She had never seen him indoors before, nor fully dressed. She realized then that she had never before really seen him at all. Now his change of clothes and change of background, as well as her new information about him made her see him with abrupt clarity.

He was wearing a light linen suit and a white shirt with a pale tie. His skin looked even darker than it had out-of-doors, and his light eyes, out of the sunlight, were wider and more attractive. Mrs. Logan looked around to where Agatha was sitting to tell her that her friend had come, when she saw that Agatha had already seen him. Agatha must have known that he was looking for her and for Johnny, but she made no sign. She simply stared at him as he stood there, her cheeks red and her eyes fixed, as if she too found him strange, as if she were looking at some remarkable visitor whose wonder she must catalogue from a distance and memorize with no thought of any further intimacy.

But the entranced look broke sharply and disappeared as soon as Clem saw her, and she poked at Johnny to tell him that it was time for them to go. Then the three of them came over to Mrs. Logan.

"It's fine out tonight," Clem said. "I just got back from Tidenham." Clem's glance still roamed over the large room as he talked. That was one of the things that made him appear younger than he was. He had a boy's way, half shy and half insolent, of being unwilling to give his eye. But Mrs. Logan now saw that the light sun-bleached hair at his temples was partly gray.

"If you're ready," he said, "we could go up now. The moon's not down yet but it's pretty low by now."

"All right," said Mrs. Logan, "I'll just stop and pick up my coat." Just as she stood up, Mrs. Devlin came toward them.

"I hope I haven't kept you waiting," she said, smiling directly at Clem.

"Oh no, that's all right," he said. "Do you know Mrs. Logan? Mrs. Devlin."

"Yes. Oh, yes," both women said at once, and then Mrs. Devlin continued, "I'm sure we'll all freeze up there. Are you positive it's going to be worth while?"

Agatha and Johnny said nothing. Mrs. Devlin had obviously been asked to join them, and just as obviously neither of them had known anything about it. Mrs. Logan saw at once that Mrs. Devlin was one of those women who are transformed by a man's presence, by the knowledge of a man's eyes upon them, actually, physically, changed and enhanced by that knowledge. Her eyes were darker and more still than they had been in the morning. Her gestures were smaller, neither so rapid nor so imperative. Her voice was lower, rounder. Her stance was easier and she carried her narrow shoulders with a bony, female delicacy. But she still kept her air of conferring the favor of her presence, and her way of asking about the weather seemed to cast discredit on the whole expedition.

If Clem was aware of the change that he had worked in her, he gave no sign of his knowledge. After all, he had probably never seen her otherwise, and her manner was neither directly flirtatious nor coy. If he had conferred womanhood upon her, he was unaware of the gift. He seemed, in fact, to share Agatha's and Johnny's impatience at the delay, even to share their childlike impertinent indifference to the woman's accomplished charm. His eyes seemed to see her, as they saw her, tiny, ugly, positive and vaguely threatening. Still she was with them only because he had asked her, because he had wanted her to be with them.

Johnny and Agatha looked at her with the same grave and curious look, with the helpless disapproval and short charity of the young. Then at the same moment they looked away from her and at one another. And at that moment, in that look, Mrs. Logan suddenly understood what she had not been able to understand before: their puzzling, partial, untalkative friendliness, their all but silent interminable sitting together and practicing together. It was Clem they shared, Clem they loved and understood together, as an innocent like themselves. He looked at the guests, the prosperous sociable guests, with their own weary, agreeable distaste. He believed in the possible perfection of a strong accurate backhand and he understood, had presented to them, the miracle of the Northern Lights.

It was with the same glance that Agatha and Johnny looked at the intruder into their circle of innocence; and then, at once, Agatha and Johnny looked at Clem for corroboration and reassurance. Reassurance, at least for a little while, they quickly received.

"All right, let's get started then," Clem said, as he turned his back on the two women. Taking Agatha and Johnny each by an arm, he started off across the room; and neither one of them had ever wanted any more of him than that.

When Mrs. Logan and her daughter went to bed that night, there was little conversation between them. Agatha was preoccupied, hardly heard when she was spoken to, and Mrs. Logan undressed in silence, not bothering her daughter, but guarding and controlling her own joy which she would neither conquer nor refuse.

She busied herself with her face and with the waves in her hair while Agatha undressed, slowly, carefully. The silence between them was not forced nor uncomfortable. In fact Agatha was probably unaware of it. She had not recognized as quickly as her mother had, what had happened to her, what she had seen. She did not yet know the exact nature of the pain, of the strangeness that she felt. There was still time to take her away. If her mother were to mention the beach, Agatha might still be glad to come with her. Next week would surely be too late. By the next day, she might understand, name her feeling, and then she would not be willing to go away, but if Mrs. Logan were to suggest going to the beach now, it might seem like a gay prank. The suddenness would be distracting in itself.

"Let's leave right away, Agatha"; she rehearsed the speech silently to herself—"I'll phone Joe and we can be there late tomorrow night and wake up Thursday morning and have a swim before breakfast."

That was what she thought. Those were the words that she said brightly to herself as she lay in her bed in the darkness, next to her quiet but sleepless daughter. Why thought and tongue did not connect; why she was not actually saying the words aloud, she did not know. She was not a woman who prepared her speeches, planned her sentences, especially with her own child. But this sentence she heard, she felt it moving in her brain, and she did not say it.

Then the moment had passed; and, as she lay there wondering, with a delightfully detached sort of curiosity what defect in her will it was that had broken the circuit between thought and speech, she fell asleep. A sense of righteousness is not after all a necessary part of the sensation of happiness. The pleasure of victory is quite apart from the pleasure of justice, and conquest, ownership, is sweet in itself while it is new.

When she woke next morning, Agatha's bed was empty except for a paper pinned to the crushed pillow. The note, scrawled in a large hand, said, "Don't worry about me—I'm out catching early worms. See you at the lake."

The bright night had given way to a sparkling morning and as Mrs. Logan looked out at the streak of bright blue where the lake showed through the dark pines, at the farflung sweep of the cloudless sky, she felt once more in herself that brilliance of sensation, that bright liveliness of perception that must be recognized as happiness however much she begrudged herself the word. It proclaimed itself in rich, independent liveliness, in the renewed pace of her blood, in the brisk bravery of her glance.

She tried hard to realize Agatha's misery, but it could not seem large to her. She could understand it. It was not strange with the strangeness of the joy those letters had brought her. It was an unhappiness from which a young girl would quickly recover. They would leave the Inn pretty soon and it would not be many months before Clem and Mrs. Devlin were forgotten. The whole unpleasant little episode would have served its purposes—thwarted love might drive some girls into nunneries, but Agatha was not one of those, her mother was sure—and it would all be forgotten.

Agatha, as a matter of fact, would never even know that there had been anything unpleasant about it. She would be able to remember her first love with the customary affection. The whole episode was dignified, as it had been created, by the girl's innocence. If Agatha had recognized, even for a moment, Mrs. Devlin's shameless, skillful pursuit, she might have been angry or jealous of its success but she would never have been struck dumb and awkward as she had been. The idea of accomplishment never occurred to Agatha, however, in connection with Clem's sudden gaiety and roughened voice and finally his tender awakened hands on Mrs. Devlin's shoulders, as they all stood together under the weird, tossed curtain of the Northern Lights, beneath the pale, reaching, borderless green, more marvelous than the crowded stars, and stranger than the brightly plodding moon.

It was something that had happened, a visitation, and once it had happened for Mrs. Devlin, Agatha knew that it should have happened for her; that she, if she had not been so stupid and so dull and so young and so awkward, might have known this voice, known the marvelous hands. Agatha forgot at once what she had seen so clearly only an hour before, that Mrs. Devlin was old and ugly and positive. For her, in her despair, Mrs. Devlin became immediately the enchantress, beautified by her conquest.

Agatha had turned at once toward the stairs but Mrs. Logan would not follow.

"It's too beautiful, Aggie. I'm so glad I didn't miss it." She did not plan, as she had not planned, but she felt the vigor of victory, as if an old plan were being fulfilled and the banners of the aurora trembled hilariously across the broad sky.

The heavy wool of their coats snapped with muffled cracks in the night wind.

"Aren't you cold, in just that linen jacket, Mr. Winn?" she called gaily.

"No," he said. Her voice had traveled with the wind, his came against it.

The word sounded high and light, diluted by the wind. It seemed to be laughing.

"And you Johnny, what will your aunt have to say to me if you take cold?" she said then, but Agatha's eyes did not turn with hers to Johnny.

Either Johnny was less observant than Agatha or less transparent in his behavior. He kept asking technical questions about the lights, and seemed to take no notice of the success of Mrs. Devlin's wooing; but that was no further loss to Agatha. Her emotion was no longer to be shared, it needed no corroboration, no longer accepted companionship.

After Mrs. Logan read Agatha's note, she dressed quickly and went down to breakfast early. Not even when she caught sight of the mailbag being handed over to the clerk, was the prolonged exhilaration, which she now chose to credit to the fine weather, interrupted for a moment. She lingered over her breakfast, sat long at the table, engrossed in her morning paper, never once lifting her eyes toward that portion of the tier of mail boxes visible from her table, until the mail had all been assorted. Then she folded her paper carefully, left it on the table and walked out to look for Mrs. Peters on the porch, walking carefully, self-consciously managing her joy, the hilarity of safety newly won.

The mail was still uncalled for at noon when she stopped at the desk. The third letter on the pile was the one for Agatha, a long white envelope, addressed in the black, looping hand. She stared at it for a moment. Then she handed it back to the clerk.

"This is for my daughter," she said. "Will you please put it back so that she can see it when she comes through." She spoke pleasantly to the clerk, but at the sight of that envelope, her joy in conquest had left her.

In the dark heavily inked letters on the envelope, she had caught a minute glimpse of her daughter talking to Father Gregory, of Agatha's eyes brilliantly lighting on the long white envelope next to her plate at the breakfast table, and she knew that she had betrayed her child. Her accomplishment which had made her so proudly joyful suddenly appeared to her as wilful and malicious, a violation, an invasion. She saw it too plainly now. As suddenly, as independently as it had come, the physical sensation of happiness was gone and in its place, from that moment on, she carried a painful knowledge of herself.

While she walked with Mrs. Peters, she knew that she had been, as so many parents are when faced with the prospect of a child's escape, however glorious, unable to rest. She had been afraid of losing her of course, but that was not the worst of it. She knew, as she and Agatha faced one another through a hasty lunch, that there was something else she had been afraid of.

It was not as if she did not believe in the value of the life that Agatha wanted to prepare for. She did believe in it. The depth of that belief was made plain to her by the astounding emotion she had felt at the sight of Father Gregory's letter, her quick, shocking gratitude to learn that he at least had been faithful. She had nevertheless been unable to stand by and allow Agatha to seek out a life that was different from her own.

She did not see Agatha all afternoon. She would not allow herself to go to the tennis court, but sat on the porch or walked up and down her room, studying her own sense of wrong-doing, flagellating herself with exaggerated views of her own shamefulness. She had not, after all, really plotted to trap her daughter, in the sense that a person makes one plan who might have made another. She had simply fallen upon the instinctive practicality with which parents protect themselves against the vision they have lost or surrendered, deafen themselves lest they hear some disturbing tale of a horizon they can no longer see. She had never really had a decision to make.

Agatha did not call for the letter until the end of the afternoon, and then Mrs. Logan saw her put it into her bureau drawer unopened, when she came up to dress for dinner.

"Johnny wants me to go to the movies with him tonight. His aunt said she'd send us in the car. Do you mind?" Agatha asked.

"Not at all. Have a good time," she said pleasantly, but Agatha had turned on the shower with a noisy rush, and waved as she stepped through the curtain to show that she would wait for her answer until she had finished her shower. Mrs. Logan could learn nothing from her voice or from her expression to help her to interpret this mild request.

Mrs. Devlin did not come in to her table at dinner time, and although Agatha talked a great deal, Mrs. Logan saw her daughter's eyes once more constantly turning away from her, as they had when she had first watched the lethargic mail clerk at breakfast time. Now however, they traveled a new course from the door to the table where Mrs. Devlin's young son was eating alone, and back to the door again.

That night, after they had been lying in bed with the lights out for a while, Mrs. Logan could no longer bear her own painful, uncertain listening. She had to speak, to win the girl's voice in response, since that voice, level and uncommunicative as it was, would still tell more than the pale whispering sound of her regular breathing.

"What are you thinking about, Aggie?" she asked.

"I was thinking about the ocean, and how I used to listen to the waves when I was lying in bed," Agatha answered, obligingly. "You know I used to think I could tell what kind of a wave it was—you know, what shape and how high and all that, and how it would break—just from the sound."

Mrs. Logan did not answer. Her heart beat with violent large beats.

"Couldn't we go there for a while, Mum? It wouldn't be too hard to open the house, would it? We wouldn't even have to get anyone, we could do the work ourselves. I'd do most of it, and it would be fun that way, just the two of us for a couple of weeks."

So it was not too late. The treachery which she had carried so heavily all day was not a thing complete and irrevocable. There was still a chance. The treachery which she had named and weighed to her dismay, all through that long afternoon, could still be undone.

"I suppose you'd cook, too," she said.

"Well, you like to cook, you know, if someone helps and cleans up. I'd do all the dirty work." Agatha advanced these arguments, but her voice was not insistent. She appeared to be coaxing herself as much as her mother.

"Oh, Aggie, it's such a short time left," Mrs. Logan said, slowly, thoughtfully. "It'll be getting cold in a couple of weeks." This time Agatha did not answer right away. Her argument was sparse as her desire was weak. She seemed to have given up the idea already.

"We could have had fires. That's the best fireplace in the world down there, you know," she said after a minute or two.

"I might have been willing at that," Mrs. Logan continued, picking up the girl's past tense, "if it weren't that the Peters' Alice and her husband are coming next week, and after she's talked about them so long, it seems awfully mean to go away just when they're coming."

"I guess it would be silly, wouldn't it?"

"Very silly," Mrs. Logan said without too much emphasis, and as she heard her daughter roll over into a sleeping position—abandoning the argument, giving up all thought of the beach—she once more felt her body filled with the sensations of joy, her veins flooded with delight.

Too Early Spring

STEPHEN VINCENT BENÉT

I'M WRITING this down because I don't ever want to forget the way it was. It doesn't seem as if I could, now, but they all tell you things change. And I guess they're right. Older people must have forgotten or they couldn't be the way they are. And that goes for even the best ones, like Dad and Mr. Grant. They try to understand but they don't seem to know how. And the others make you feel dirty or else they make you feel like a goof. Till, pretty soon, you begin to forget yourself—you begin to think, "Well, maybe they're right and it was that way." And that's the end of everything. So I've got to write this down. Because they smashed it forever —but it wasn't the way they said.

Mr. Grant always says in comp. class: "Begin at the beginning." Only I don't know quite where the beginning was. We had a good summer at Big Lake but it was just the same summer. I worked pretty hard at the practice basket I rigged up in the barn, and I learned how to do the back jackknife. I'll never dive like Kerry but you want to be as all-around as you can. And, when I took my measurements, at the end of the summer, I was 5 ft. 9¾ and I'd gained 12 lbs. 6 oz. That isn't bad for going on sixteen and the old chest expansion was O. K. You don't want to get too heavy, because basketball's a fast game, but the year before was the year when I got my height, and I was so skinny, I got tired. But this year, Kerry helped me practice, a couple of times, and he seemed to think I had a good chance for the team. So I felt pretty set up—they'd never had a Sophomore on it before. And Kerry's a natural athlete, so that means a lot from him. He's a pretty good brother too. Most Juniors at State wouldn't bother with a fellow in High.

It sounds as if I were trying to run away from what I have to write down, but I'm not. I want to remember that summer, too, because it's the last happy one I'll ever have. Oh, when I'm an old man—thirty or forty—things may be all right again. But that's a long time to wait and it won't be the same.

And yet, that summer was different, too, in a way. So it must have started then, though I didn't know it. I went around with the gang as usual and we had a good time. But, every now and then, it would strike me we were acting like awful kids. They thought I was getting the big head, but I wasn't. It just wasn't much fun—even going to the cave. It was like going on shooting marbles when you're in High.

I had sense enough not to try to tag after Kerry and his crowd. You can't do that. But when they all got out on the lake in canoes, warm evenings, and somebody brought a phonograph along, I used to go down to the Point, all by myself, and listen and listen. Maybe they'd be talking or maybe they'd be singing, but it all sounded mysterious across the water. I wasn't trying to hear what they said, you know. That's the kind of thing Tot Pickens does. I'd just listen, with my arms around my knees—and somehow it would hurt me to listen—and yet I'd rather do that than be with the gang.

I was sitting under the four pines, one night, right down by the edge of the water. There was a big moon and they were singing. It's funny how you can be unhappy and nobody know it but yourself.

I was thinking about Sheila Coe. She's Kerry's girl. They fight but they get along. She's awfully pretty and she can swim like a fool. Once Kerry sent me over with her tennis racket and we had quite a conversation. She was fine. And she didn't pull any of this big sister stuff, either, the way some girls will with a fellow's kid brother.

And when the canoe came along, by the edge of the lake, I thought for a moment it was her. I thought maybe she was looking for Kerry and maybe she'd stop and maybe she'd feel like talking to me again. I don't know why I thought that—I didn't have any reason. Then I saw it was just the Sharon kid, with a new kind of bob that made her look grown-up, and I felt sore. She didn't have any business out on the lake at her age. She was just a Sophomore in High, the same as me.

I chunked a stone in the water and it splashed right by the canoe, but she didn't squeal. She just said, "Fish," and chuckled. It struck me it was a kid's trick, trying to scare a kid.

"Hello, Helen," I said. "Where did you swipe the gunboat?"

"They don't know I've got it," she said. "Oh, hello, Chuck Peters. How's Big Lake?"

"All right," I said. "How was camp?"

"It was peachy," she said. "We had a peachy counselor, Miss Morgan. She was on the Wellesley field-hockey team."

"Well," I said, "we missed your society." Of course we hadn't, because they're across the lake and don't swim at our raft. But you ought to be polite.

"Thanks," she said. "Did you do the special reading for English? I thought it was dumb."

"It's always dumb," I said. "What canoe is that?"

"It's the old one," she said. "I'm not supposed to have it out at night. But you won't tell anybody, will you."

"Be your age," I said. I felt generous. "I'll paddle awhile, if you want," I said.

"All right," she said, so she brought it in and I got aboard. She went back in the bow and I took the paddle. I'm not strong on carting kids around, as a rule. But it was better than sitting there by myself.

"Where do you want to go?" I said.

"Oh, back towards the house," she said in a shy kind of voice. "I ought to, really. I just wanted to hear the singing."

"K. O.," I said. I didn't paddle fast, just let her slip. There was a lot of moon on the water. We kept around the edge so they wouldn't notice us. The singing sounded as if it came from a different country, a long way off.

She was a sensible kid, she didn't ask fool questions or giggle about nothing at all. Even when we went by Petters' Cove. That's where the lads from the bungalow colony go and it's pretty well populated on a warm night. You can hear them talking in low voices and now and then a laugh. Once Tot Pickens and a gang went over there with a flashlight, and a big Bohunk chased them for half a mile.

I felt funny, going by there with her. But I said, "Well, it's certainly Old Home Week"—in an offhand tone, because, after all, you've got to be sophisticated. And she said, "People are funny," in just the right sort of way. I took quite a shine to her after that and we talked. The Sharons have only been in town three years and somehow I'd never really noticed her before. Mrs. Sharon's awfully good-looking but she and Mr. Sharon fight. That's hard on a kid. And she was a quiet kid. She had a small kind of face and her eyes were sort of like a kitten's. You could see she got a great kick out of pretending to be grown-up—and yet it wasn't all pretending. A couple of times, I felt just as if I were talking to Sheila Coe. Only more comfortable, because, after all, we were the same age.

Do you know, after we put the canoe up, I walked all the way back home, around the lake? And most of the way, I ran. I felt swell too. I felt as if I could run forever and not stop. It was like finding something. I hadn't imagined anybody could ever feel the way I did about some things. And here was another person, even if it was a girl.

Kerry's door was open when I went by and he stuck his head out, and grinned.

"Well, kid," he said. "Stepping out?"

"Sure. With Greta Garbo," I said, and grinned back to show I didn't mean it. I felt sort of lightheaded, with the run and everything.

"Look here, kid—" he said, as if he was going to say something. Then he stopped. But there was a funny look on his face.

And yet I didn't see her again till we were both back in High. Mr. Sharon's uncle died, back East, and they closed the cottage suddenly. But all the rest of the time at Big Lake, I kept remembering that night and her little face. If I'd seen her in daylight, first, it might have been different. No, it wouldn't have been.

All the same, I wasn't even thinking of her when we bumped into each other, the first day of school. It was raining and she had on a green slicker and her hair was curly under her hat. We grinned and said hello and had to run. But something happened to us, I guess.

I'll say this now—it wasn't like Tot Pickens and Mable Palmer. It wasn't like Junior David and Betty Page—though they've been going together ever since kindergarten. It wasn't like any of those things. We didn't get sticky and sloppy. It wasn't like going with a girl.

Gosh, there'd be days and days when we'd hardly see each other, except in class. I had basketball practice almost every afternoon and sometimes evenings and she was taking music lessons four times a week. But you don't have to be always twos-ing with a person, if you feel that way about them. You seem to know the way they're thinking and feeling, the way you know yourself.

Now let me describe her. She had that little face and the eyes like a kitten's. When it rained, her hair curled all over the back of her neck. Her hair was yellow. She wasn't a tall girl but she wasn't chunky—just light and well made and quick. She was awfully alive without being nervous—she never bit her fingernails or chewed the end of her pencil, but she'd answer quicker than anyone in the class. Nearly everybody liked her, but she wasn't best friends with any particular girl, the mushy way they get. The teachers all thought a lot of her, even Miss Eagles. Well, I had to spoil that.

If we'd been like Tot and Mabel, we could have had a lot more time together, I guess. But Helen isn't a liar and I'm not a snake. It wasn't easy, going over to her house, because Mr. and Mrs. Sharon would be polite to each other in front of you and yet there'd be something wrong. And she'd have to be fair to both of them and they were always pulling at her.

But we'd look at each other across the table and then it would be all right.

I don't know when it was that we knew we'd get married to each other, some time. We just started talking about it, one day, as if we always had. We were sensible, we knew it couldn't happen right off. We thought maybe when we were eighteen. That was two years but we knew we had to be educated. You don't get as good a job, if you aren't. Or that's what people say.

We weren't mushy either, like some people. We got to kissing each other good-by, sometimes, because that's what you do when you're in love. It was cool, the way she kissed you, it was like leaves. But lots of the time we wouldn't even talk about getting married, we'd just play checkers or go over the old Latin, or once in a while go to the movies with the gang. It was really a wonderful winter. I played every game after the first one and she'd sit in the gallery and watch and I'd know she was there. You could see her little green hat or her yellow hair. Those are the class colors, green and gold.

And it's a queer thing, but everybody seemed to be pleased. That's what I can't get over. They liked to see us together. The grown people, I mean. Oh, of course, we got kidded too. And old Mrs. Withers would ask me about "my little sweetheart," in that awful damp voice of hers. But, mostly, they were all right. Even Mother was all right, though she didn't like Mrs. Sharon. I did hear her say to Father, once, "Really, George, how long is this going to last? Sometimes I feel as if I just couldn't stand it."

Then Father chuckled and said to her, "Now, Mary, last year you were worried about him because he didn't take any interest in girls at all."

"Well," she said, "he still doesn't. Oh, Helen's a nice child—no credit to Eva Sharon—and thank heaven she doesn't giggle. Well, Charles is mature for *his* age too. But he acts so solemn about her. It isn't natural."

"Oh, let Charlie alone," said Father. "The boy's all right. He's just got a one-track mind."

But it wasn't so nice for us after the spring came.

In our part of the state, it comes pretty late, as a rule. But it was early this year. The little kids were out with scooters when usually they'd still be having snowfights and, all of a sudden, the radiators in the classrooms smelt dry. You'd got used to that smell for months—and then, there was a day when you hated it again and everybody kept asking to open the windows. The monitors had a tough time, that first week—they always do when spring starts—but this year it was worse than ever because it came when you didn't expect it.

Usually, basketball's over by the time spring really breaks, but this year it hit us while we still had three games to play. And it certainly played hell with us as a team. After Bladesburg nearly licked us, Mr. Grant called off all practice till the day before the St. Matthew's game. He knew we were stale—and they've been state champions two years. They'd have walked all over us, the way we were going.

The first thing I did was telephone Helen. Because that meant there were six extra afternoons we could have, if she could get rid of her music lessons any way. Well, she said, wasn't it wonderful, her music teacher had a cold? And that seemed just like Fate.

Well, that was a great week and we were so happy. We went to the movies five times and once Mrs. Sharon let us take her little car. She knew I didn't have a driving license but of course I've driven ever since I was thirteen and she said it was all right. She was funny—sometimes she'd be awfully kind and friendly to you and sometimes she'd be like a piece of dry ice. She was that way with Mr. Sharon too. But it was a wonderful ride. We got stuff out of the kitchen—the cook's awfully sold on Helen—and drove way out in the country. And we found an old house, with the windows gone, on top of a hill, and parked the car and took the stuff up to the house and ate it there. There weren't any chairs or tables but we pretended there were.

We pretended it was our house, after we were married. I'll never forget that. She'd even brought paper napkins and paper plates and she set two places on the floor.

"Well, Charles," she said, sitting opposite me, with her feet tucked under, "I don't suppose you remember the days we were both in school."

"Sure," I said—she was always much quicker pretending things than I was—"I remember them all right. That was before Tot Pickens got to be President." And we both laughed.

"It seems very distant in the past to me—we've been married so long," she said, as if she really believed it. She looked at me.

"Would you mind turning off the radio, dear?" she said. "This modern music always gets on my nerves."

"Have we got a radio?" I said.

"Of course, Chuck."

"With television?"

"Of course, Chuck."

"Gee, I'm glad," I said. I went and turned it off.

"Of course, if you *want* to listen to the late market reports—" she said just like Mrs. Sharon.

"Nope," I said. "The market—uh—closed firm today. Up twenty-six points."

"That's quite a long way up, isn't it?"

"Well, the country's perfectly sound at heart, in spite of this damn-fool Congress," I said, like Father.

She lowered her eyes a minute, just like her mother, and pushed away her plate.

"I'm not very hungry tonight," she said. "You won't mind if I go upstairs?"

"Aw, don't be like that," I said. It was too much like her mother.

"I was just seeing if I could," she said. "But I never will, Chuck."

"I'll never tell you you're nervous, either," I said. "I—oh, gosh!"

She grinned and it was all right. "Mr. Ashland and I have never had a serious dispute in our wedded lives," she said—and everybody knows who runs *that* family. "We just talk things over calmly and reach a satisfactory conclusion, usually mine."

"Say, what kind of house have we got?"

"It's a lovely house," she said. "We've got radios in every room and lots of servants. We've got a regular movie projector and a library full of good classics and there's always something in the icebox. I've got a shoe closet."

"A what?"

"A shoe closet. All my shoes are on tipped shelves, like Mother's. And all my dresses are on those padded hangers. And I say to the maid, 'Elise, Madam will wear the new French model today.' "

"What are my clothes on?" I said. "Christmas trees?"

"Well," she said. "You've got lots of clothes and dogs. You smell of pipes and the open and something called Harrisburg tweed."

"I do not," I said. "I wish I had a dog. It's a long time since Jack."

"Oh, Chuck, I'm sorry," she said.

"Oh, that's all right," I said. "He was getting old and his ear was always bothering him. But he was a good pooch. Go ahead."

"Well," she said, "of course we give parties—"

"Cut the parties," I said.

"Chuck! They're grand ones!"

"I'm a homebody," I said. "Give me—er—my wife and my little family and—say, how many kids have we got, anyway?"

She counted on her fingers. "Seven."

"Good Lord," I said.

"Well, I always wanted seven. You can make it three, if you like."

"Oh, seven's all right, I suppose," I said. "But don't they get awfully in the way?"

"No," she said. "We have governesses and tutors and send them to boarding school."

"O. K.," I said. "But it's a strain on the old man's pocketbook, just the same."

"Chuck, will you ever talk like that? Chuck, this is when we're rich." Then suddenly, she looked sad. "Oh, Chuck, do you suppose we ever will?" she said.

"Why, sure," I said.

"I wouldn't mind if it was only a dump," she said. "I could cook for you. I keep asking Hilda how she makes things."

I felt awfully funny. I felt as if I were going to cry.

"We'll do it," I said. "Don't you worry."

"Oh, Chuck, you're a comfort," she said.

I held her for a while. It was like holding something awfully precious. It wasn't mushy or that way. I know what that's like too.

"It takes so long to get old," she said. "I wish I could grow up tomorrow. I wish we both could."

"Don't you worry," I said. "It's going to be all right."

We didn't say much, going back in the car, but we were happy enough. I thought we passed Miss Eagles at the turn. That worried me a little because of the driving license. But, after all, Mrs. Sharon had said we could take the car.

We wanted to go back again, after that, but it was too far to walk and that was the only time we had the car. Mrs. Sharon was awfully nice about it but she said, thinking it over, maybe we'd better wait till I got a license. Well, Father didn't want me to get one till I was seventeen but I thought he might come around. I didn't want to do anything that would get Helen in a jam with her family. That shows how careful I was of her. Or thought I was.

All the same, we decided we'd do something to celebrate if the team won the St. Matthew's game. We thought it would be fun if we could get a steak and cook supper out somewhere—something like that. Of course we could have done it easily enough with a gang, but we didn't want a gang. We wanted to be alone together, the way we'd been at the house. That was all we wanted. I don't see what's wrong about that. We even took home the paper plates, so as not to litter things up.

Boy, that was a game! We beat them 36-34 and it took an extra period and I thought it would never end. That two-goal lead they had looked as big as the Rocky Mountains all the first half. And they gave me the full school cheer with nine Peters when we tied them up. You don't forget things like that.

Afterwards, Mr. Grant had a kind of spread for the team at his house and a lot of people came in. Kerry had driven down from State to see the game and that made me feel pretty swell. And what made me feel better yet was his taking me aside and saying, "Listen, kid, I don't want you to get the swelled head, but you did a good job. Well, just remember this. Don't let anybody kid you out of going to State. You'll like it up there." And Mr. Grant heard him and laughed and said, "Well, Peters, I'm not proselytizing. But your brother might think about some of the Eastern colleges." It was all like the kind of dream you have when you can do anything. It was wonderful.

Only Helen wasn't there because the only girls were older girls. I'd seen her for a minute, right after the game, and she was fine, but it was only a minute. I wanted to tell her about that big St. Matthew's forward and—oh, everything. Well, you like to talk things over with your girl.

Father and Mother were swell but they had to go on to some big shindig at the country club. And Kerry was going there with Sheila Coe. But Mr. Grant said he'd run me back to the house in his car and he did. He's a great guy. He made jokes about my being the infant phenomenon of basketball, and they were good jokes too. I didn't mind them. But, all the same, when I'd said good night to him and gone into the house, I felt sort of let down.

I knew I'd be tired the next day but I didn't feel sleepy yet. I was too excited. I wanted to talk to somebody. I wandered around downstairs and wondered if Ida was still up. Well, she wasn't, but she'd left half a chocolate cake, covered over, on the kitchen table, and a note on top of it, "Congratulations to Mister Charles Peters." Well, that was awfully nice of her and I ate some. Then I turned the radio on and got the time signal—eleven—and some snappy music. But still I didn't feel like hitting the hay.

So I thought I'd call up Helen and then I thought—probably she's asleep and Hilda or Mrs. Sharon will answer the phone and be sore. And then I thought—well, anyhow, I could go over and walk around the block and look at her house. I'd get some fresh air out of it, anyway, and it would be a little like seeing her.

So I did—and it was a swell night—cool and a lot of stars—and I felt like a king, walking over. All the lower part of the Sharon house was dark but a window upstairs was lit. I knew it was her window. I went around back of the driveway and whistled once—the whistle we made up. I never expected her to hear.

But she did, and there she was at the window, smiling. She made motions that she'd come down to the side door.

Honestly, it took my breath away when I saw her. She had on a kind of yellow thing over her night clothes and she looked so pretty. Her feet were so pretty in those slippers. You almost expected her to be carrying one of those animals kids like—she looked young enough. I know I oughtn't to have gone into the house. But we didn't think anything about it—we were just glad to see each other. We hadn't had any sort of chance to talk over the game.

We sat in front of the fire in the living room and she went out to the kitchen and got us cookies and milk. I wasn't really hungry, but it was like that time at the house, eating with her. Mr. and Mrs. Sharon were at the country club, too, so we weren't disturbing them or anything. We turned off the lights because there was plenty of light from the fire and Mr. Sharon's one of those people who can't stand having extra lights burning. Dad's that way about saving string.

It was quiet and lovely and the firelight made shadows on the ceiling. We talked a lot and then we just sat, each of us knowing the other was there. And the room got quieter and quieter and I'd told her about the game and I didn't feel excited or jumpy any more—just rested and happy. And then I knew by her breathing that she was asleep and I put my arm around her for just a minute. Because it was wonderful to hear that quiet breathing and know it was hers. I was going to wake her in a minute. I didn't realize how tired I was myself.

And then we were back in that house in the country and it was our home and we ought to have been happy. But something was wrong because there still wasn't any glass in the windows and a wind kept blowing through them and we tried to shut the doors but they wouldn't shut. It drove Helen distracted and we were both running through the house, trying to shut the doors, and we were cold and afraid. Then the sun rose outside the windows, burning and yellow and so big it covered the sky. And with the sun was a horrible, weeping voice. It was Mrs. Sharon's saying, "Oh, my God, oh my God."

I didn't know what had happened, for a minute, when I woke. And then I did and it was awful. Mrs. Sharon was saying "Oh, Helen—I trusted you . . ." and looking as if she were going to faint. And Mr. Sharon looked at her for a minute and his face was horrible and he said, "Bred in the bone," and she looked as if he'd hit her. Then he said to Helen—

I don't want to think of what they said, I don't want to think of any of the things they said. Mr. Sharon is a bad man. And she is a bad woman, even if she is Helen's mother. All the same, I could stand the things he said better than hers.

I don't want to think of any of it. And it is all spoiled now. Everything is spoiled. Miss Eagles saw us going to that house in the country and she said horrible things. They made Helen sick and she hasn't been back at school. There isn't any way I can see her. And if I could, it would be spoiled. We'd be thinking about the things they said.

I don't know how many of the people know, at school. But Tot Pickens passed me a note. And, that afternoon, I caught him behind his house. I'd have broken his nose if they hadn't pulled me off. I meant to. Mother cried when she heard about it and Dad took me into his room and talked to me. He said you can't lick the whole town. But I will anybody like Tot Pickens. Dad and Mother have been all right. But they say things about Helen and that's almost worse. They're for me because I'm their son. But they don't understand.

I thought I could talk to Kerry but I can't. He was nice but he looked at me such a funny way. I don't know—sort of impressed. It wasn't the way I wanted him to look. But he's been decent. He comes down almost every weekend and we play catch in the yard.

You see, I just go to school and back now. They want me to go with the gang, the way I did, but I can't do that. Not after Tot. Of course my marks are a lot better because I've got more time to study now. But it's lucky I haven't got Miss Eagles though Dad made her apologize. I couldn't recite to her.

I think Mr. Grant knows because he asked me to his house once and we had a conversation. Not about that, though I was terribly afraid he would. He showed me a lot of his old college things and the gold football he wears on his watch chain. He's got a lot of interesting things.

Then we got talking, somehow, about history and things like that and how times had changed. Why, there were kings and queens who got married younger than Helen and me. Only now we lived longer and had a lot more to learn. So it couldn't happen now. "It's civilization," he said. "And all civilization's against nature. But I suppose we've got to have it. Only sometimes it isn't easy." Well somehow or other, that made me feel less lonely. Before that I'd been feeling that I was the only person on earth who'd ever felt that way.

I'm going to Colorado, this summer, to a ranch, and next year I'll go East to school. Mr. Grant says he thinks I can make the basketball team, if I work hard enough, though it isn't as big a game in the East as it is with us. Well, I'd like to show them something. It would be some satisfaction. He says not to be too fresh at first, but I won't be that.

It's a boy's school and there aren't even women teachers. And, maybe, afterwards, I could be a professional basketball player or something, where you don't have to see women at all. Kerry says I'll get over that; but I won't. They all sound like Mrs. Sharon to me now, when they laugh.

They're going to send Helen to a convent—I found out that. Maybe they'll let me see her before she goes. But, if we do, it will be all wrong and in front of people and everybody pretending. I sort of wish they don't—though I want to, terribly. When her mother took her upstairs that night—she wasn't the same Helen. She looked at me as if she was afraid of me. And no matter what they do for us now, they can't fix that.

Sunset at Sixteen

DOROTHY CANFIELD

THEY WERE the same old couple Trigger had seen in the dining room of the hotel. She knew them the minute she swung herself up, panting, to the other end of the ledge where they were sitting. It was cold, now the sun was so low over there beyond the lake, and they had on coats and scarfs and hats—all the hateful junk old people pile on when they go outdoors. They looked different, but she recognized their faces—those wrinkled faces with the dead-looking skin, and their gray dead-looking hair, and their withered hands with the ridged brittle fingernails. Collapsing for a moment to get her breath, at the far end of the ledge, Trigger remembered sickly that other withered, horribly soft old hand with the ridged fingernails which had been laid on hers in the room where that almost imperceptible, that overpowering, that horrible smell. . . .

Yet Great-Great-Aunt Henrietta had had a nurse, a starched white-linen nurse who did little but wash and clean and brush and bathe and powder her old patient, and dust and sweep and polish the determinedly cheery-looking sickroom. There had been flowers there the day Trigger had been taken to see her great-grandmother's sister, red velvet roses pouring their perfume into the air. When Trigger and her mother had first gone in, the room had smelled only of soap and flowers and disinfectants. Trigger had walked forward, trustingly, unsuspecting, to the big bed. She had been tall at twelve, tall enough to look down on it.

The figure in it had moved, the dried-parchment face creasing into a million-wrinkled smile, the old woman had shifted her position and laid her hand on Trigger's—and from the stirred bedclothes, from the old body, from the rotten-soft flesh of the old hand that held hers, had come faint, invisible wave upon wave of that horrible smell.

The child, transfixed, her startled eyes wide and set, had needed no one to tell her what it was. Every fibre in her body knew that it was the smell of death—and every fibre recoiled in indignant horror. She had stood perfectly still, not moving so much as an eyelash, gazing fixedly down at the old woman and seeing now how much of her was already dead—the lifeless white hair, the parchment-dry skin, those fingernails ridged and brittle, —they had died. They were already dead, and rotting with this faint dreadful odor of decay, which was an unbearable indignity to the blossoming life in the tall child.

Around her, people had said things, the usual things. "She looks as Peggy did." "Something about the forehead like Gerland's family." Trigger's ears had heard nothing. All her being was focused in burning resentment at the extravagance of death's presumption in entering *her* presence. That odor of decay in *her* nostrils—it was an unforgivable affront. Immortal that she was, what had she to do with death?

She had been twelve then, she was sixteen now, four inches taller, older by an eternity. And after the week, four years ago, of pallor and nausea and starvation, inexplicable to her parents, during which her body washed itself clean from that affront, she never thought of the unclean old age that had been half death—except sometimes with a passing qualm when she smelled red roses dying in their vase, or saw other old people, like these two who had been eating their supper together in the rough wooden room when Trigger and the girls from her camp had come cantering in on their long bare legs, steaming hot with youth and vitality and the stiff climb up the mountain.

After that one look as she passed, she had paid no attention to them. She had gone on yelling, and laughing, and screeching with the other girls as they clattered to their places. She had fallen on her hot soup with a scream of joy like that of her neighbors on each side. But far under this fine lusty zest, was the imprint on her vision of the old woman's dry, gray hair, the deep wrinkles in the back of the old man's neck, in his forehead. The clean, cool, mountain room smelled only of wood-smoke, coffee and fresh wood. But, faint and sickening, there came to her nostrils the memory of another odor. She bent her head low to her plate, spooning up the soup fast, and when she had swallowed it all, greedily, she wiped her mouth with the back of her hand.

"Shaggsy'd skin you alive if she saw you do that," said the girl next to her.

Trigger did not hear her. Those two with their sparse lifeless hair and leathery skin were not really old like the great-great-aunt. She had only just passed her sixteenth birthday, but she knew enough to know that they were only old like her grandparents, or like the principal of her school, sixty years old perhaps, but quite old enough to be partly dead—hair and skin and fingernails all ready for the coffin—how she hated, hated the way old people looked! How she hated, hated, hated the incredible idea that she would ever look like that.

The soup plates were taken away, and while they waited for the next round of food, they sang—the counsellor in charge of this outing was a great believer in "keeping things going." They sang a Mozart song which the music counsellor at camp had made them learn, and then "The Man with the Mandolin," which nobody had suggested their learning. And then ruddy-brown slabs of roast beef came and heaps of mashed potato and thick cups of coffee (they were allowed coffee out on hikes away from camp), the knives and forks began to rattle, the voices died down.

Across the room the gray-haired couple pushed away from the table and went out. But Trigger did not see them. She had forgotten them. She had gone back to thinking of what she was always thinking of—that she would never see him again, that she never wanted to see him again—that she would die if she didn't see him again, looking at her out of those deep eyes—how could she *not,* when there was—was something between them that could never be broken, never, never, no, not if they never saw each other again, no, not though all the continent lay between—although it was really only half the continent, since he lived in Minneapolis, not in San Francisco.

They *were* something to each other, she thought with passion, something that nobody else could ever be to either one of them. Something had happened to them—to them together, that was different from anything else that ever could happen—and *they* were different from that minute on, changed to the bone, to the marrow, colored all through a new color. How wonderful it was that he wasn't one of the home boys she'd have to go on seeing. After, after that moment they had lived through, together, it would be too dreadful to *see* him again, to have to go to class with him, or—how could she go on living if she did not see him tomorrow, today, this hour!

She had emptied her plate, passed it back, hungrily, for more roast beef and joined the chorus shouting out "Lilacs in the Rain," looking around her at the round, smooth, girls' faces, glowing with youth, at the tousled, wind-roughened hair anointed with youngness. What kids they were, she thought, You could tell by looking at them that they had never been shaken as she had been shaken—as a dog shakes a rat.

The pale slabs of ice cream were there, the wedges of cake. Talk rose with a clatter like a Niagara of breaking dishes.

"I would not either, I tell you! He's just a drip!"

"Oh go on! You never! Forty-fifteen! I don't believe it!"

"There was I all gussied up, and waiting for the telephone to ring, and he. . . ."

"To do a decent swan, you gotta get up in the *air*! That lousy old diving board's too slimsy! It ought to be. . . ."

Trigger ate her ice cream in silence, deaf to the pandemonium around her, passively obeying that inexorable law of her being which, once she thought of him, made her live all through it again, day by day, from the first time she had seen him, just as it had happened.

By the time dessert was eaten he had come to visit her cousin, her cousin had brought him to the rehearsal of the junior play and he had looked up at her on the stage—her heart turned over!

The troop of girls were clattering out now, the long, bare, bramble-scratched legs moving sluggishly. Trigger was once more seeing for the first time the red-brown lights in his eyes when he stood near one of the big flood lamps.

On the porch of the hotel, the counsellor struck her hands together hard and shouted like a train-announcer in a station, "All out to see the sunset. Everybody out to see the sunset."

The girls cried, "Oh gosh! Do we have to climb clear up on that old rock *every* year? Why can't we. . . ."

"Aw, Shaggsy now, let us just roost around here. My legs are ready to drop off."

But Shaggsy was firm. They always went up on top of Hurricane Rock to see the sunset when they came on this hike: there was no reason to change, this year. Trigger floated dreamily with the current, as the girls trudged down the wooden steps of the porch and set off along the rocky moss-grown trail. She was thinking that she had been only fifteen when it happened—just think, only three months ago! She had been a kid, a child, like these girls shoving and pushing their way forward around her on the trail. Now she was sixteen—but it was not with her birthday that she had grown up, it was when. . . .

She walked more and more slowly. The others passed her, whooping back and forth, she was alone in the green tunnel of the trail; the thick green of the spruce-trees dwarfed by the altitude, shut her off from the world. She was back on the stage at school, rehearsing her part, the coach shouting at her, the others standing close to her—and far off, down on the floor of the deserted assembly room he stood, intently watching. And when their eyes met it was as though nobody else was there—she walked more slowly yet, her heart beginning to pound as though she were hurrying. The trail was now rocky and steep, her feet took her up with no thought from her, for she was back on that stage—they had hardly said a word to each other, all those two weeks he had been in town, hardly really spoken to each other, not in words, that is. They had hardly even touched each other till—except by their plunging pulses and that dizzy swimming of their eyes. . . .

She was climbing now, although she had no idea what she was doing, her strong tennis-playing, basketball-throwing arms were hauling her up, ledge by ledge; she was panting, she was hardly breathing at all, her heart was fluttering against its bars—it almost stopped. She leaned faintly against the face of the rock and went through it again, living and dying. . . .

It was the day he was going away back to his home. This was the last time he would be there. It was the last time she had seen him. He had looked at her all the time, during the rehearsal. At the end, the others had gone on out into the corridor. He stood below on the floor looking up at her on the platform, and said in a low hurried voice, "Jump!"

He had held out his arms, and she had jumped. And for a moment he had held her.

Leaning now against the rock, her face very white, she shut her eyes and closed her hand around a sharp projection of the ledge, hard, hard, *hard,* with all her might—as she would hold hard, hard, with all her might in a like rending of pain and glory, years later when her first child was born.

Behind her shut lids she was gazing once more deep into his eyes, at last so close to hers, so close that she was lost in them. They were as wide, as startled, as terrified as hers. She was fifteen and he was sixteen, but they needed no one to tell them what it was that held them there, shaking them as a dog shakes a rat—it was life. Thunder rolled in their ears, a jagged lightning bolt struck down clean through their vitals, they clung to each other, not in love—in terror—lest they should fall.

She who had been so alive, alive, that the very presence of death in the same room with her was an indignity—she knew, that instant, in his arms, that she had never lived at all, she had been wrapped in a cocoon—she had not yet been born.

From high on the cliff above, they shouted down, the girls who had clambered on ahead, they shouted and peered and tried to see her in the thicket of green. "Trigger! T-r-r-r-igger! Are you dead or something?" they called, and, "Shaggsy'll be in your hair if you don't step on the gas."

She came to herself. Her hand was bleeding.

She shouted back, "Okay. Be with you in a sec! Just stopped to tie my shoe."

"Oh yeah?" they jeered, waiting above till they saw her emerge from the last of the spruces, and start up the trail along the open face of the rocks.

She climbed up, oblivious of the cut hand that left a bloodstain on every rock she leaned on, straddling her long strong legs from ledge to ledge. Inside her head, her mind was thinking, "What of it? What of it? What is he to me? I didn't even know him. We'd never even had a date. Lots of the boys had done more than that. He didn't even kiss me. It was nothing. It was just a notion." Inside her body, her heart was still quaking and trembling like a cowering tame animal, a dog, a cat, a horse, to which the wind brings the strange feral scent of a tiger which sees crossing its path a fierce, striped, dangerous and magnificent beauty.

It had been life that struck her that blow, she knew that, although she had never felt it before, wrapped in her cocoon as she had been, as yet unborn. Those other times when boys had touched her and clasped her, the two well-remembered kisses she had had from boys, she scorned them now as mere vague brushings against the outside of the cocoon. This, *this,* which she could not for a moment forget, this had been a thrust, deep into her very self, bared and defenseless. Those bared and defenseless fibres, quivering under that thrust, they knew what she did not—they knew what was before them, they knew and they told her with their dumb wordless trembling.

Flying at the face of the cliff, her teeth set, her muscles taut, she yearned passionately back to the cocoon. "I will never grow up. I will never be in love. It scares me to death. It's too big. I won't be able to help myself. I hate it. I won't!" As passionately she flung herself forward, farther and farther out from the riven cocoon, tearing away its broken threads, flinging them from her contemptuously, laughing at the befooled childishness in which she had been kept till now, playing with toys, when, waiting for her on the path ahead, was this—this—this!

The hot fit passed. The cold chills came again. She climbed more slowly, stopping to suck the blood from the cut in her hand. "Marriage. . . ." She knew marriage—she had seen it in every house she went into—"it was nothing—it was just tiresomeness!" The faces of married women she had known came before her, patient, extinguished, unexpectant. It was keeping house for somebody who complained when you didn't get it just right. And she would never get it just right. It was having to bring up children. How could anybody ever know how to bring up children? *She* would never know! The children would think she knew all about everything and what to do, always, and she didn't. She'd have to feed them, and wash them. And they'd be sick. How did anybody ever know what to do when they were sick?

And then she swung herself up on the ledge where the two old people sat, whom she had seen in the dining room.

They did not see her. At least they gave her but one passing absent glance as she dropped down to breathe at the other end of the ledge. They were looking out over the lake.

For the first time the girl looked at what was there. The sun was setting in limpid gold, a few rosy clouds floating in a line above it. The lake was like beaten gold, the little strokes of the hammer glimmering in tiny semicircular waves. Drawing in a few long breaths she really looked at it. It was nice. It was really and truly like a picture, she thought, with those pink clouds and the sky all flame color.

She looked back at the couple on the other end of the ledge. They were sitting close together. The wife had pulled up the hood of the cape. It had rumpled her gray hair. Untidy wisps floated around her forehead. She did not put up her hand to arrange them. She looked across the lake out of tranquil blue eyes. Her face had the quiet intent look of someone who is listening as well as seeing. She *was* listening. The girl saw now that her husband's lips were moving. He was saying something to her. Yet he was not looking at her. He too was gazing steadfastly out over the lake to where the sun sank lower behind the blue, blue, far mountains. What could he be saying? She trained her ears to hear.

"Breathless with adoration; the broad sun
Is sinking down in its tranquillity,
The gentleness of heaven broods o'er the sea."

She stopped listening, astonished. It was poetry. He was saying poetry to her!

Her cut hand was still bleeding. She got out a crumpled handkerchief and tied it up. When she looked up from this and listened again, she heard,

"There in a season of calm weather
Though inland far we be
Our souls have sight of that immortal sea
That brought us thither."

The sun sank lower. The fiery glow in the sky paled from orange to pale gold. The line of small rosy clouds turned from rose to mauve to lavender. The girl's eyes were fixed on it, but she was trying to follow the murmuring voice, which presently rose till she heard,

"Yet in these woods and by this sea
Beauty has lifted eyes to me,
While a clear voice chanted, 'They who find
Me not upon their doorsteps,
Know me never
Know me never
Though forever to and fro. . . .'"

The sun, mildly, slowly sinking, was now hidden behind the line of mountains. The sunset was almost past. The man was silent. The girl saw that he moved his hand till it held his wife's. Without turning her gray head she leaned it closer to his shoulder. Their eyes were fixed on the magnificent long rays of translucent light throbbing up from where the sun had sunk, turning all the world to gold. This was the most beautiful moment of all.

Then the glory of fire ebbed swiftly away, and blue came swiftly in from the distance, closing in on the mountain with solemnly dropping transparent blue veils.

A small breeze began to breathe gently. The man turned his gray head and smiled at his old wife.

The girl gazed wildly at them, smiling at each other. Why, they were safe! They had gone through it all, the thunder and the lightning and the storm, the struggles and the failures, and had come out into this peace. Oh, to be where they were, safe!— Or to be a little girl again!

She turned her head to hide her face; she bent it down. Violent, exquisite tears burst from her eyes—the delicious, broken-hearted, nonsensical tears of sixteen—because she was not six, or sixty.

University Days

JAMES THURBER

I PASSED ALL the other courses that I took at my university, but I could never pass botany. This was because all botany students had to spend several hours a week in a laboratory looking through a microscope at plant cells, and I could never see through a microscope. I never once saw a cell through a microscope. This used to enrage my instructor. He would wander around the laboratory pleased with the progress all the students were making in drawing the involved and, so I am told, interesting structure of flower cells, until he came to me. I would just be standing there. "I can't see anything," I would say. He would begin patiently enough, explaining how anybody can see through a microscope, but he would always end up in a fury, claiming that I could *too* see through a microscope but just pretended that I couldn't. "It takes away from the beauty of flowers anyway," I used to tell him. "We are not concerned with beauty in this course," he would say. "We are concerned solely with what I may call the *mechanics* of flars." "Well," I'd say, "I can't see anything." "Try it just once again," he'd say, and I would put my eye to the microscope and see nothing at all, except now and again a nebulous milky substance—a phenomenon of maladjustment. You were supposed to see a vivid, restless clockwork of sharply defined plant cells. "I see what looks like a lot of milk," I would tell him. This, he claimed, was the result of my not having adjusted the microscope properly, so he would readjust it for me, or rather, for himself. And I would look again and see milk.

I finally took a deferred pass, as they called it, and waited a year and tried again. (You had to pass one of the biological sciences or you couldn't graduate.) The professor had come back from vacation brown as a berry, bright-eyed, and eager to explain cell-structure again to his classes. "Well," he said to me, cheerily, when we met in the first laboratory hour of the semester, "we're going to see cells this time, aren't we?" "Yes, sir," I said. Students to right of me and to left of me and in front of me were seeing cells; what's more, they were quietly drawing pictures of them in their notebooks. Of course, I didn't see anything.

"We'll try it," the professor said to me, grimly, "with every adjustment of the microscope known to man. As God is my witness, I'll arrange this glass so that you see cells through it or I'll give up teaching. In twenty-two years of botany, I—" He cut off abruptly for he was beginning to quiver all over, like Lionel Barrymore, and he genuinely wished to hold onto his temper; his scenes with me had taken a great deal out of him.

So we tried it with every adjustment of the microscope known to man. With only one of them did I see anything but blackness or the familiar lacteal opacity, and that time I saw, to my pleasure and amazement, a variegated constellation of flecks, specks, and dots. These I hastily drew. The instructor, noting my activity, came back from an adjoining desk, a smile on his lips and his eyebrows high in hope. He looked at my cell drawing. "What's that?" he demanded, with a hint of a squeal in his voice. "That's what I saw," I said. "You didn't, you didn't, you *did*n't!" he screamed, losing control of his temper instantly, and he bent over and squinted into the microscope. His head snapped up. "That's your eye!" he shouted. "You've fixed the lens so that it reflects! You've drawn your eye!"

Another course that I didn't like, but somehow managed to pass, was economics. I went to that class straight from the botany class, which didn't help me any in understanding either subject. I used to get them mixed up. But not as mixed up as another student in my economics class who came there direct from a physics laboratory. He was a tackle on the football team, named Bolenciecwcz. At that time Ohio State University had one of the best football teams in the country, and Bolenciecwcz was one of its outstanding stars. In order to be eligible to play it was necessary for him to keep up in his studies, a very difficult matter, for while he was not dumber than an ox he was not any smarter. Most of his professors were lenient and helped him along. None gave him more hints, in answering questions, or asked him simpler ones than the economics professor, a thin, timid man named Bassum. One day when we were on the subject of transportation and distribution, it came Bolenciecwcz's turn to answer a question. "Name one means of transportation," the professor said to him. No light came into the big tackle's eyes. "Just any means of transportation," said the professor. Bolenciecwcz sat staring at him. "That is," pursued the professor, "any medium, agency, or method of going from one place to another." Bolenciecwcz had the look of a man who is being led into a trap. "You may choose among steam, horse-drawn, or electrically propelled vehicles," said the instructor. "I might suggest the one which we commonly take in making long journeys across land." There was a profound silence in which everybody stirred uneasily, including Bolenciecwcz and Mr. Bassum. Mr. Bassum abruptly broke this silence in an amazing manner. "Choo-choo-choo," he said, in a low voice, and turned instantly scarlet. He glanced appealingly around the room. All of us, of course, shared Mr. Bassum's desire that Bolenciecwcz should stay abreast of the class in economics, for the Illinois game, one of the hardest and most important of the season was only a week off. "Toot, toot, tootooooooot!" some student with a deep voice moaned, and we all looked encouragingly at Bolenciecwcz. Somebody else gave a fine imitation of a locomotive letting off steam. Mr. Bassum himself rounded off the little show. "Ding, dong, ding, dong," he said, hopefully. Bolenciecwcz was staring at the floor now, trying to think, his great brow furrowed, his huge hands rubbing together, his face red.

"How did you come to college this year, Mr. Bolenciecwcz?" asked the professor. "*Chuf*fa chuffa, *chuf*fa chuffa."

"M'father sent me," said the football player.

"What on?" asked Bassum.

"I git an 'lowance," said the tackle, in a low, husky voice, obviously embarrassed.

"No, no," said Bassum. "Name a means of transportation. What did you *ride* here on?"

"Train," said Bolenciecwcz.

"Quite right," said the professor. "Now, Mr. Nugent, will you tell us—"

If I went through anguish in botany and economics—for different reasons—gymnasium work was even worse. I don't even like to think about it. They wouldn't let you play games or join in the exercises with your glasses on and I couldn't see with mine off. I bumped into professors, horizontal bars, agricultural students, and swinging iron rings. Not being able to see, I could take it but I couldn't dish it out. Also, in order to pass gymnasium (and you had to pass it to graduate) you had to learn to swim if you didn't know how. I didn't like the swimming pool, I didn't like swimming, and I didn't like the swimming instructor, and after all these years I still don't. I never swam but I passed my gym work anyway, by having another student give my gymnasium number (978) and swim across the pool in my place. He was a quiet, amiable blond youth, number 473, and he would have seen through a microscope for me if we could have got away with it, but we couldn't get away with it. Another thing I didn't like about gymnasium work was that they made you strip the day you registered. It is impossible for me to be happy when I am stripped and being asked a lot of questions. Still, I did better than a lanky agricultural student who was cross-examined just before I was. They asked each student what college he was in—that is, whether Arts, Engineering, Commerce, or Agriculture. "What college are you in?" the instructor snapped at the youth in front of me. "Ohio State University," he said promptly.

It wasn't that agricultural student but it was another a whole lot like him who decided to take up journalism, possibly on the ground that when farming went to hell he could fall back on newspaper work. He didn't realize, of course, that that would be very much like falling back full-length on a kit of carpenter's tools. Haskins didn't seem cut out for journalism, being too embarrassed to talk to anybody and unable to use a typewriter, but the editor of the college paper assigned him to the cow barns, the sheep house, the horse pavilion, and the animal husbandry department generally. This was a genuinely big "beat," for it took up five times as much ground and got ten times as great a legislative appropriation as the College of Liberal Arts. The agricultural student knew animals, but nevertheless his stories were dull and colorlessly written. He took all afternoon on each of them, on account of having to hunt for each letter on the typewriter. Once in a while he had to ask somebody to help him hunt. "C" and "L," in particular, were hard letters for him to find. His editor finally got pretty much annoyed at the farmer-journalist because his pieces were so uninteresting. "See here, Haskins," he snapped at him one day, "why is it we never have anything hot from you on the horse pavilion? Here we have two hundred head of horses on this campus—more than any other university in the Western Conference except Purdue—and yet you never get any real low-down on them. Now shoot over to the horse barns and dig up something lively." Haskins shambled out and came back in about an hour; he said he had something. "Well, start it off snappily," said the editor. "Something people will read." Haskins set to work and in a couple of hours brought a sheet of typewritten paper to the desk; it was a two-hundred-word story about some disease that had broken out among the horses. Its opening sentence was simple but arresting. It read: "Who has noticed the sores on the tops of the horses in the animal husbandry building?"

Ohio State was a land grant university and therefore two years of military drill was compulsory. We drilled with old Springfield rifles and studied the tactics of the Civil War even though the World War was going on at the time. At 11 o'clock each morning thousands of freshmen and sophomores used to deploy over the campus, moodily creeping up on the old chemistry building. It was good training for the kind of warfare that was waged at Shiloh but it had no connection with what was going on in Europe. Some people used to think there was German money behind it, but they didn't dare say so or they would have been thrown in jail as German spies. It was a period of muddy thought and marked, I believe, the decline of higher education in the Middle West.

As a soldier I was never any good at all. Most of the cadets were glumly indifferent soldiers, but I was no good at all. Once General Littlefield, who was commandant of the cadet corps, popped up in front of me during regimental drill and snapped, "You are the main trouble with this university!" I think he meant that my type was the main trouble with the university but he may have meant me individually. I was mediocre at drill, certainly —that is, until my senior year. By that time I had drilled longer than anybody else in the Western Conference, having failed at military at the end of each preceding year so that I had to do it all over again. I was the only senior still in uniform. The uniform which, when new, had made me look like an interurban railway conductor, now that it had become faded and too tight made me look like Bert Williams in his bellboy act. This had a definitely bad effect on my morale. Even so, I had become by sheer practise little short of wonderful at squad manoeuvres.

One day General Littlefield picked our company out of the whole regiment and tried to get it mixed up by putting it through one movement after another as fast as we could execute them: squads right, squads left, squads on right into line, squads right about, squads left front into line, etc. In about three minutes one hundred and nine men were marching in one direction and I was marching away from them at an angle of forty degrees, all alone. "Company, halt!" shouted General Littlefield, "That man is the only man who has it right!" I was made a corporal for my achievement.

The next day General Littlefield summoned me to his office. He was swatting flies when I went in. I was silent and he was silent too, for a long time. I don't think he remembered me or why he had sent for me, but he didn't want to admit it. He swatted some more flies, keeping his eyes on them narrowly before he let go with the swatter. "Button up your coat!" he snapped. Looking back on it now I can see that he meant me although he was looking at a fly, but I just stood there. Another fly came to rest on a paper in front of the general and began rubbing its hind legs together. The General lifted the swatter cautiously. I moved restlessly and the fly flew away. "You startled him!" barked General Littlefield, looking at me severely. I said I was sorry. "That won't help the situation!" snapped the General, with cold military logic. I didn't see what I could do except offer to chase some more flies toward his desk, but I didn't say anything. He stared out the window at the faraway figures of co-eds crossing the campus toward the library. Finally, he told me I could go. So I went. He either didn't know which cadet I was or else he forgot what he wanted to see me about. It may have been that he wished to apologize for having called me the main trouble with the university; or maybe he had decided to compliment me on my brilliant drilling of the day before and then at the last minute decided not to. I don't know. I don't think about it much any more.

Green Tunnels

ALDOUS HUXLEY

"In the Italian gardens of the thirteenth century . . ." Mr. Buzzacott interrupted himself to take another helping of the *risotto* which was being offered him. "Excellent *risotto* this," he observed. "Nobody who was not born in Milan can make it properly. So they say."

"So they say," Mr. Topes repeated in his sad, apologetic voice, and helped himself in his turn.

"Personally," said Mrs. Topes, with decision, "I find all Italian cooking abominable. I don't like the oil—especially hot. No, thank you." She recoiled from the proffered dish.

After the first mouthful Mr. Buzzacott put down his fork. "In the Italian gardens of the thirteenth century," he began again, making with his long, pale hand a curved and flowery gesture that ended with a clutch at his beard, "a frequent and most felicitous use was made of green tunnels."

"Green tunnels?" Barbara woke up suddenly from her tranced silence. "Green tunnels?"

"Yes, my dear," said her father. "Green tunnels. Arched alleys covered with vines or other creeping plants. Their length was often very considerable."

But Barbara had once more ceased to pay attention to what he was saying. Green tunnels—the word had floated down to her, through profound depths of reverie, across great spaces of abstraction, startling her like the sound of a strange-voiced bell. Green tunnels—what a wonderful idea. She would not listen to her father explaining the phrase into dullness. He made everything dull; an inverted alchemist, turning gold into lead. She pictured caverns in a great aquarium, long vistas between rocks and scarcely swaying weeds and pale, discoloured corals; endless dim green corridors with huge lazy fishes loitering aimlessly along them. Green-faced monsters with goggling eyes and mouths that slowly opened and shut. Green tunnels . . .

"I have seen them illustrated in illuminated manuscripts of the period," Mr. Buzzacott went on; once more he clutched his pointed brown beard—clutched and combed it with his long fingers.

Mr. Topes looked up. The glasses of his round owlish spectacles flashed as he moved his head. "I know what you mean," he said.

"I have a very good mind to have one planted in my garden here."

"It will take a long time to grow," said Mr. Topes. "In this sand, so close to the sea, you will only be able to plant vines. And they come up very slowly—very slowly indeed." He shook his head and the points of light danced wildly in his spectacles. His voice drooped hopelessly, his grey moustache drooped, his whole person drooped. Then, suddenly, he pulled himself up. A shy, apologetic smile appeared on his face. He wriggled uncomfortably. Then, with a final rapid shake of the head, he gave vent to a quotation:

"But at my back I always hear
Time's winged chariot hurrying near."

He spoke deliberately, and his voice trembled a little. He always found it painfully difficult to say something choice and out of the ordinary; and yet what a wealth of remembered phrase, what apt new coinages were always surging through his mind!

"They don't grow so slowly as all that," said Mr. Buzzacott confidently. He was only just over fifty, and looked a handsome thirty-five. He gave himself at least another forty years; indeed, he had not yet begun to contemplate the possibility of ever concluding.

"Miss Barbara will enjoy it, perhaps—your green tunnel." Mr. Topes sighed and looked across the table at his host's daughter.

Barbara was sitting with her elbows on the table, her chin in her hands, staring in front of her. The sound of her own name reached her faintly. She turned her head in Mr. Topes's direction and found herself confronted by the glitter of his round, convex spectacles. At the end of the green tunnel—she stared at the shining circles—hung the eyes of a goggling fish. They approached, floating, closer and closer, along the dim submarine corridor.

Confronted by this fixed regard, Mr. Topes looked away. What thoughtful eyes! He couldn't remember ever to have seen eyes so full of thought. There were certain Madonnas of Montagna, he reflected, very like her: mild little blonde Madonnas with slightly snub noses and very, very young. But he was old; it would be many years, in spite of Buzzacott, before the vines grew up into a green tunnel. He took a sip of wine; then, mechanically, sucked his drooping grey moustache.

"Arthur!"

At the sound of his wife's voice Mr. Topes started, raised his napkin to his mouth. Mrs. Topes did not permit the sucking of moustaches. It was only in moments of absent-mindedness that he ever offended, now.

"The Marchese Prampolini is coming here to take coffee," said Mr. Buzzacott suddenly. "I almost forgot to tell you."

"One of these Italian marquises, I suppose," said Mrs. Topes, who was no snob, except in England. She raised her chin with a little jerk.

Mr. Buzzacott executed an upward curve of the hand in her direction. "I assure you, Mrs. Topes, he belongs to a very old and distinguished family. They are Genoese in origin. You remember their palace, Barbara? Built by Alessi."

Barbara looked up. "Oh yes," she said vaguely. "Alessi. I know." Alessi: Aleppo—where a malignant and a turbaned Turk. *And* a turbaned; that had always seemed to her very funny.

"Several of his ancestors," Mr. Buzzacott went on, "distinguished themselves as viceroys of Corsica. They did good work in the suppression of rebellion. Strange, isn't it"—he turned parenthetically to Mr. Topes—"the way in which sympathy is always on the side of rebels? What a fuss people made of Corsica! That ridiculous book of Gregorovius, for example. And the Irish, and the Poles, and all the rest of them. It always seems to me very superfluous and absurd."

"Isn't it, perhaps, a little natural?" Mr. Topes began timorously and tentatively; but his host went on without listening.

"The present marquis," he said, "is the head of the local Fascisti. They have done no end of good work in this district in the way of preserving law and order and keeping the lower classes in their place."

"Ah, the Fascisti," Mrs. Topes repeated approvingly. "One would like to see something of the kind in England. What with all these strikes . . ."

"He has asked me for a subscription to the funds of the organisation. I shall give him one, of course."

"Of course." Mrs. Topes nodded. "My nephew, the one who was a major during the war, volunteered in the last coal strike. He was sorry, I know, that it didn't come to a fight. 'Aunt Annie,' he said to me, when I saw him last, 'if there had been a fight we should have knocked them out completely—completely.' "

In Aleppo, the Fascisti, malignant *and* turbaned, were fighting, under the palm trees. Weren't they palm trees, those tufted green plumes?

"What, no ice to-day? *Niente gelato?*" inquired Mr. Buzzacott as the maid put down the compote of peaches on the table.

Concetta apologised. The ice-making machine in the village had broken down. There would be no ice till to-morrow.

"Too bad," said Mr. Buzzacott. *"Troppo male, Concetta."*

Under the palm trees, Barbara saw them: they pranced about, fighting.

They were mounted on big dogs, and in the trees were enormous many-coloured birds.

"Goodness me, the child's asleep." Mrs. Topes was proffering the dish of peaches. "How much longer am I to hold this in front of your nose, Barbara?"

Barbara felt herself blushing. "I'm so sorry," she mumbled, and took the dish clumsily.

"Day-dreaming. It's a bad habit."

"It's one we all succumb to sometimes," put in Mr. Topes deprecatingly, with a little nervous tremble of the head.

"You may, my dear," said his wife. "I do not."

Mr. Topes lowered his eyes to his plate and went on eating.

"The *marchese* should be here at any moment now," said Mr. Buzzacott, looking at his watch. "I hope he won't be late. I find I suffer so much from any postponement of my siesta. This Italian heat," he added, with growing plaintiveness, "one can't be too careful."

"Ah, but when I was with my father in India," began Mrs. Topes in a tone of superiority: "he was an Indian civilian, you know . . ."

Aleppo, India—always the palm trees. Cavalcades of big dogs, and tigers too.

Concetta ushered in the marquis. Delighted. Pleased to meet. Speak English? Yés, yéss. *Pochino*. Mrs. Topes: and Mr. Topes, the distinguished antiquarian. Ah, of course; know his name very well. My daughter. Charmed. Often seen the signorina bathing. Admired the way she dives. Beautiful—the hand made a long, caressing gesture. These athletic English signorine. The teeth flashed astonishingly white in the brown face, the dark eyes glittered. She felt herself blushing again, looked away, smiled foolishly. The marquis had already turned back to Mr. Buzzacott.

"So you have decided to settle in our Carrarese."

Well, not settled exactly; Mr. Buzzacott wouldn't go so far as to say settled. A villino for the summer months. The winter in Rome. One was forced to live abroad. Taxation in England. . . . Soon they were all talking. Barbara looked at them. Beside the marquis they all seemed half dead. His face flashed as he talked; he seemed to be boiling with life. Her father was limp and pale, like something long buried from the light; and Mr. Topes was all dry and shrivelled; and Mrs. Topes looked more than ever like something worked by clockwork. They were talking about Socialism and Fascisti, and all that. Barbara did not listen to what they were saying; but she looked at them, absorbed.

Good-bye, good-bye. The animated face with its flash of a smile was turned like a lamp from one to another. Now it was turned on her. Perhaps one evening she would come, with her father, and the Signora Topes. He and his sister gave little dances sometimes. Only the gramophone, of course. But that was better than nothing, and the signorina must dance divinely—another flash—he could see that. He pressed her hand again. Good-bye.

It was time for the siesta.

"Don't forget to pull down the mosquito netting, my dear," Mr. Buzzacott exhorted. "There is always a danger of anophylines."

"All right, father." She moved towards the door without turning round to answer him. He was always terribly tiresome about mosquito nets. Once they had driven through the Campagna in a hired cab, completely enclosed in an improvised tent of netting. The monuments along the Appian Way had loomed up mistily as through bridal veils. And how everyone had laughed. But her father, of course, hadn't so much as noticed it. He never noticed anything.

"Is it at Berlin, that charming little Madonna of Montagna's?" Mr. Topes abruptly asked. "The one with the Donor kneeling in the left-hand corner as if about to kiss the foot of the Child." His spectacles flashed in Mr. Buzzacott's direction.

"Why do you ask?"

"I don't know. I was just thinking of it."

"I think you must mean the one in the Mond Collection."

"Ah yes; very probably. In the Mond . . ."

Barbara opened the door and walked into the twilight of her shuttered room. It was hot even here; for another three hours it would hardly be possible to stir. And that old idiot, Mrs. Topes, always made a fuss if one came in to lunch with bare legs and one's after-bathing tunic. "In India we always made a point of being properly and adequately dressed. An Englishwoman must keep up her position with natives, and to all intents and purposes Italians *are* natives." And so she always had to put on shoes and stockings and a regular frock just at the hottest hour of the day. What an old ass that woman was! She slipped off her clothes as fast as she could. That was a little better.

Standing in front of the long mirror in the wardrobe door she came to the humiliating conclusion that she looked like a piece of badly toasted bread. Brown face, brown neck and shoulders, brown arms, brown legs from the knee downwards; but all the rest of her was white, silly, effeminate, townish white. If only one could run about with no clothes on till one was like those little coppery children who rolled and tumbled in the burning sand! Now she was just underdone, half-baked, and wholly ridiculous.

For a long time she looked at her pale image. She saw herself running, bronzed all over, along the sand; or through a field of flowers, narcissus and wild tulips; or in soft grass under grey olive trees. She turned round with a sudden start. There, in the shadows behind her. . . . No, of course there was nothing. It was that awful picture in a magazine she had looked at, so many years ago, when she was a child. There was a lady sitting at her dressing-table, doing her hair in front of the glass; and a huge, hairy black monkey creeping up behind her. She always got the creeps when she looked at herself in a mirror. It was very silly. But still. She turned away from the mirror, crossed the room, and, without lowering the mosquito curtains, lay down on her bed. The flies buzzed about her, settled incessantly on her face. She shook her head, flapped at them angrily with her hands. There would be peace if she let down the netting. But she thought of the Appian Way seen mistily through the bridal veil and preferred to suffer the flies. In the end she had to surrender; the brutes were too much for her. But, at any rate, it wasn't the fear of anophylines that made her lower the netting.

Undisturbed now and motionless, she lay stretched stiffly out under the transparent bell of gauze. A specimen under a glass case. The fancy possessed her mind. She saw a huge museum with thousands of glass cases, full of fossils and butterflies and stuffed birds and mediæval spoons and armour and Florentine jewellery and mummies and carved ivory and illuminated manuscripts. But in one of the cases was a human being, shut up there alive.

All of a sudden she became horribly miserable. "Boring, boring, boring," she whispered, formulating the words aloud. Would it never stop being boring? The tears came into her eyes. How awful everything was! And perhaps it would go on being as bad as this all her life. Seventeen from seventy was fifty-three. Fifty-three years of it. And if she lived to a hundred there would be more than eighty.

The thought depressed her all the evening. Even her bath after tea did her no good. Swimming far out, far out, she lay there, floating on the warm water. Sometimes she looked at the sky, sometimes she turned her head towards the shore. Framed in their pinewoods, the villas looked as small and smug as the advertisement of a seaside resort. But behind them, across the level plain, were the mountains. Sharp, bare peaks of limestone, green woodland slopes and grey-green expanses of terraced olive trees—they seemed marvellously close and clear in this evening light. And beautiful, beautiful beyond words. But that, somehow, only made things worse. And Shelley had lived a few miles farther up the coast, there, behind the headland guarding the Gulf of Spezia. Shelley had been drowned in this milk-warm sea. That made it worse too.

The sun was getting very low and red over the sea. She swam slowly in. On the beach Mrs. Topes waited, disapprovingly. She had known somebody, a strong man, who had caught a cramp from staying in too long. He sank like a stone. Like a stone. The queer people Mrs. Topes had known! And the funny things they did, the odd things that happened to them!

Dinner that evening was duller than ever. Barbara went early to bed. All night long the same old irritating cicada scraped and scraped among the pine trees, monotonous and regular as clockwork. Zip zip, zip zip zip. Boring, boring. Was the animal never bored by its own noise? It seemed odd that it shouldn't be. But, when she came to think of it, nobody ever did get bored with their own noise. Mrs. Topes, for example; she never seemed to get bored. Zip zip, zip zip zip. The cicada went on without pause.

Concetta knocked at the door at half-past seven. The morning was as bright and cloudless as all the mornings were. Barbara jumped up, looked from one window at the mountains, from the other at the sea; all seemed to be well with them. All was well with her, too, this morning. Seated at the mirror, she did not so much as think of the big monkey in the far obscure corner of the room. A bathing dress and a bath-gown, sandals, a handkerchief round her head, and she was ready. Sleep had left no recollection of last night's mortal boredom. She ran downstairs.

"Good morning, Mr. Topes."

Mr. Topes was walking in the garden among the vines. He turned round, took off his hat, smiled a greeting.

"Good morning, Miss Barbara." He paused. Then, with an embarrassed wriggle of introduction he went on; a queer little falter came into his voice. "A real Chaucerian morning, Miss Barbara. A May-day morning—only it happens to be September. Nature is fresh and bright, and there is at least one specimen in this dream garden"—he wriggled more uncomfortably than ever, and there was a tremulous glitter in his round spectacle lenses—"of the poet's 'yonge fresshe folkes.'" He bowed in her direction, smiled deprecatingly, and was silent. The remark, it seemed to him, now that he had finished speaking, was somehow not as good as he had thought it would be.

Barbara laughed. "Chaucer! They used to make us read the *Canterbury Tales* at school. But they always bored me. Are you going to bathe?"

"Not before breakfast." Mr. Topes shook his head. "One is getting a little too old for that."

"Is one?" Why did the silly old man always say 'one' when he meant 'I'?

She couldn't help laughing at him. "Well, I must hurry, or else I shall be late for breakfast again, and you know how I catch it."

She ran out, through the gate in the garden wall, across the beach, to the striped red-and-white bathing cabin that stood before the house. Fifty yards away she saw the Marchese Prampolini, still dripping from the sea, running up towards his bathing hut. Catching sight of her, he flashed a smile in her direction, gave a military salute. Barbara waved her hand, then thought that the gesture had been too familiar—but at this hour of the morning it was difficult not to have bad jolly manners—and added the corrective of a stiff bow. After all, she had only met him yesterday. Soon she was swimming out to sea, and, ugh! what a lot of horrible huge jelly-fish there were.

Mr. Topes had followed her slowly through the gate and across the sand. He watched her running down from the cabin, slender as a boy, with long, bounding strides. He watched her go jumping with great splashes through the deepening water, then throw herself forward and begin to swim. He watched her till she was no more than a small dark dot far out.

Emerging from his cabin, the marquis met him walking slowly along the beach, his head bent down and his lips slightly moving as though he were repeating something, a prayer or a poem, to himself.

"Good morning, signore." The marquis shook him by the hand with a more than English cordiality.

"Good morning," replied Mr. Topes, allowing his hand to be shaken. He resented this interruption of his thoughts.

"She swims very well, Miss Buzzacott."

"Very," assented Mr. Topes, and smiled to himself to think what beautiful, poetical things he might have said, if he had chosen.

"Well, so, so," said the marquis, too colloquial by half. He shook hands again, and the two men went their respective ways.

Barbara was still a hundred yards from the shore when she heard the crescendo and dying boom of the gong floating out from the villa. Damn! she'd be late again. She quickened her stroke and came splashing out through the shallows, flushed and breathless. She'd be ten minutes late, she calculated; it would take her at least that to do her hair and dress. Mrs. Topes would be on the warpath again; though what business that old woman had to lecture her as she did, goodness only knew. She always succeeded in making herself horribly offensive and unpleasant.

The beach was quite deserted as she trotted, panting, across it, empty to right and left as far as she could see. If only she had a horse to go galloping at the water's edge, miles and miles. Right away down to Bocca d'Arno she'd go, swim the river—she saw herself crouching on the horse's back, as he swam, with legs tucked up on the saddle, trying not to get her feet wet—and gallop on again, goodness only knew where.

In front of the cabin she suddenly halted. There in the ruffled sand she had seen a writing. Big letters, faintly legible, sprawled across her path.

O CLARA D'ELLÉBEUSE.

She pieced the dim letters together. They hadn't been there when she started out to bathe. Who? . . . She looked round. The beach was quite empty. And what was the meaning? "O Clara d'Ellébeuse." She took her bath-gown from the cabin, slipped on her sandals, and ran back towards the house as fast as she could. She felt most horribly frightened.

It was a sultry, headachy sort of morning, with a hot sirocco that stirred the bunting on the flagstaffs. By midday the thunderclouds had covered half the sky. The sun still blazed on the sea, but over the mountains all was black and indigo. The storm broke noisily overhead just as they were drinking their after-luncheon coffee.

"Arthur," said Mrs. Topes, painfully calm, "shut the shutters, please."

She was not frightened, no. But she preferred not to see the lightning. When the room was darkened, she began to talk, suavely and incessantly.

Lying back in her deep arm-chair, Barbara was thinking of Clara d'Ellébeuse. What did it mean and who was Clara d'Ellébeuse? And why had he written it there for her to see? He—for there could be no doubt who had written it. The flash of teeth and eyes, the military salute; she knew she oughtn't to have waved to him. He had written it there while she was swimming out. Written it and then run away. She rather liked that—just an extraordinary word on the sand, like the footprint in *Robinson Crusoe*.

"Personally," Mrs. Topes was saying, "I prefer Harrod's."

The thunder crashed and rattled. It was rather exhilarating, Barbara thought; one felt, at any rate, that something was happening for a change. She remembered the little room half-way up the stairs at Lady Thingumy's house, with the bookshelves and the green curtains and the orange shade on the light; and that awful young man like a white slug who had tried to kiss her there, at the dance last year. But that was different—not at all serious; and the young man had been so horribly ugly. She saw the marquis running up the beach, quick and alert. Copper coloured all over, with black hair. He was certainly very handsome. But as for being in love, well . . . what did that exactly mean? Perhaps when she knew him better. Even now she fancied she detected something. O Clara d'Ellébeuse. What an extraordinary thing it was!

With his long fingers Mr. Buzzacott combed his beard. This winter, he was thinking, he would put another thousand into Italian money when the exchange was favourable. In the spring it always seemed to drop back again. One could clear three hundred pounds on one's capital if the exchange went down to seventy. The income on three hundred was fifteen pounds a year, and fifteen pounds was now fifteen hundred lire. And fifteen hundred lire, when you came to think of it, was really sixty pounds. That was to say that one would make an addition of more than one pound a week to one's income by this simple little speculation. He became aware that Mrs. Topes had asked him a question.

"Yes, yes, perfectly," he said.

Mrs. Topes talked on; she was keeping up her morale. Was she right in believing that the thunder sounded a little less alarmingly loud and near?

Mr. Topes sat, polishing his spectacles with a white silk handkerchief. Vague and myopic between their puckered lids, his eyes seemed lost, homeless, unhappy. He was thinking about beauty. There were certain relations between the eyelids and the temples, between the breast and the shoulder; there were certain successions of sounds. But what about them? Ah, that was the problem—that was the problem. And there was youth, there was innocence. But it was all very obscure, and there were so many phrases, so many remembered pictures and melodies; he seemed to get himself entangled among them. And he was after all so old and so ineffective.

He put on his spectacles again, and definition came into the foggy world beyond his eyes. The shuttered room was very dark. He could distinguish the Renaissance profile of Mr. Buzzacott, bearded and delicately featured. In her deep arm-chair Barbara appeared, faintly white, in an attitude relaxed and brooding. And Mrs. Topes was nothing more than a voice in the darkness. She had got on to the marriage of the Prince of Wales. Who would they eventually find for him?

Clara d'Ellébeuse, Clara d'Ellébeuse. She saw herself so clearly as the *marchesa*. They would have a house in Rome, a palace. She saw herself in the Palazzo Spada—it had such a lovely vaulted passage leading from the courtyard to the gardens at the back. "MARCHESA PRAMPOLINI, PALAZZA-SPADA, ROMA."—a great big visiting-card beautifully engraved. And she would go riding every day in the Pincio. *"Mi porta il mio cavallo,"* she would say to the footman, who answered the bell. *Porta?* Would that be quite correct? Hardly. She'd have to take some proper Italian lessons to talk to the servants. One must never be ridiculous before servants. *"Voglio il mio cavallo."* Haughtily one would say it sitting at one's writing-table in a riding-habit, without turning round. It would be a green riding-habit, with a black tricorne hat, braided with silver.

"Prendero la mia collazione al letto." Was that right for breakfast in bed? Because she would have breakfast in bed, always. And when she got up there would be lovely looking-glasses with three panels where one could see oneself sideface. She saw herself leaning forward, powdering her nose, carefully, scientifically. With the monkey creeping up behind? Ooh! Horrible! *Ho paura di questa scimmia, questo scimmione.*

She would come back to lunch after her ride. Perhaps Prampolini would be there; she had rather left him out of the picture so far. *"Dov' è il Marchese" "Nella sala di pranza, signora."* I began without you, I was so hungry. *Pasta asciutta.* Where have you been, my love? Riding, my dove. She supposed they'd get into the habit of saying that sort of thing. Everyone seemed to. And you? I have been out with the Fascisti.

Oh, these Fascisti! Would life be worth living when he was always going out with pistols and bombs and things? They would bring him back one day on a stretcher. She saw it. Pale, pale, with blood on him. *Il signore è ferito. Nel petto. Gravamente. E morto.*

How could she bear it? It was too awful; too, too terrible. Her breath came in a kind of sob; she shuddered as though she had been hurt. *E morto. E morto.* The tears came into her eyes.

She was roused suddenly by a dazzling light. The storm had receded far enough into the distance to permit of Mrs. Topes's opening the shutters.

"It's quite stopped raining."

To be disturbed in one's intimate sorrow and self-abandonment at a death-bed by a stranger's intrusion, an alien voice. . . . Barbara turned her face away from the light and surreptitiously wiped her eyes. They might see and ask her why she had been crying. She hated Mrs. Topes for opening the shutters; at the inrush of the light something beautiful had flown, an emotion had vanished, irrecoverably. It was a sacrilege.

Mr. Buzzacott looked at his watch. "Too late, I fear, for a siesta now," he said. "Suppose we ring for an early tea."

"An endless succession of meals," said Mr. Topes, with a tremolo and a sigh. "That's what life seems to be—real life."

"I have been calculating"—Mr. Buzzacott turned his pale green eyes towards his guest—"that I may be able to afford that pretty little *cinque cassone*, after all. It would be a bit of a squeeze." He played with his beard. "But still . . ."

After tea, Barbara and Mr. Topes went for a walk along the beach. She didn't much want to go, but Mrs. Topes thought it would be good for her; so she had to. The storm had passed and the sky over the sea was clear. But the waves were still breaking with an incessant clamour on the outer shallows, driving wide sheets of water high up the beach, twenty or thirty yards above the line where, on a day of calm, the ripples ordinarily expired. Smooth, shining expanses of water advanced and receded like steel surfaces moved out and back by a huge machine. Through the rain-washed air the mountains appeared with an incredible clarity. Above them hung huge masses of cloud.

"Clouds over Carrara," said Mr. Topes, deprecating his remark with a little shake of the head and a movement of the shoulders. "I like to fancy sometimes that the spirits of the great sculptors lodge among these marble hills, and that it is their unseen hands that carve the clouds into these enormous splendid shapes. I imagine their ghosts"—his voice trembled—"feeling about among superhuman conceptions, planning huge groups and friezes and monumental figures with blowing draperies; planning, conceiving, but never quite achieving. Look, there's something of Michelangelo in that white cloud with the dark shadows underneath it." Mr. Topes pointed, and Barbara nodded and said, "Yes, yes," though she wasn't quite sure which cloud he meant. "It's like Night on the Medici tomb; all the power and passion are brooding inside it, pent up. And there, in that sweeping, gesticulating piece of vapour—you see the one I mean—there's a Bernini. All the passion's on the surface, expressed; the gesture's caught at its most violent. And that sleek, smug white fellow over there, that's a delicious absurd Canova." Mr. Topes chuckled.

"Why do you always talk about art?" said Barbara. "You bring these dead people into everything. What do I know about Canova or whoever it is?" They were none of them alive. She thought of that dark face, bright as a lamp with life. He at least wasn't dead. She wondered whether the letters were still there in the sand before the cabin. No, of course not; the rain and the wind would have blotted them out.

Mr. Topes was silent; he walked with slightly bent knees and his eyes were fixed on the ground; he wore a speckled black-and-white straw hat. He always thought of art; that was what was wrong with him. Like an old tree he was; built up of dead wood, with only a few fibres of life to keep him from rotting away. They walked on for a long time in silence.

"Here's the river," said Mr. Topes at last.

A few steps more and they were on the bank of a wide stream that came down slowly through the plain to the sea. Just inland from the beach it was fringed with pine trees; beyond the trees one could see the plain, and beyond the plain were the mountains. In this calm light after the storm everything looked strange. The colours seemed deeper and more intense than at ordinary times. And though all was so clear, there was a mysterious air of remoteness about the whole scene. There was no sound except the continuous breathing of the sea. They stood for a little while, looking; then turned back.

Far away along the beach two figures were slowly approaching. White flannel trousers, a pink skirt.

"Nature," Mr. Topes enunciated, with a shake of the head. "One always comes back to nature. At a moment such as this, in surroundings like these, one realises it. One lives now—more quietly, perhaps, but more profoundly. Deep waters. Deep waters. . . ."

The figures drew closer. Wasn't it the marquis? And who was with him? Barbara strained her eyes to see.

"Most of one's life," Mr. Topes went on, "is one prolonged effort to prevent oneself thinking. Your father and I, we collect pictures and read about the dead. Other people achieve the same results by drinking, or breeding rabbits, or doing amateur carpentry. Anything rather than think calmly about the important things."

Mr. Topes was silent. He looked about him, at the sea, at the mountains, at the great clouds, at his companion. A frail Montagna madonna, with the sea and the westering sun, the mountains and the storm, all eternity as a background. And he was sixty, with all a life, immensely long and yet timelessly short, behind him, an empty life. He thought of death and the miracles of beauty; behind his round, glittering spectacles he felt inclined to weep.

The approaching couple were quite near now.

"What a funny old walrus," said the lady.

"Walrus? Your natural history is quite wrong." The marquis laughed. "He's much too dry to be a walrus. I should suggest some sort of an old cat."

"Well, whatever he is, I'm sorry for that poor little girl. Think of having nobody better to go about with!"

"Pretty, isn't she?"

"Yes, but too young, of course."

"I like the innocence."

"Innocence? Cher ami! These English girls. Oh, la la! They may look innocent. But, believe me . . ."

"Sh, sh. They'll hear you."

"Pooh, they don't understand Italian."

The marquis raised his hand. "The old walrus . . ." he whispered; then addressed himself loudly and jovially to the newcomers.

"Good evening, signorina. Good evening, Mr. Topes. After a storm the air is always the purest, don't you find, eh?"

Barbara nodded, leaving Mr. Topes to answer. It wasn't his sister. It was the Russian woman, the one of whom Mrs. Topes used to say that it was a disgrace she should be allowed to stay at the hotel. She had turned away, dissociating herself from the conversation; Barbara looked at the line of her averted face. Mr. Topes was saying something about the Pastoral Symphony. Purple face powder in the daylight; it looked hideous.

"Well, au revoir."

The flash of the marquis's smile was directed at them. The Russian woman turned back from the sea, slightly bowed, smiled languidly. Her heavy white eyelids were almost closed; she seemed the prey of an enormous ennui.

"They jar a little," said Mr. Topes when they were out of earshot—"they jar on the time, on the place, on the emotion. They haven't the innocence for this . . . this . . ."—he wriggled and tremoloed out the just, the all too precious word—"this prelapsarian landscape."

He looked sideways at Barbara and wondered what she was so thoughtfully frowning over. Oh, lovely and delicate young creature! What could he adequately say of death and beauty and tenderness? Tenderness . . .

"All this," he went on desperately, and waved his hand to indicate the sky, the sea, the mountains, "this scene is like something remembered, clear and utterly calm; remembered across great gulfs of intervening time."

But that was not really what he wanted to say.

"You see what I mean?" he asked dubiously. She made no reply. How could she see? "This scene is so clear and pure and remote; you need the corresponding emotion. Those people were out of harmony. They weren't clear and pure enough." He seemed to be getting more muddled than ever. "It's an emotion of the young and of the old. You could feel it, I could feel it. Those people couldn't." He was feeling his way through obscurities. Where would he finally arrive? "Certain poems express it. You know Francis Jammes? I have thought so much of his work lately. Art instead of life, as usual; but then I'm made that way. I can't help thinking of Jammes. Those delicate, exquisite things he wrote about Clara d'Ellébeuse?"

"Clara d'Ellébeuse?" She stopped and stared at him.

"You know the lines?" Mr. Topes smiled delightedly. "This makes me think, you make me think of them. '*J'aime dans les temps Clara d'Ellébeuse . . .*' But, my dear Barbara, what is the matter?"

She had started crying, for no reason whatever.

Sophistication

SHERWOOD ANDERSON

IT WAS early evening of a day in the late fall and the Winesburg County Fair had brought crowds of country people into town. The day had been clear and the night came on warm and pleasant. On the Trunion Pike, where the road after it left town stretched away between berry fields now covered with dry brown leaves, the dust from passing wagons arose in clouds. Children, curled into little balls, slept on the straw scattered on wagon beds. Their hair was full of dust and their fingers black and sticky. The dust rolled away over the fields and the departing sun set it ablaze with colors.

In the main street of Winesburg crowds filled the stores and the sidewalks. Night came on, horses whinnied, the clerks in the stores ran madly about, children became lost and cried lustily, an American town worked terribly at the task of amusing itself.

Pushing his way through the crowds in Main Street, young George Willard concealed himself in the stairway leading to Doctor Reefy's office and looked at the people. With feverish eyes he watched the faces drifting past under the store lights. Thoughts kept coming into his head and he did not want to think. He stamped impatiently on the wooden steps and looked sharply about. "Well, is she going to stay with him all day? Have I done all this waiting for nothing?" he muttered.

George Willard, the Ohio village boy, was fast growing into manhood and new thoughts had been coming into his mind. All that day, amid the jam of people at the Fair, he had gone about feeling lonely. He was about to leave Winesburg to go away to some city where he hoped to get work on a city newspaper and he felt grown up. The mood that had taken possession of him was a thing known to men and unknown to boys. He felt old and a little tired. Memories awoke in him. To his mind his new sense of maturity set him apart, made of him a half-tragic figure. He wanted someone to understand the feeling that had taken possession of him after his mother's death.

There is a time in the life of every boy when he for the first time takes the backward view of life. Perhaps that is the moment when he crosses the line into manhood. The boy is walking through the street of his town. He is thinking of the future and of the figure he will cut in the world. Ambitions and regrets awake within him. Suddenly something happens; he stops under a tree and waits as for a voice calling his name. Ghosts of old things creep into his consciousness; the voices outside of himself whisper a message concerning the limitations of life. From being quite sure of himself and his future he becomes not at all sure. If he be an imaginative boy a door is torn open and for the first time he looks out upon the world, seeing, as though they marched in procession before him, the countless figures of men who before his time have come out of nothingness into the world, lived their lives and again disappeared into nothingness. The sadness of sophistication has come to the boy. With a little gasp he sees himself as merely a leaf blown by the wind through the streets of his village. He knows that in spite of all the stout talk of his fellows he must live and die in uncertainty, a thing blown by the winds, a thing destined like corn to wilt in the sun. He shivers and looks eagerly about. The eighteen years he has lived seem but a moment, a breathing space in the long march of humanity. Already he hears death calling. With all his heart he wants to come close to some other human, touch someone with his hands, be touched by the hand of another. If he prefers that the other be a woman, that is because he believes that a woman will be gentle, that she will understand. He wants, most of all, understanding.

When the moment of sophistication came to George Willard, his mind turned to Helen White, the Winesburg banker's daughter. Always he had been conscious of the girl growing into womanhood as he grew into manhood. Once on a summer night when he was eighteen, he had walked with her on a country road and in her presence had given way to an impulse to boast, to make himself appear big and significant in her eyes. Now he wanted to see her for another purpose. He wanted to tell her of the new impulses that had come to him. He had tried to make her think of him as a man when he knew nothing of manhood and now he wanted to be with her and to try to make her feel the change he believed had taken place in his nature.

As for Helen White, she also had come to a period of change. What George felt, she in her young woman's way felt also. She was no longer a girl and hungered to reach into the grace and beauty of womanhood. She had come home from Cleveland, where she was attending college, to spend a day at the Fair. She also had begun to have memories. During the day she sat in the grandstand with a young man, one of the instructors from the college, who was a guest of her mother's. The young man was of a pedantic turn of mind and she felt at once he would not do for her purpose. At the Fair she was glad to be seen in his company as he was well dressed and a stranger. She knew that the fact of his presence would create an impression. During the day she was happy, but when night came on she began to grow restless. She wanted to drive the instructor away, to get out of his presence. While they sat together in the grandstand and while the eyes of former schoolmates were upon them, she paid so much attention to her escort that he grew interested. "A scholar needs money. I should marry a woman with money," he mused.

Helen White was thinking of George Willard even as he wandered gloomily through the crowds thinking of her. She remembered the summer evening when they had walked together and wanted to walk with him again. She thought that the months she had spent in the city, the going to theatres and the seeing of great crowds wandering in lighted thoroughfares, had changed her profoundly. She wanted him to feel and be conscious of the change in her nature.

The summer evening together that had left its mark on the memory of both the young man and woman had, when looked at quite sensibly, been rather stupidly spent. They had walked out of town along a country road. Then they had stopped by a fence near a field of young corn and George had taken off his coat and let it hang on his arm. "Well, I've stayed here in Winesburg—yes—I've not yet gone away but I'm growing up," he had said. "I've been reading books and I've been thinking. I'm going to try to amount to something in life.

"Well," he explained, "that isn't the point. Perhaps I'd better quit talking."

The confused boy put his hand on the girl's arm. His voice trembled. The two started to walk back along the road toward town. In his desperation George boasted, "I'm going to be a big man, the biggest that ever lived here in Winesburg," he declared. "I want you to do something, I don't know what. Perhaps it is none of my business. I want you to try to be different from other women. You see the point. It's none of my business I tell you. I want you to be a beautiful woman. You see what I want."

The boy's voice failed and in silence the two came back into town and went along the street to Helen White's house. At the gate he tried to say something impressive. Speeches he had thought out came into his head, but they seemed utterly pointless. "I thought—I used to think—I had it in my mind you would marry Seth Richmond. Now I know you won't," was all he could find to say as she went through the gate and toward the door of her house.

On the warm fall evening as he stood in the stairway and looked at the crowd drifting through Main Street, George thought of the talk beside the field of young corn and was ashamed of the figure he had made of himself. In the street the people surged up and down like cattle confined in a pen. Buggies and wagons almost filled the narrow thoroughfare. A band played and small boys raced along the sidewalk, diving between the legs of men. Young men with shining red faces walked awkwardly about with girls on their arms. In a room above one of the stores, where a dance was to be held, the fiddlers tuned their instruments. The broken sounds floated down through an open window and out across the murmur of voices and the loud blare of the horns of the band. The medley of sounds got on young Willard's nerves. Everywhere, on all sides, the sense of crowding, moving life closed in about him. He wanted to run away by himself and think. "If she wants to stay with that fellow she may. Why should I care? What difference does it make to me?" he growled and went along Main Street and through Hern's grocery into a side street.

George felt so utterly lonely and dejected that he wanted to weep but pride made him walk rapidly along, swinging his arms. He came to Westley Moyer's livery barn and stopped in the shadows to listen to a group of men who talked of a race Westley's stallion, Tony Tip, had won at the Fair during the afternoon. A crowd had gathered in front of the barn and before the crowd walked Westley, prancing up and down and boasting. He held a whip in his hand and kept tapping the ground. Little puffs of dust arose in the lamplight. "Hell, quit your talking," Westley exclaimed. "I wasn't afraid, I knew I had 'em beat all the time. I wasn't afraid."

Ordinarily George Willard would have been intensely interested in the boasting of Moyer, the horseman. Now it made him angry. He turned and hurried away along the street. "Old wind-bag," he sputtered. "Why does he want to be bragging? Why don't he shut up?"

George went into a vacant lot and as he hurried along, fell over a pile of rubbish. A nail protruding from an empty barrel tore his trousers. He sat down on the ground and swore. With a pin he mended the torn place and then arose and went on. "I'll go to Helen White's house, that's what I'll do. I'll walk right in. I'll say that I want to see her. I'll walk right in and sit down, that's what I'll do," he declared, climbing over a fence and beginning to run.

On the veranda of Banker White's house Helen was restless and distraught. The instructor sat between the mother and daughter. His talk wearied the girl. Although he had also been raised in an Ohio town, the instructor began to put on the airs of the city. He wanted to appear cosmopolitan. "I like the chance you have given me to study the background out of which most of our girls come," he declared. "It was good of you, Mrs. White, to have me down for the day." He turned to Helen and laughed. "Your life is still bound up with the life of this town?" he asked. "There are people here in whom you are interested?" To the girl his voice sounded pompous and heavy.

Helen arose and went into the house. At the door leading to a garden at the back she stopped and stood listening. Her mother began to talk. "There is no one here fit to associate with a girl of Helen's breeding," she said.

Helen ran down a flight of stairs at the back of the house and into the garden. In the darkness she stopped and stood trembling. It seemed to her that the world was full of meaningless people saying words. Afire with eagerness she ran through a garden gate and turning a corner by the banker's barn, went into a little side street. "George! Where are you, George?" she cried, filled with nervous excitement. She stopped running, and leaned against a tree to laugh hysterically. Along the dark little street came George Willard, still saying words. "I'm going to walk right into her house. I'll go right in and sit down," he declared as he came up to her. He stopped and stared stupidly. "Come on," he said and took hold of her hand. With hanging heads they walked away along the street under the trees. Dry leaves rustled under foot. Now that he had found her George wondered what he had better do and say.

At the upper end of the fair ground, in Winesburg, there is a half-decayed old grand-stand. It has never been painted and the boards are all warped out of shape. The fair ground stands on top of a low hill rising out of the valley of Wine Creek and from the grand-stand one can see at night, over a cornfield, the lights of the town reflected against the sky.

George and Helen climbed the hill to the fair ground, coming by the path past Waterworks Pond. The feeling of loneliness and isolation that had come to the young man in the crowded streets of his town was both broken and intensified by the presence of Helen. What he felt was reflected in her.

In youth there are always two forces fighting in people. The warm unthinking little animal struggles against the thing that reflects and remembers, and the older, the more sophisticated thing had possession of George Willard. Sensing his mood, Helen walked beside him filled with respect. When they got to the grandstand they climbed up under the roof and sat down on one of the long benchlike seats.

There is something memorable in the experience to be had by going into a fair ground that stands at the edge of a Middle Western town on a night after the annual fair has been held. The sensation is one never to be forgotten. On all sides are ghosts, not of the dead, but of living people. Here, during the day just passed, have come the people pouring in from the town and the country around. Farmers with their wives and children and all the people from the hundreds of little frame houses have gathered within these board walls. Young girls have laughed and men with beards have talked of the affairs of their lives. The place has been filled to overflowing with life. It has itched and squirmed with life and now it is night and the life has all gone away. The silence is almost terrifying. One conceals oneself standing silently beside the trunk of a tree and what there is of a reflective tendency in his nature is intensified. One shudders at the thought of the meaninglessness of life while at the same instant, and if the people of the town are his people, one loves life so intensely that tears come into the eyes.

In the darkness under the roof of the grandstand, George Willard sat beside Helen White and felt very keenly his own insignificance in the scheme of existence. Now that he had come out of town where the presence of the people stirring about, busy with a multitude of affairs, had been so irritating the irritation was all gone. The presence of Helen renewed and refreshed him. It was as though her woman's hand was assisting him to make some minute readjustment of the machinery of his life. He began to think of the people in the town where he had always lived with something like reverence. He had reverence for Helen. He wanted to love and to be loved by her, but he did not want at the moment to be confused by her womanhood. In the darkness he took hold of her hand and when she crept close put a hand on her shoulder. A wind began to blow and he shivered. With all his strength he tried to hold and to understand the mood that had come upon him. In that high place in the darkness the two oddly sensitive human atoms held each other tightly and waited. In the mind of each was the same thought. "I have come to this lonely place and here is this other," was the substance of the thing felt.

In Winesburg the crowded day had run itself out into the long night of the late fall. Farm horses jogged away along lonely country roads pulling their portion of weary people. Clerks began to bring samples of goods in off the sidewalks and lock the doors of stores. In the Opera House a crowd had gathered to see a show and farther down Main Street the fiddlers, their instruments tuned, sweated and worked to keep the feet of youth flying over a dance floor.

In the darkness in the grandstand Helen White and George Willard remained silent. Now and then the spell that held them was broken and they turned and tried in the dim light to see into each other's eyes. They kissed but that impulse did not last. At the upper end of the fair ground a half dozen men worked over horses that had raced during the afternoon. The men had built a fire and were heating kettles of water. Only their legs could be seen as they passed back and forth in the light. When the wind blew the little flames of the fire danced crazily about.

George and Helen arose and walked away into the darkness. They went along a path past a field of corn that had not yet been cut. The wind whispered among the dry corn blades. For a moment during the walk back into town the spell that held them was broken. When they had come to the crest of Waterworks Hill they stopped by a tree and George again put his hands on the girl's shoulders. She embraced him eagerly and then again they drew quickly back from that impulse. They stopped kissing and stood a little apart. Mutual respect grew big in them. They were both embarrassed and to relieve their embarrassment dropped into the animalism of youth. They laughed and began to pull and haul at each other. In some way chastened and purified by the mood they had been in they became, not man and woman, not boy and girl, but excited little animals.

It was so they went down the hill. In the darkness they played like two splendid young things in a young world. Once, running swiftly forward, Helen tripped George and he fell. He squirmed and shouted. Shaking with laughter, he rolled down the hill. Helen ran after him. For just a moment she stopped in the darkness. There is no way of knowing what woman's thoughts went through her mind but, when the bottom of the hill was reached and she came up to the boy, she took his arm and walked beside him in dignified silence. For some reason they could not have explained they had both got from their silent evening together the thing needed. Man or boy, woman or girl, they had for a moment taken hold of the thing that makes the mature life of men and women in the modern world possible.

About the Authors

SHERWOOD ANDERSON was born September 13, 1876 in Camden, Ohio and died March 8, 1941. "Sophistication," his contribution to *Time to Be Young*, appeared as the final story in his most widely known book *Winesburg, Ohio*, the volume which initiated his career as probably the most significant American short story writer of his generation.

LUDWIG BEMELMANS, Americanized native of the Austrian Tyrol and widely known for his painting and illustrating as well as for several novels and books for juveniles, selected for this volume a story about his little daughter Barbara. When this story appeared in a magazine, he reports, he was swamped with letters from other parents who had great sympathy for Barbara and her reactions to a summer camp.

ROBERT BENCHLEY, who was born in Worcester, Massachusetts in September, 1889 is author of many books of humorous sketches. His discourse on the dilemma of a father suffering from "The Visiting Schoolmate Problem" first appeared in his collection of sketches *The Treasurer's Report*. Mr. Benchley graduated from Harvard in 1912 and was married in that year; he is the father of two sons. He has done much dramatic criticism and has written dialogue and acted in motion pictures.

STEPHEN VINCENT BENÉT, one of the best-loved American writers of his day, was born July 22, 1898 in Bethlehem, Pennsylvania. He died March 13, 1943. He wrote many books of poetry and short stories. He was married in 1921 to Rosemary Carr and was the father of three children.

SALLY BENSON is the author of some of the best stories of childhood published in America. Some of these short stories grew into books and later to stage plays and motion pictures, to wit: *Junior Miss* and *Meet Me in St. Louis*. Most of her short stories have first appeared in *The New Yorker*. She is the mother of a grown daughter, who recently presented her with a grandchild.

KAY BOYLE, short story writer and novelist who was born in St. Paul, Minnesota, February 19, 1903, spent her youth in Philadelphia, Atlantic City, Cincinnati and Europe. Her first husband was a Frenchman. She married twice again and is the mother of six children. At present her husband is in the Armed Forces and she has been sent abroad by the government.

FRANK BROOKHOUSER is a Philadelphia newspaperman at present with the U. S. Army in France. He is married. "Easter Egg" was one of Mr. Brookhouser's earliest stories and introduced him as a writer through the pages of the magazine *Story*.

MORLEY CALLAGHAN was born in Toronto, Canada in 1903, of Irish descent. He is a graduate of the University of Toronto and a member of the Canadian Bar. He has written several volumes of short stories. He was married in 1929 and has two children and at present is in the Canadian Armed Forces. "Very Special Shoes" first appeared in *Story*.

DOROTHY CANFIELD (Dorothy Canfield Fisher), is one of America's most widely known women novelists, a judge of the Book-of-the-Month Club and active in a civic way in her home state of Vermont. She has still found time to write many novels and short stories. She was born February 17, 1879, and in 1907 married John Redwood Fisher. She has written a great deal about the relationship of parents and children, including the books *Montessori Mother, Mothers and Children, Self-Reliance, and Tell Me a Story,* as well as *Fables for Parents.* The names of Mrs. Fisher's children are Sarah and Jane.

WINSTON S. CHURCHILL in his fragment in *Time to Be Young* confesses to having stood near the bottom of his class in both scholarship and alphabetically because then at school his name was Spencer-Churchill. Today he is one of the Big Three running the world and is the Prime Minister of the British government. His "Examinations at Harrow" originally appeared in his autobiography, published in England and Canada under the title *My Early Life* and in America under *A Roving Commission.* He is of course a family man as well as a statesman, father of one son and three daughters, and has been accompanied at times on official missions by his wife or one of his daughters.

BERTHA DAMON was born in North Stonefield, Connecticut, and graduated from Pembroke College in New England. She is married to Professor Lindsay Todd Damon. Her contribution to *Time to Be Young* comes from her book *Grandma Called It Carnal.* She has written one other book, *A Sense of Humus.*

CLARENCE DAY, who died in 1935, was best known for his autobiographical works, *Life with Father, Life with Mother, God and My Father,* etc. *Life with Father* which was dramatized in 1939 is still running as a Broadway play. He is survived by his widow.

IRWIN EDMAN, author, educator, and critic, was born in New York City November 28, 1896 and after taking his Ph.D. at Columbia began to lecture on Philosophy at that institution in which he has been full Professor of Philosophy since 1935. He has written poetry, history of philosophy and philosophical criticism. He is one of the few unmarried contributors to *Time to Be Young.*

FRANCES EISENBERG, whose story about Joey first appeared in the magazine *Story* and later was launched as part of a book, *There's One in Every Family,* now being made into a play, comes from Knoxville, Tennessee, but at present is doing defense work in Lakeland, Florida. She comes of an old Knoxville family and spent several years with the young as a teacher in the grade schools. She has not had time yet to get married and have her own children although she understands her family and somebody's brother, unless Joey is everybody's brother.

HAVELOCK ELLIS, author of *The Dance of Life,* in which he wrote of life as an art and the dance as its symbol, is the author of numerous other volumes. He was born in 1859, taught school in the Australian Bush in 1877, and in 1891 he married Edith Lees who died in 1916. He died July 8, 1939.

ALICE FARNHAM, a relatively young writer, is a discovery of the magazine *Story.* She is an adventurous young woman who, for research in her stories, lived for some time among the Florida scrub-brush natives. She is the mother of three children and has written of love, marriage, divorce and other peoples' children extensively in her forthcoming novel *Lover, Come Back.* She lives in Pennsylvania.

WILLIAM FAULKNER, born September 25, 1897, in Mississippi where he now lives, enlisted in the Canadian Air Force in the first World War. He was wounded in France. He was a friend of Sherwood Anderson and through him came into print in *The Double Dealer,* a little literary magazine of the 'twenties. He has written several novels, some of which have also been made into motion pictures. In 1939 he married Mrs. Estelle Oldham Franklin, a widow with two children. They now have a child of their own.

MICHAEL FESSIER, whose "That's What Happened to Me" appeared first in *Story,* was born in Angels Camp, California. His story about the fifteen-year-old boy who was the world's champion standing high-jumper has been translated into several languages. He is married and has worked several years in the motion picture industry.

WILLIAM FIFIELD, descendant of a family of Congregational ministers, has done considerable radio writing. One of his stories "The Fishermen of Patzcuaro," written in Mexico City and published in *Story,* won an O. Henry Memorial Prize Award. His wife is an actress and they have one small son.

W. E. FISHBAUGH was born in Rochester, N. Y., in 1906.

WOLCOTT GIBBS, writer and critic, was born in New York City March 15, 1902. He worked as a newspaperman for some years. Since 1927 he has been connected with *The New Yorker*. In 1933 he married Eleanor Sherwin and has a son and a daughter. He lives in New York City.

BRENDAN GILL, who is connected with *The New Yorker,* was born in 1914 in Hartford, Connecticut and attended Yale. He is married and has three children born in 1937, 1940 and 1942.

KENNETH GRAHAME, British story writer, was born March 3, 1859, and died July 6, 1932. His parents having died when he was a very young man he was reared by relatives. He went into banking and combined banking with literature. In 1899 he married a Scotswoman and it was for their one son, Alastair, sometimes known as "Mouse" for whom the *Wind in the Willows* was written. The son died in an accident at twenty. Grahame is buried beside his son at Pangbourne on the Thames. His books, ostensibly written for children, have been characterized by *The Nation* as "books not really for children to read but for adults to remember." He said he wrote for children because they were "the only really living people." He has been often compared to Lewis Carroll.

WALT GROVE, whose story "The Brothers Patton" is first printed here in book form, was born April 23, 1921 at Dallas, Texas. He is now a Sergeant with the Intelligence and Security Sections overseas. His post-war plans: "to marry, live in Mexico in the shade of a lime tree clutching both Mrs. Grove and a glass of tequila and to raise six children and a girl."

ERNEST HEMINGWAY, who has written more extensively about childhood than most readers realize, is the son of a doctor. He was born July 21, 1898 in Oak Park, Illinois and has recorded some of his boyhood experiences with fishing rod and shotgun in short stories in which the chief character is Nick. He has done newspaper work, was in the Italian infantry in the first World War, has been a war correspondent in this war, and written numerous novels and short stories. His present wife is the writer, Martha Gellhorn. He has had three sons by earlier marriages.

ALDOUS HUXLEY was born July 26, 1894. The noted English novelist has been living for some years in Southern California.

MACKINLAY KANTOR, who was born in Iowa in 1904, has written several historical novels and is one of the few living authors to tackle a subject as young as the baby in "And These Went Down to Burlington." He spent some years in newspaper work and with the scenario departments of several of the motion picture companies. He was married in 1926 and has two children.

HELEN KELLER, who has written her own biography in her unique and moving *The Story of My Life,* has been deaf and blind as the result of illness since the age of nineteen months. Although *The Story of My Life* appeared first in 1902, it has been kept in print and sells extensively to this day. She has written much since then and has lectured throughout the world. She has appeared frequently at rallies in connection with the present war effort. She was born at Tuscumbia, Alabama, June 27, 1880. She is descended on her father's side from Alexander Spottswood, colonial governor of Virginia, and is related on her mother's side to the Adams and Everett families of New England.

VICTORIA LINCOLN, who lives in a suburb of Columbus, Ohio, is the wife of Victor Lowe, Professor of English at Ohio State University, and the mother of three children. She is the author of many short stories, poems and sketches as well as the novel *February Hill* which was later dramatized as *The Primrose Path.*

KATHERINE MANSFIELD, who was born October 14, 1888, and died January 9, 1923, was a native of New Zealand. Her large output of short stories has influenced women writers for many years. She was the wife of John Middleton Murry, editor and critic. Much of her life was spent fighting ill health and ill success and her death came about through an illness of the lungs.

MARJORIE MARKS' little short story has been read by several millions since its republication from *Story* in the *Readers Digest.* "The child, Norma, in 'Death in the Fifth Grade' was in my daughter's class at school," says Marjorie Marks. "She would be twenty now—like my daughter—and no doubt equally dignified. But she still wins all the races in the schoolyard of my mind." Marjorie Marks was born in 1901 in New York City and received her M.A. Degree from Columbia. She is married, has three children, a cocker spaniel, and a cat.

H. L. MENCKEN, editor, critic, national convention reporter and piano player of Baltimore, has covered his biography fairly extensively in three volumes and he still has some to go. He was born in Baltimore in 1880 and has been in and out of newspaper work since then. He was co-editor of *The Smart Set* with George Jean Nathan between 1914 and 1923 and he and Nathan founded *The American Mercury* which they edited until 1933. His critical views gave encouragement to such writers as Theodore Dreiser, James Branch Cabell, Sherwood Anderson, and many others. He is the author of *The American Language* among numerous other books. His contribution to *Time to Be Young* comes from his earliest recollections in his autobiographical volume *Happy Days.* A noted bachelor, he did not marry until 1930. His wife, Sara Powell Haardt, died in 1935. He lives in Baltimore.

GEORGE JEAN NATHAN, a distinguished bachelor contributor to a book about childhood and early youth, lives in the heart of the theater district of New York City in a hotel convenient to the best restaurants and box offices. He was born in Fort Wayne, Indiana, in 1882 and was educated at Cornell and the University of Bologna, Italy. He has written numerous books of dramatic criticism and has served on scores of periodicals and newspapers as a dramatic critic. He currently edits the *Theater Book of the Year.* His selection for this book was from a volume no one expected him to write, *Beware of*

Parents, in which he explains what makes parents and children go wrong, particularly in the presence of each other.

KATHERINE ANNE PORTER was born in Texas in 1894 and has written several volumes of distinguished short stories. She was awarded a Guggenheim Fellowship in 1931. She married Albert Erskine Russell, Jr. in 1938.

MARCEL PROUST who died, unmarried, in France on November 18, 1922, left in his many-volumed novel *Remembrance of Things Past* one of the most complete pictures of marriage, love, jealousy and childhood in contemporary literature. He is represented in this book with a long segment from his first novel *Swann's Way.* He suffered from asthma. From the age of thirty-five, after his association with the aristocrats of the upper Parisian world, he became a recluse and devoted himself exclusively to writing.

MARJORIE KINNAN RAWLINGS, whose book *The Yearling,* is known throughout the country, was born in Washington, D. C., August 8, 1896. Since 1931 she has been writing fiction. She lives in Hawthorn, Florida, the wife of Norton Boskin, whom she married in 1941. In 1928 she went into the "hummock" country of Florida where she cut herself off from "civilized ties" to study and write about the vanishing frontier. She owns and manages a seventy-two-acre orange grove.

GEORGE SANTAYANA, Spanish-born philosopher, who taught for years at Harvard, has written the beginning of his autobiography in *Persons and Places* from which "Early Memories" has been taken. The author was born December 16, 1863. Although he has spent the better part of his life in the United States and writes his books in the English language he still feels he retains his Spanish nationality and sentiments. At present he lives in Rome. Like Mr. Edman, the only other philosopher-contributor to *Time to Be Young,* Santayana has never married.

WILLIAM SAROYAN, who has written as many short stories as Pirandello, is represented in this book with his earliest published story. It appeared in an Armenian weekly in Boston under the pseudonym of Sirak Goryan and somewhat preceded the publication in *Story* of "The Daring Young Man on the Flying Trapeze" which swung him into the limelight. Since then Mr. Saroyan has written several hundred stories and several prize-winning plays and one motion picture. He was born in Fresno, California, August 31, 1908. He married in New York City and is the father of an infant son, Aram. He is at present in the U. S. Army.

JEANNE SINGER was born and brought up in Manhattan. She graduated from Radcliffe in 1929 and after several months with the *New York World News Service* was married. She did not start writing until after her second son was born in 1934. She now works for the Office of War Information.

CORNELIA OTIS SKINNER, humorist, actress, and playwright, is the daughter of the late Otis Skinner, the actor. She was married to Alden Blodgett in 1928. She lives in New York City and she has written off and on about the problems, at least the humorous ones, besetting a mother. She has one son, in his teens, who attends St. Paul's School in Concord, New Hampshire.

JOHN STEINBECK, whose stories about Jody, a young boy on a California ranch, reflect some of the author's own boyhood observations, was born in Salinas, California, February 27, 1902. His wife is the former Gwynn Conger. He has written several novels including *The Grapes of Wrath, Of Mice and Men, The Moon Is Down,* etc. In 1943 he was a war columnist overseas. His latest book is *Cannery Row*.

JAMES STREET was born in Lumberton, Mississippi, October 15, 1903. He was married in 1923 and has three children. He was for several years a newspaper man but since 1937 has been writing stories and novels.

JESSE STUART, Kentucky writer who has written several hundred poems, several hundred short stories and a novel *Taps for Private Tussie,* which was distributed by the Book-of-the-Month Club, is at present an officer in the United States Navy. His wife and young daughter live on the farm in Kentucky in the country about which "Thanksgiving Hunter" is written.

BOOTH TARKINGTON, Indiana novelist who was born in 1869 and has written numerous novels of American life, is perhaps even more noted among certain readers for his books about boys and adolescence, particularly his stories and books about Penrod, the first of which began to appear in 1914. Mr. Tarkington lives with his family in Indianapolis. He has been twice married.

JAMES THURBER, humorist with both pen and typewriter, is a native of Columbus, Ohio where he was born December 8, 1894. Since 1927 he has been a regular staff contributor to *The New Yorker*. He is married and lives in Connecticut. He has one daughter, in her teens.

ROBERT TRAVER is the pen name for a prosecuting attorney of a city in Michigan. He is married and has three children. His first book, *Trouble-Shooter,* was published by The Viking Press.

MARK TWAIN, the pen name of Samuel Clemens, who left America a legacy of boyhood in *Tom Sawyer* and *Huckleberry Finn,* wrote of his own special boyhood in his Autobiography, a fragment of which constitutes his contribution to this volume.

EDMUND WARE, whose story of the boy who crawled through the sewer pipe first appeared in *Story,* won a Doubleday-Doran novel prize contest and has appeared frequently in the magazines.

EUDORA WELTY was born in Jackson, Mississippi where she now lives and devotes her time to fiction. Her books of short stories include *Curtain of Green* and *The Wide Net.*

THOMAS WOLFE died in his thirty-eighth year, Sept. 15, 1938. He was born and reared in Asheville, North Carolina. His several books of an autobiographical nature were a contribution to American writing. The fragment in this book was taken from his first book, *Look Homeward, Angel.*